Completely Revised

America's Best-Loved Book on Infant Care

Prenatal and postnatal care of the mother and child, from infancy through the sixth year.

Developed by leading practicing obstetricians and pediatricians, this book provides the latest scientific advances in child psychology, care and training for the new mother. It brings within her reach everything she needs to know to bring up her child with happy confidence.

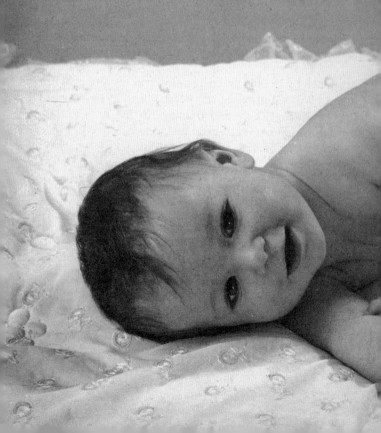

BETTER HOMES AND GARDENS

BABY

Revised Edition

BOOK

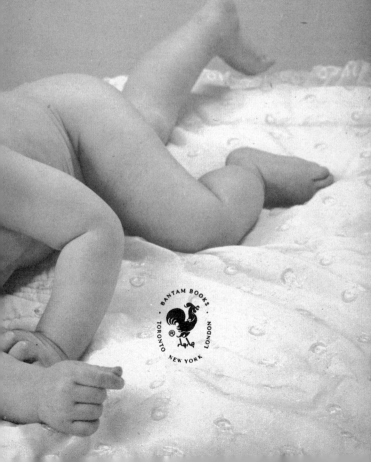

BANTAM BOOKS
TORONTO · NEW YORK · LONDON

*This low-priced Bantam Book
has been completely reset in a type face
designed for easy reading, and was printed
from new plates. It contains the complete
text of the original hard-cover edition.*
NOT ONE WORD HAS BEEN OMITTED.

BETTER HOMES AND GARDENS® BABY BOOK

*A Bantam Book / published by arrangement with
Meredith Corporation*

PRINTING HISTORY

*Meredith edition published 1943
27 printings through 1968
Revised Meredith edition published 1969*

*Bantam edition / August 1965
18 printings through July 1970
Revised Bantam edition / November 1970
20 printings through February 1979*

ISBN 0-553-12849-3

Published simultaneously in the United States and Canada

*Bantam Books are published by Bantam Books, Inc. Its trade-
mark, consisting of the words "Bantam Books" and the por-
trayal of a bantam, is Registered in U.S. Patent and Trademark
Office and in other countries. Marca Registrada. Bantam
Books, Inc., 666 Fifth Avenue, New York, New York 10019.*

PRINTED IN THE UNITED STATES OF AMERICA

About this book

The Better Homes and Gardens Baby Book, prepared with the cooperation and advice of leading child-care authorities, is a complete day-by-day guide for the mother—before Baby comes and through the first six years. It is a helpful supplement to your doctor's instructions, and a reliable authority to turn to between visits with your physician.

We believe you will find that the book gives you comforting reassurance when doubts and fears arise, and that it serves as a most reliable guide to answer your questions. We suggest that you begin its use by quickly skimming through the book to familiarize yourself with its organization and contents. Later, as a chapter becomes more applicable to you, read that chapter intensively—and the one following it. In this way, you'll be helped to keep abreast—and ahead—of your ever-changing needs and those of your child.

Pictures show step-by-step how to feed, bathe, dress, and care for your baby. His changing physical needs are outlined month by month, and you'll see how to guide his unfolding personality as he learns about the world around him. More than 16,000 doctors own the Baby Book. It is recommended by leading physicians.

The Baby Book is the most authoritative guide in the child-care field. Continuing research, consultation with child-health authorities, the cooperation of leading child psychologists—all have gone into the preparation of this book.

Accuracy and completeness have earned for the Baby Book endorsements of eminent specialists in child-care and training. Millions of mothers have given their hearty approval of the Baby Book's commonsense writing and easy-to-follow directions (almost three million copies of this book have been purchased making it the best-selling hardbound baby book of all time). It is revised regularly with the latest reliable information—new technological advances including new medicines, immunizations, and practices are given; also the use of the latest equipment is presented.

Your children can provide you with more hours of enjoyment and pleasure than anything else in this world. The Better Homes and Gardens Baby Book can serve as a helpful guide for their happy, healthy development.

The Editors
Better Homes and Gardens

Acknowledgments

We wish to express our appreciation to these authorities on infant and child care, maternal health, and child development for their help in the preparation and revision of this book.

JACK SPEVAK, M.D.

Certified by the American Board of Pediatrics; Fellow of the American Academy of Pediatrics; Teaching staff and Director of Hematology Clinic, Raymond Blank Memorial Hospital for Children, Des Moines, Iowa; Chief of Staff, Broadlawns County General Hospital, Des Moines; Chief of Pediatrics, Northwest Hospital, Des Moines; former Associate Professor of Pediatrics, University of Indiana School of Medicine.

GEORGE GRAY CAUDILL, M.D.

Certified by the American Board of Pediatrics; Fellow of the American Academy of Pediatrics; Fellow of the American Association of Clinical Immunology and Allergy; Staff of Raymond Blank Memorial Hospital for Children, Des Moines.

PARKER K. HUGHES, M.D.

Chief of Department of Obstetrics and Gynecology, Methodist Hospital, Des Moines; Founding Fellow, American College of Obstetrics and Gynecology; Diplomate, American Board of Obstetrics and Gynecology; former Vice-President of the Central Association of Obstetricians and Gynecologists.

DENNIS H. KELLY, M.D.

Des Moines, Fellow of the American Academy of Pediatrics.

VAN C. ROBINSON, M.D.

Retired Member of the staffs of Iowa Methodist Hospital, Iowa Lutheran Hospital, and Mercy Hospital, Des Moines.

FRANCIS KODL, M.D.

Berwyn, Ill., Fellow of the American Academy of Pediatrics.

WILLARD W. HARTUP, Ed.D.

Professor of Child Psychology; Associate Director, Institute of Child Development, University of Minnesota, Minneapolis, Minnesota.

HOWARD V. MEREDITH, Ph.D.

Institute of Child Behavior and Development, University of Iowa, Iowa City, Iowa.

Photography: Kathryn Abbe, Wesley Bowman, Ralph Cowan, William Hopkins, Vivienne Lapham, Joan Liffring, Vincent Maselli, William Maxheim, Charles R. Pearson, Doris Pinney, H. Armstrong Roberts.

Contents

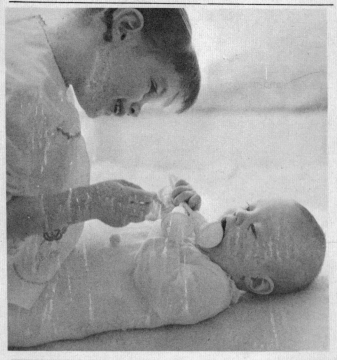

SECTION ONE • BEFORE THE BABY COMES

CHAPTER

SECTION TWO · YOUR BABY FROM BIRTH TO TWO YEARS

SECTION THREE · YOUR CHILD FROM TWO TO SIX YEARS

SECTION FOUR · GENERAL INFORMATION

Looking to the future is a happy experience for expectant parents

Not long ago, you were told that the two of you would soon become parents. With this news, together you embark upon one of the most exciting, most satisfying of human adventures—the birth and rearing of your child. Take full advantage of the months of waiting ahead of you. Use this time to learn as much as possible about child rearing. With your mate, discuss your ideas, likes, and dislikes concerning your child's upbringing. Thus, your own philosophy of parenthood will evolve. With this shared knowledge and understanding, you as husband and wife will understand the meaningful way your love is being fulfilled with the birth of your child.

1

The miracle of life

Comprehend, if you can, how the most minute fragment of life—a single cell, just on the fringe of the microscopic world —can divide and redivide to make the billions of cells in the body of a baby. Think of the uncountable number of tissues and organs that sprang from this initial fleck of life; the hair, the nails, the skin, the brain, the eyes, the ductless glands. Each step of the creative process represents a series of exquisitely intricate events, each timed to the other in almost unbelievable hairline sequence.

Almost any high-school biology student feels competent to explain the facts of life. The research man lacks this self-assurance. There are, he readily admits, great gaps in his knowledge. At best, he can supply only the crudest outline of the stirring drama.

Scientists have pieced together the picture as best they can. They have used X rays to peer into the womb and observe the growing life. The electric activity of the brain can be recorded. Studies have been made of thousands of fetuses which, through miscarriage, have been delivered at various stages of pregnancy, and which help to visualize the steps of fetal development.

Furthermore, they have checked their findings with studies of animals—the development of all mammalian life being remarkably the same. The sperms of horses and the eggs of sheep look almost exactly like their human counterparts. A whale and a mouse spring from eggs approximately the same size as those that produce a human life.

OVULATION Time plays an important role. It is believed that ovulation takes place fourteen days before the beginning of the menstrual flow (about the thirteenth day of the menstrual cycle). Although the ovum itself lives for only twelve hours, there are about twenty-four to forty-eight hours each month during which time a fertile woman can conceive.

Each month one or the other of a woman's two ovaries—

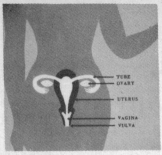

This familiar illustration shows both the external and internal female sex organs. These terms will be used throughout the book.

Male sperm, similar in size to a red blood cell, are 1/30 the size of a female egg.

Female eggs are barely visible to the naked eye, yet 2 million could be held in a thimble.

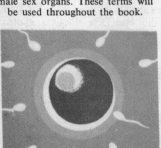

The female egg–admits only one sperm. After that, all others are rejected.

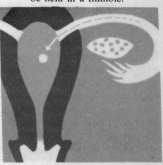

After fertilization in the Fallopian tube, the egg begins a 3-day journey to the uterus.

small (an inch and a half long), almond-shaped glands that hang on either side of the pelvis—produces a single egg. The egg is a minute, fragile, opalescent thing so tiny as to be barely visible to the sharpest eyes. Globe-shaped, the egg is barely 1/200 of an inch in diameter. It would require 2,000,000 eggs to fill a sewing thimble yet it is the largest cell in the human body.

At the other extreme, the sperm produced by man is infinitely small. Resembling a microscopic tadpole, it whips itself along with a thread-like tail to the uterus and into the Fallopian tube. Although sperm can survive for several days, they are thought to retain their fertilizing ability for only forty-eight hours. The spermatozoon has remarkable traits. The most striking trait being its selectivity. It passes millions of body

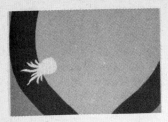

On the sixth day, the egg implants itself on the uterine wall for food and shelter.

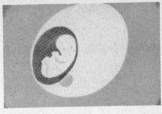

At the end of two months, your baby weighs only 1/15 of an ounce yet primitive nervous and circulatory systems have already formed.

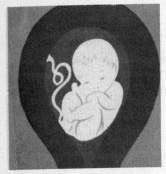

At 4½ months, all organs are formed and now only growth takes place. About this time, Mother feels the first stirrings of life.

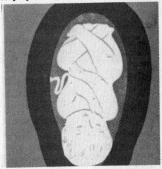

In preparing for birth, 95 percent of all babies turn to this position. Flexible tissues in the head allow the baby to pass through the birth canal without difficulty.

cells on its journey, yet displays interest in none of them. Another unique fact about sperm cells is their staggering number—225,000,000 of them will be implanted at a single time. Yet, out of this vast number, only one will complete its destiny: fertilization of the egg.

SPERM DETERMINES SEX OF CHILD The actual mating occurs on the surface of the ovary in the Fallopian tube, the 3- to 5-inch canal that conveys the egg from ovary to uterus. The process of fertilization has been observed in animals. Not long ago, Drs. John Rock and Arthur T. Hertig, of Harvard, conducted an epochal research. They recovered human ova from Fallopian tubes removed from women because of disease. They mated these eggs with male sperm.

Under their microscopes they watched sperm attack eggs—and saw the first halting steps toward life as cell division started in the egg.

At the same time, the process is no less wondrous for the fact that it has been observed. It is astonishing that the minute, fragile sperm can bore its way into the large and relatively tough egg. Possibly it produces a chemical which softens the shell, or possibly the shell itself weakens to permit entrance. In either case, only one sperm is admitted. After that, all others are turned away. To accomplish this turning away, the eggs of some creatures shoot out tiny fingers pushing away unwanted sperms. It has also been suggested that once a sperm cell has gained admittance, the shell hardens instantly to bar the way to all others.

The particular sperm the egg accepts determines the sex of the child which will be born 266 days later (for comparison, the gestation period of an opossum is 11 days, of an elephant 600 days). Half of all male cells carry girl-producing X chromosomes, half boy-producing Y chromosomes. The egg carries only the X's. Hence, if an X-bearing chromosome enters the egg, a girl baby will result; if a Y, there will be a boy. Sex, therefore, is dependent on the father.

Once the cells fuse, the curtain slowly rises on the most fundamental of all dramas. The egg, now fertilized, is still in the Fallopian tube—a threadlike opening, no larger than a broom straw. This channel contains thousands of minute *cilia* —hairlike protrusions which wave like wheat in the wind. It is their job to move the fragile egg on a leisurely journey toward the uterus—a trip that requires something like three days. During this time, cell division has started in the egg. The original cell has split apart to make two cells, these two to make four, etc.

UTERINE CHANGES OCCUR Almost immediately uterine changes occur. A stirring rush of events gets under way with perfect timing. First, the ovary secretes a hormone, estrogen, which it empties into the blood stream. This remarkable chemical has an all-important job to perform. It has a specific action on the uterus. Under its influence, the lining of that organ thickens. Networks of new blood vessels spring up with amazing rapidity, and there is an enormous increase in uterine glands. The purpose of this activity is to provide nourishment for the new life. Once this job is completed, the ovary springs to new activity. The tiny crater from which the egg erupted rapidly fills with a yellowish, waxy stuff—the corpus luteum. It, too, produces a hormone—progesterone. The main function of progesterone is to produce secretory activity on the uterine lining which provides food for the recently fertilized ovum. It is also the job of this chemical to quiet the rhythmic contractions of the uterus—otherwise, the fragile egg might be injured or discarded.

In a sense, all of this activity is like preparing a house—the uterus—for an honored guest. If the guest—a fertilized ovum —does not arrive, all the preparations have been in vain. Excess tissue breaks down and is discarded. Bleeding results which is menstruation. But in the case we are interested in, the guest *does* arrive, right on schedule.

Once the fertilized egg reaches the uterus—a muscular organ approximately the size and shape of a small pear—it leads an apparently aimless existence for six days. It drifts around the uterine cavity, carried by fluid currents. Were any foreign body placed in the uterus, that organ would contract to expel it. But it makes no effort to discard the new life.

EMBRYO IS SEPARATE BEING This six-day period of apparently aimless—or at least unexplained—drifting represents a highly critical period for the fertilized egg. By now its food supply, the microscopic yolk of the original egg, is near exhaustion. The life it carries is dangerously near extinction. The egg reacts to this hazard. It selects a spot on the red, velvet-smooth uterine wall. It apparently secretes something— possibly an enzyme—which eats a tiny niche in the wall. Then it shoots out tiny feelers with which to draw nourishment. Now, at last, the embryo is safe. It has a nest, and has tapped an always dependable source of food.

From this point out, one wonder piles rapidly on top of another. The rounded clump of cells becomes the *morula*— which is Latin for mulberry. Then this minute berry of life grows into a tiny hollow sphere, which is filled with fluid. Over it, a membrane forms which will become the placenta.

Through this placenta the growing life will take nourishment from the mother, and will discharge its body wastes—to be excreted by her kidneys. From now on, until the moment of birth, it will live an aquatic life, immersed in a bath of amniotic fluid—the watery substance that fills the sac in which the baby is forming. At one point in its development, the baby will have primitive gill slits.

By the end of the third week, the constantly growing particle of life is a tiny fleck of gray tissue. But even at this point, it has a primitive heart, a tiny pulsating tube; and its own system of blood vessels. Already it is manufacturing its own blood, which is quite independent of the mother's blood supply and separated from the mother's circulatory system by the placental barrier. The baby's blood, note in passing, may be an entirely different type of blood from that of the mother.

During this third week, other striking things have happened. A brain of microscopic proportions, a threadlike spinal cord, and an even smaller network of nerves have been forming to create an, as yet, incomplete nervous system.

The first evidence of a bony structure doesn't appear until the end of the sixth week. Up to this point, the embryo has been indistinguishable from the embryos of other mammals. By the end of the sixth week, it is recognizable, even to the unaided eye, as a human being. The head is forming and during the following week, fingers and toes will appear. By the end of the ninth week, a tiny miniature face is completely formed. At this point, the baby is still unbelievably small, weighing only 1/15 of an ounce.

By the end of the third month, most organs are complete and functioning, but it is not nearly ready for an independent existence in a hostile world.

Up to this point, the mother is aware of the new life only by external signs. She may feel morning sickness and has ceased menstruating. Now she can feel a small lump just above the pelvic area—the rapidly enlarging uterus. At first pear-shaped, the uterus assumes a globular form, then, later on, an ovoid, or bottle shape. By the end of the ninth month, the uterus, a predominantly muscular organ, has undergone almost unbelievable expansion. By volume, it has increased 500 times! It has pushed other organs aside, nearly filling the abdominal cavity, and pushing against the diaphragm to cause mild breathing difficulties.

There is a general misconception that for approximately nine months the developing infant leads a cramped life tightly folded within the uterus. This is not true, at least in its early stage of development. The infant floats lazily about in the amniotic fluid—which acts as a kind of shock absorber. This is nature's way of supplying protection for the baby. A prospective mother may undergo violent injury—she may fall down stairs, slip on ice, or be involved in an auto accident—but thanks to this built-in safety feature, there is little likelihood of her baby suffering, even up to the time that birth is imminent. Without this liquid environment, the baby would receive shocks which might be fatal.

By the middle of the fourth month, all organs are formed, and now only growth takes place. The infant can twist its face into a grimace and contract eyes into a wink—even though eyelids are still fused together. It can swallow, and it discharges urine into the fluid in which it floats. At this time, the mother feels the first stirrings of life within her. The baby thrashes his arms and legs but lacks energy and oxygen for prolonged movement. It cannot gulp air into its lungs to get oxygen needed for any extended exercise—it has to depend on the supply available in the mother's blood. So, after a short period of wakefulness, it is tired and goes back to sleep and its movements cease.

By the fifth month, it has hair, eyebrows, and lashes, and weighs nearly two pounds. Its heartbeat is now detectable by the ordinary clinical means of a stethoscope. Earlier, the faint beat could be heard only with amplifiers. At this point, let's straighten out another common misconception. There is a widespread, and erroneous, belief that hearts of girl babies beat more rapidly than those of boys—and the physician can therefore tell the unborn child's sex with a stethoscope. There is no clinical support whatsoever for this belief.

By now, the baby is an altogether remarkable individual. The original single cell has grown to a point where the new life now has its full lifetime complement of nerve cells—a staggering total of 12 billion!

By the seventh month, the baby has grown enough to stand a good chance of survival if born prematurely. The old wives' tale stating that a seven-months baby has a better chance of survival than an eight-months baby is not true. The longer a baby stays within its mother, the better its chances for life. The eighth and ninth months are nature's safety factors. The child has a chance if born before, but it has far better chances if given these two months to grow sturdier and stronger.

During this period, the placenta assumes tasks other than just nourishing the baby and disposing of wastes. It has become a gland of internal secretion. It would be impossible for the ovaries to secrete enough progesterone to keep the enormously enlarged uterus quiet, to keep it from contracting and expelling the fetus. Hence, the placenta starts producing progesterone. It also begins to make estrogen, another ovarian hormone, which is needed to stimulate tissue building in the uterus. There is now evidence of a third female sex hormone, relaxin. Its job is exactly what the name implies: To facilitate birth by relaxing the tendons and tissues in the pelvic area to facilitate birth.

In its final stages of development, the baby takes steps toward acquiring a personality. He makes breathing motions with his chest, may engage in thumb-sucking, and is subject to hiccups. All of these monumental first steps in the development of a personality can and *will* be felt by Mother.

The forming baby reacts to external environment. If his mother smokes a cigarette, he might derive enough nicotine from her blood to speed up his heart. For this reason, the mother who smokes would be wise in discussing this situation with her doctor. Some sounds apparently cause irritation—or at least excitement—to the baby. Research men have found that certain sounds cause rapid movement of the baby's arms and legs. Thus we have learned that Baby is affected by his environment.

While living his nesting existence, the baby is the world's supreme egotist. He is an utterly selfish sprout of life, interested only in his own well-being.

Without regard for his mother's welfare, he draws on her for essential proteins with which to build tissue. He burdens her kidneys with his own wastes; pushes her organs aside to make room for himself.

To build a blood supply of his own, he draws heavily on her reserve of iron—possibly producing anemia in her while remaining robustly healthy himself.

He robs her of calcium to build bones for himself, and takes glycogen—a starchy substance that provides energy—from her liver. He helps himself to whatever he wants.

Yet, as always, there is a pattern and a wisdom here. Only by such selfishness can the baby insure his own survival. A mother can seek help from hundreds of thousands of sources. The baby is completely dependent on one individual, you, his mother.

Thus, the baby prepares himself for the supreme moment: His birth.

BODY PREPARES FOR BIRTH Once again, the mother's body has undergone elaborate preparations for the event. Nothing has been forgotten in the whole, vastly complex procedure. The placenta has generated enough surplus hormones to prepare the breasts for their waiting job. Both external and internal changes occur. The breasts contain a treelike structure of milk ducts, the nipples representing the trunks. Under pressure of increased hormone production, these tree structures become enlarged—shooting out thousands of new branches and twigs.

Everything is in readiness to provide food for the new life. Actual milk production, however, won't start until the pituitary gland at the base of the mother's brain goes into action. A few hours after birth, it gives the signal and starts producing minute amounts of the hormone, prolactin. This, in turn, starts the breasts functioning.

Other dramatic things have taken place within the mother's body. The normally hard cervix, or mouth of the womb, through which the baby must pass, has softened. Blood vessels in the birth canal have expanded tremendously and are bringing a large amount of additional blood to the area to help sustain the infant. The pelvic joints become more movable than normal so that the baby's head can pass through the pelvic canal at birth. At no other time in your life will so many metabolic and physiologic changes occur. Nothing in the miracle of life has been forgotten. The moment of birth is at hand.

WHAT STARTS LABOR? How does the body decide that the infant is ready to be born? Physicians are still searching for the answer to this question. If they knew what triggered labor, they might find a means of stopping labor when it started prematurely. As things stand, there are only guesses— some of them feeble—as to how the body decides the moment has come.

One theory is that the vastly enlarged uterus has been stretched beyond its endurance. The uterus then expresses itself by contracting in an effort to expel the irritant—the baby. Another theory is that the body chooses this moment to produce a mysterious chemical which initiates labor, but no such chemical has ever been found.

A third theory has some support in experimental evidence. Just before the birth process begins, there is a dramatically sharp decline in the amounts of sex hormones circulating in the blood. It appears possible that the placenta has become senile and is no longer able to produce the hormones which have made the uterus lie quiet for nine months. In any case, this rapid decline of hormones in the blood system is a signal that labor is about to begin. The uterus, which is made up almost entirely of muscular tissue, starts rhythmic contractions. The moment you have prepared for has arrived.

HOW BIRTH TAKES PLACE The head of the baby—over 95 percent of all babies are in a head-downward position at the time of birth—pushes with increasing force against the now softened cervix. This opening, no larger than a pencil lead in nonpregnant women, must expand to four or five inches. To achieve this expansion, relatively enormous forces are required.

Once again, the uterus has prepared itself for the job awaiting it. As pregnancy advanced, it grew thicker and stronger at its upper levels, adding new strands of muscle tissues. At lower levels, it grew thinner. Thus, when the moment arrives, it will be able to apply the greatest force where most needed.

So a new life comes into the world—using its first lungful of air to announce its arrival with a healthy cry. It is not a wonder that there are so many people on earth. The wonder is that there are people at all. For the process which created each man or woman is a miracle almost beyond comprehension.

CHAPTER 2

Care during the waiting period

The good care you've determined to give your baby begins, not the day he is born, but the day you realize that he has probably been conceived. And even before that—for in the years prior to this time, your good health, good nutrition, and good physical development have all been building up to contribute to your baby's well-being.

Right now, taking care of your baby means putting yourself immediately under the guidance of the doctor you have chosen, and following his instructions for keeping yourself in good health and rested and, most important of all, *well nourished*.

Happily, this kind of prenatal care pays double dividends. First, you're giving your baby the best chance to be strong and healthy; and second, you are helping to make your pregnancy comfortable and your labor and delivery as easy as possible.

As tests given prior to the sixth week have a tendency to be inaccurate, doctors generally prefer that a patient contact them immediately following the second missed menstrual period. This is because the difficulty of confirming pregnancy varies greatly from one patient to another. A visit too soon will only result in a repeated visit. But an early diagnosis will enable the doctor to make you as comfortable as possible.

He will give you a thorough examination and will take a specimen of your blood for testing early in your pregnancy.

He'll make note of your initial weight, blood pressure, measurements, and urinalysis. These records will be an invaluable aid to him in later months in determining your weight gain, and whether there has been any important change in your urine.

Many serious complications can sometimes be avoided by the early examination your doctor makes, and regularly scheduled checkups that you have thereafter.

SIGNS OF PREGNANCY How can you tell if you're pregnant?

Usually, the first sign is a missed period. If you're very regular, and go over 10 days or more, you'll begin to surmise that conception has taken place. If you miss two periods, it's fairly certain. If you've gone over your period and begin feeling nauseated in the mornings, or start urinating frequently, you'd better see your doctor.

There are other signs by which your doctor judges—for one, the breasts grow larger, and the brown circle around the nipple widens—though sometimes it's hard for him to be sure before about the third month. In times of stress especially, women sometimes simulate the symptoms of pregnancy. It's not at all uncommon for a bride, though she isn't pregnant, to skip a period and even feel morning nausea because the possibility of pregnancy is in her thoughts.

If you must find out immediately whether you're pregnant, there are tests which are from 95 to 100 percent accurate. You have to pay for such a test. There is no need for one, unless you've personal reasons for wanting an early, accurate diagnosis.

During the first half or so of pregnancy, if all goes well, you should visit your doctor once a month. In the latter half, he may ask you to come every two or three weeks, and in the last month or so, perhaps every week. When you first go to your doctor, ask him frankly about his charges. Have an understanding as to how his fee is to be paid—whether in advance, as you go, or at the conclusion of your pregnancy.

As pregnancy is a perfectly normal condition, your doctor's role isn't so much to treat you as a patient, but rather to manage your pregnancy. With his expert guidance and direction, you will be a comfortable, calm, and happy leading lady.

CARE DURING THE WAITING PERIOD · 25

WHEN TO EXPECT YOUR BABY The doctor will give you a date on which your baby may be expected, but don't hold him to it too closely! The length of normal pregnancies varies from woman to woman and sometimes there are other factors which make close calculations difficult. The doctors usually figure on 280 days, or 10 lunar months, from the first day of your last menstrual period. Count back three calendar months from the first day of your last menstrual period, and add seven days. Let's say that your last period began on December 16. Count back three months to September 16, and add seven days, which makes the expected date of your baby's birth next September 23. Remember, though, this is only an educated guess not a timetable. Even with all of the recent advancements in medical science, no one knows exactly how long it will take your child to develop, or for that matter, how your body decides that the child is ready to be born. Therefore, the password must be patience so, two weeks one way or the other should not be alarming.

Toward the end, your frequent trips to the doctor, and his examinations of the baby's heartbeats, will assure you that all's well, and that when your baby gets ready, he'll be coming along! Don't urge your doctor to speed things along. If he decides the birth should be hastened, he'll take proper measures. Rely upon his knowledge.

ACTIVITIES WHICH ARE PERMITTED What you do at this time depends upon what you have been in the habit of doing previously. The amount of exercise you can take depends a great deal on what you have already been accustomed to. The most important thing is to avoid exhaustion. A good rule is to stop *before* you're tired, not after. Golf may be indulged in moderately, provided your doctor consents and you feel no ill effects. Forceful exercise, such as horseback riding, tennis, fast dancing, and swimming may be harmful. Be sure to talk these matters over with your doctor.

If you're accustomed to doing your own housework, you'll benefit by continuing to do it. It is really the best kind of diversion and exercise for you, provided you delegate the heavy tasks to others and don't overtire yourself. If you tire at a task, stop and rest before completing it. Sit down at your work whenever possible and avoid pushing, carrying, and lifting heavy or cumbersome objects.

If you continue working at a job, take advantage of rest periods and really rest! Lie down, if facilities are available, even though it's only for short periods. Your doctor will probably suggest that you stop working about the seventh month of your pregnancy. This will be an excellent opportunity for you to catch up on your rest and finish some of those necessary, last-minute details before going to the hospital.

Some exercise is a necessity, but it should conform, as nearly as possible, to your habits. Most doctors advise a healthy woman to walk every day, even though she's doing housework. Perhaps the best answer to the exercise problem is a morning and evening walk, beginning with short ones and gradually increasing them to any amount which doesn't tire you. You might make this a family affair. In addition to the fresh air and exercise, walking can produce a calming, peaceful effect.

SHOULD YOU TRAVEL? Frequently expectant mothers ask if they may travel. Your doctor must decide how much traveling you ought to do, and what means of transportation is permissible. Short trips, to places less than one hour away from your doctor, are generally permitted. If you are contemplating a long trip for any reason, consult your doctor before making any of your final plans.

When considering a trip, remember that you'll be away from the doctor who is so familiar with your case and there's a tendency not to seek medical care when you need it if you're away from home. If you still feel that a trip is necessary, plan to take it by easy stages. Air travel is generally preferable, provided you have no history of premature birth or miscarriage and are not nauseous. During the last two months of pregnancy, it's wise for you to stay in your city or, at the beginning of the eighth month, go to the locality where you intend the baby's birth to take place and remain there.

SMOKING AND LIQUOR To date much has been done to inform the general public of the harmful effects of smoking. However, opinion is divided as to whether or not smoking is more hazardous during pregnancy. If you're a heavy smoker, doctors advise that you cut down to a great extent, but you needn't quit entirely, unless your doctor recommends it.

An alcoholic beverage contains between 70 and 160 calories and might be well worth eliminating from your diet if the doctor suggests cutting down on your caloric intake. Alcohol adds calories without nourishment to your diet, and for other reasons may be harmful. Ask your doctor whether or not you may drink on occasion.

DRUGS AND MEDICINES In recent years there has been a great deal of concern and publicity concerning the possible harmful effects of various drugs taken during the early stages of pregnancy. Most drugs or medicines have no effect on the pregnancy one way or another. However, it is important that during your pregnancy you take only those drugs prescribed or approved by your doctor.

INTERCOURSE Refrain from intercourse altogether during the last six weeks of pregnancy.

BABY GROWS ON WHAT YOU EAT Since your baby, before birth, depends solely on you for nourishment, your diet is most vital.

We know that now as an expectant mother you don't need any more food than at any other time, but the quality of the food you eat is enormously significant.

It's true that you're eating for two, yet you must cautiously watch your weight. Excess weight may cause complications during your pregnancy, at the time of delivery, and is terribly hard to lose afterwards! The up-to-date doctor therefore "weighs in" his patients when they come for their regular examinations, and in most cases insists that they don't gain more than 20 pounds all told. Doctors are usually real sticklers about weight gain, so take his advice seriously or you'll be taking a scolding instead.

This means that without eating any more, and generally less than you did before, you must include all the food elements your baby needs for normal development. It is your responsibility to eat the right foods in the proper amounts.

A POOR DIET ENDANGERS BOTH YOU AND YOUR BABY Various studies made in hospitals and research centers have proved conclusively that the baby's development can be seriously affected if the mother's diet during pregnancy is deficient. These babies may weigh less and be too short. The development of their bones and teeth may be impaired. And they are thought to be more susceptible to illness than the babies of mothers who have had good diets throughout their pregnancies.

In addition to the possible effect on the baby, a poor diet can also cause trouble for you. It may result in more difficult labor, major complications, and even the loss of your baby because of prematurity or stillbirth. A poor prenatal diet can affect your ability to nurse the baby. So, you see, the importance of the best possible diet all through your pregnancy cannot be overemphasized.

Your baby is developing continuously and needs these vital food elements every day. Many of the needed vitamins cannot be stored, so you can't eat a good diet one day, then backslide for a few days, still thinking you're doing an adequate job.

LEARN THE GOOD FOODS On the next few pages, the good foods are discussed. Learn them and then stick to them every day. Fathers-to-be can help by adopting this food plan, too. If you don't have to prepare the "outlawed" foods, you won't be as tempted to eat them.

After learning the good foods, learn how to save their nutritional content. Save vitamins and minerals by purchasing the freshest possible fruits and vegetables. Exposure to heat, air, and water robs food of its nutritional value. Some uncooked fruits and vegetables should be included in your diet every day. Cooking should be done quickly in a covered container in as little water as possible. Avoid reheating cooked foods when possible. Cooking foods in their skins also cuts down on nutrient loss.

VITAMINS The subject of vitamins in pregnancy can be overworked. Vitamins are essential for growth and during pregnancy the body's demand will increase for them. However, today's expectant mother receives a near-adequate supply by taking a prenatal multivitamin supplement prescribed by her doctor.

With the multivitamin supplements and enriched and fortified foods now on the market, a mother-to-be need not worry about vitamin deficiency if she eats sensibly and gets additional daily amounts of vitamin C.

She must now concentrate on calcium, proteins, and carbohydrates.

THE NUTRIENTS: WHAT, WHY, AND HOW

NUTRIENT	REASONS WHY WE NEED IT	FOOD SOURCES
Protein	Build and repair all tissue; form antibodies; supply food energy.	Meat; fish; poultry, eggs; milk and grain products.
Fat	Supply food energy and essential fatty acids.	Butter; margarine; cream; oils; bacon.
Carbohydrate	Supply food energy; to help the body use other nutrients.	Grain products; potatoes; any of the many sweet, fattening foods.
Calcium	Build bones and teeth.	Milk products.
Iron	Combine with protein to make hemoglobin.	Liver; egg yolk; shellfish; dried fruit; grain products.
Vitamin A	Healthy mucous membranes and inner organs; nerve and eye development; resistance to infections.	Green and yellow vegetables; liver; milk products; egg yolk.
Vitamin B_1	Normal appetite, digestion, and carbohydrate utilization.	Grain and poultry products; meat; fish; milk; peas.
Vitamin B_2	Appetite and digestion; nervous system; skin and eye tissue.	Dark green vegetables; milk and grain products; meat.
Vitamin C	Blood regeneration; tissue respiration; resistance to infection.	Fruit; potatoes; green vegetables.
Vitamin D	Strong bones and teeth; body utilization of calcium and phosphorus.	Milk; eggs; butter; exposure to direct sunlight.
Vitamin E	Normal fetus development; completion of pregnancy.	Lettuce; wheat germ. Adequate in any balanced diet.
Vitamin K	Normal blood clotting; prevention of hemorrhage.	Egg yolk; liver; spinach; tomatoes; cauliflower.

YOU NEED MILK FOR CALCIUM Milk contains the minerals needed for the baby's bones and teeth and in a form easy for you and the baby to use. It's also a rich source of tissue-building protein, carbohydrates for energy, and important vitamins.

You should have a quart of milk a day. It may be taken as a beverage or in foods, such as cream soup, custards, creamed vegetables, and the like. If possible, drink most of your milk as a beverage. It's the simplest way of getting your full quota.

If you don't like to drink milk, try slightly diluted evaporated milk in cooking, or on your cereal. Since it is concentrated, it will give you more nutritional value with less fluid. Or mix powdered milk with other foods as another way of getting your milk in a highly concentrated form.

Cheese is another concentrated milk product and has a food value similar to milk. A one and a quarter-inch cube of yellow American cheese has about the same amount of calcium, phosphorus, proteins, and vitamins as a 6-ounce glass of whole milk. But cheese shouldn't be used to replace more than one glass of milk in your daily diet.

If you seem to gain more weight than you should, in spite of cutting out sweets, starches, and other fattening foods, ask your doctor about substituting skimmed milk for whole milk. Whole milk is preferred for the vitamin A in its butterfat. Do not substitute calcium tablets for milk. In fact, if you are gaining too much weight, cut down on something else—but don't cut out milk!

PROTEINS BUILD NEW LIFE The woman who is pregnant requires about 50 percent more protein than she normally would so protein requirements demand careful attention. While calcium and phosphorus in milk supply the framework of your unborn's body, protein provides the actual building materials for his tissues and organs.

Proteins can come from two sources—animal and vegetable. Animal protein is considered our richest source and includes meat, eggs, seafood, milk, and cheese. Over half of your protein requirement should come from this group. The rest can be obtained from vegetables, breads, cereals, and other foods.

Meat and eggs are the richest protein sources and are practically equal in value. Eggs also are rich in iron and vitamins. Remember, you are harboring a little iron-hoarder; so eat at least one egg every day (unless you're allergic to eggs. If so you should consult your doctor). Most doctors also advise a serving (about ¼ pound) of lean meat every day, with liver at least once a week. Chicken, lamb, mutton, veal, kidney, heart, lean pork, and lean beef are allowed.

In addition to its protein, liver contains iron, copper, and valuable vitamins, so it gives extra value. Oysters, too, are rich in these nutritional areas, and may be eaten liberally when you can get them.

Fresh fish is also excellent, and seafood is especially good because it contains iodine, essential for proper mental and physical development.

If protein needs are not met in pregnancy, the mother-to-be often complains of swelling, tiredness, and anemia. Liver damage and edema may also result from protein deficiency.

Proper protein balance isn't difficult if you have two servings of meat, four glasses of milk, and two eggs every day.

CHOOSE THE BEST CARBOHYDRATES Carbohydrates, the energy foods, are needed in pregnancy as at other times. These include cereals, breads, potatoes, and sweets. While they're fattening foods and need to be eaten sparingly, they have a definite place in your diet, especially whole-grain breads and cereals.

Choose the breads and cereals you eat from the whole-wheat or enriched variety, so you'll get extra vitamins.

FOODS NOT TO EAT Avoid foods rich in fats, sugars, and starches, such as gravies, bacon, mayonnaise, fat meats, dough-nuts, potato chips, macaroni, spaghetti, rice, pies, cakes, rich puddings, ice cream, candy, soft drinks, popcorn, peanuts, and the like. Reject food that's highly spiced or seasoned.

As salt encourages retention of water in the tissues, use it sparingly. When you're cooking, cut down on the amount of salt you normally add to foods and don't add any more while at the table. Foods such as bacon, ham, salt pork, salt fish, chipped beef, and other salty prepared meats and dark rye bread should not be used. The best rule to apply is: When in doubt, don't use it.

DIETARY "MUSTS" IN PREGNANCY Here are the foods which you should eat every day for your own well-being and to enable your baby to grow as you would like him to do:

1. Milk. One quart. (Or its equivalent in evaporated or powdered milk, and cheese.)

2. Vegetables. Two or more servings of cooked vegetables. A serving is 4 heaping tablespoonfuls or ½ measuring cup. Include some dark-green leafy or deep-yellow vegetables every day. One small potato, boiled or baked in the skin. (Potato, in addition to its other nutritional value, furnishes vitamin C and iron.)

3. Fruit and fruit juices. One measuring cup (8 ounces) of unstrained orange juice, or the juice of other citrus fruit or tomato in amounts that will supply as much vitamin C as 1 cup of orange juice. For instance, ¾ measuring cup (6 ounces) of grapefruit juice equals ½ cup of orange juice; 1 cup tomato juice equals ½ cup of orange juice; ½ cup of strawberries, ¼ cantaloupe, or 2 tangerines are equal to ½ cup of orange juice. In addition to meeting your vitamin C requirements, eat at least one other serving of fruit each day. Dried fruits are excellent sources of iron—apricots, especially—and they're also high in vitamin A. Fruit also helps prevent constipation.

4. Meat, fish, or fowl. At least one serving.

5. At least one egg.

6. Whole-grain or enriched cereals. One serving.

7. Vitamin D as prescribed by your doctor.

From these groups, choose those foods that are high in nutrients and low in calories.

A GOOD DIET DURING PREGNANCY

Breakfast:

4 ounces of orange juice (or its equivalent in citrus fruit)

¾ cup whole-grain cereal, with 1 teaspoon sugar

½ cup skim milk

1 cup coffee

10 a.m.

1 glass of skim milk

Luncheon:

1 slice whole-wheat or enriched bread

1 egg or cottage cheese

1 serving raw or cooked vegetable

½ cup of skim milk

1 teaspoon of butter or margarine

½ cup any kind of fruit or berries, or 1 piece of melon, or 1 peach, pear, or apple

3 p.m.

1 glass skim milk

Dinner:

1 serving lean meat, fish, or fowl

1 small potato, cooked in skin

1 teaspoon butter

½ cup cooked vegetables

1 liberal serving raw vegetable salad

1 glass of skim milk (or at bedtime)

½ cup orange juice or its equivalent

1 multivitamin capsule, or vitamin D in form that has been prescribed

Ideally, it's probably a better practice to have your large meal at noon, and a lighter one at night. Most American families, however, have dinner at night. The point is not important enough for you to prepare one meal for your family, another for yourself.

CARE OF THE BOWELS It's easy to understand that you need to keep bowels functioning regularly, since the waste products of the baby's body as well as of your own must be carried off through your excretory system. If you have a tendency to be constipated, it may be a little increased during pregnancy, causing temporary discomfort. As far as possible, the bowels should be controlled through diet and regular habits.

If you choose your foods from the list just given and eat large quantities of vegetables and fruits, you should have little trouble. However, should you have trouble, the following foods will be especially helpful: Green vegetables, figs, dates, stewed fruit, prunes, oranges, baked apples, whole-wheat bread, and rough cereals.

The other constipation preventive is regularity in going to the toilet. If you haven't already done so, you should form the habit of going to the toilet every morning after breakfast and staying there for some time. Don't strain to force a movement. Instead, relax as much as possible. This practice, combined with the diet described, will in most cases establish a daily movement.

If you need further help, try this regimen:

1. Drink a glass of warm water when you get up in the morning.

2. Eat a coarse, laxative bran cereal for breakfast with one of the laxative fruits just mentioned. Marmalade on your toast is also a stimulus to bowel action.

3. Eat some fruit before going to bed at night.

4. If suggestions 1–3 do not work, ask your doctor for a mild laxative. Don't take any other laxative except on doctor's orders.

CARE OF THE KIDNEYS The importance of the kidneys at this time is recognized in the regular examination of urine which every reliable doctor gives his obstetrical cases. Aside from having this examination, you usually need to do nothing except drink the six to eight glasses of liquids a day in addition to your quart of milk, or a total of 3 quarts of liquid, and observe the other hygienic rules. In early and late pregnancy, there is a tendency to urinate frequently because at this time the uterus presses upon the bladder and urethra. There's nothing abnormal about this. If, however, the urine becomes scant, hard to pass, dark colored, or has a strong odor, have your doctor examine a specimen at once.

SIGNS OF DANGER If any of the following occur between your visits to the doctor, don't delay, but let him know AT ONCE.

1. Swelling of the face, hands or feet

2. Dimness or blurring of vision

3. Pain in the abdomen

4. Fever

5. Any vaginal bleeding

6. Persistent vomiting

7. Continuous headache

8. A rush of water from the vagina

9. A hard fall. If you have one, notify your doctor, go to bed, and remain still until examined.

These may be of slight importance, but they may indicate a condition that needs immediate attention. Only your doctor can decide.

TAKE CARE OF YOUR TEETH There is a tendency toward

Maternity-nursing bras play a dual role. Before the baby arrives, they provide added support. Afterward, they make nursing more convenient.

decay in the teeth of pregnant women. This may be because the child-bearing years occur at the same periods when teeth ordinarily show signs of decay. Whatever the cause, you should be under the watchful eye of your dentist as well as of your doctor.

Consult your dentist early in pregnancy and have a thorough dental checkup. It's desirable to have the necessary work done as early in pregnancy as possible.

CARE OF THE NIPPLES The condition of your nipples when your baby is born will have a good deal to do with your success in nursing him.

The nipples should be washed every morning, with mild soap and water. Then dash cold water over them lightly to toughen them.

If the nipples are stiff or hard, apply petroleum jelly, lanolin, or warm cocoa butter. Cover with squares of clean linen or gauze to protect your clothes.

Any time from the fourth month on, some fluid may come from the nipples, sometimes enough that your clothes must be protected by pads. If the fluid stays on the nipples, it may make them sore. They should be washed often with tepid boiled water.

Use an uplift type of brassiere, which lifts the breasts up and out and doesn't press the nipples. Never wear a brassiere which presses the nipples in, as this makes nursing more dif-

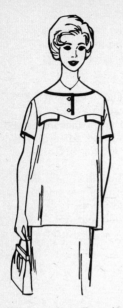 

Two-piece outfits offer mix-and-match opportunities and provide plenty of combinations for the months ahead. Boost the morale with bright colors.

Fashionable one-piece dresses may make you look and feel slimmer. Make them yourself or buy ready-mades. Now you can be a fashion-minded mother-to-be.

ficult for your baby.

If cracks appear in your nipples, wash them with tepid boiled water and keep them covered with sterile gauze. Report the condition to your doctor.

STREAKS ON THE ABDOMEN The streaks or lines which often appear on the abdomen, and even down on the thighs, result from overstretching of your skin. You may succeed in keeping these streaks (called striae) to a minimum if you watch your weight diligently. If you avoid a rapid weight gain, this condition should be of very little or no concern to you.

If, however, you are alarmed by these streaks, some authorities recommend massaging your abdomen with lanolin or cold cream daily during the last four months to ease the stretched condition of your skin. This may or may not help avoid the streaking, but it certainly does no harm to try it.

These marks will lighten in time, after delivery, but they never disappear completely.

PERSONAL HYGIENE You have undoubtedly heard people say that a woman is never more beautiful than when she is carrying a child. Probably you have given this some thought lately and may have gone so far as to look for proof! This is only natural as every woman wants to look her best—an expectant mother is no exception.

In the coming months, you may find this more difficult if your energy dwindles by late afternoon. A leisurely bath (neither steaming hot nor so cold that you become chilled), a dab of perfume, and a fresh outfit will help restore your appearance, energy, and spirits. Take care not to slip while getting in or out of the tub. Place a mat or towel in the tub to prevent accidents.

During the last six weeks of pregnancy, you may find getting in and out of the tub a bit awkward. If so, you may prefer taking a sponge bath or shower.

CLOTHING In the past one hundred years, the mother-to-be has been emancipated. No longer does society demand that she seek seclusion during her waiting period. In more recent years, clothing manufacturers increased her freedom by allowing her to be both pregnant and fashionable. Today's lady-in-waiting has a nearly inexhaustible selection of both style and colors from which to choose.

In selecting your maternity wardrobe, combine maximum appeal with wearability. Buy these clothes in the same size you always wear, because most well-made maternity fashions have stretch, pleat, and tab features that expand as you progress in your pregnancy. Keep in mind that all clothing should hang from the shoulders as much as possible. Avoid tight or confining clothing, especially at the waist and around the legs.

What should you buy? The one-piece dress is the most comfortable and popular selection. However, skirts and jumpers are far more versatile. Because they can be worn with many different blouses, they become both wardrobe stretchers and therefore, dollar stretchers. Add a few sports outfits for homewear. Washable slacks of denim or corduroy worn with colorful tops printed with flowers, checks, stripes, and plaids will keep you looking both pretty and comfortable.

Your underwear or "briefs" should fit closely around your thighs, as a sanitary precaution. However, they must not bind either at the legs or the waist.

If your regular bra size is 34 B, you will probably increase to a 36 or 38 C by the third month. Select bras which provide good support and a full enough cup to prevent pressure against the nipple.

Unless your physician recommends otherwise, you may get adequate support and comfort from an ordinary "two-way-stretch" girdle, provided there are no reinforcing panels or stays and it is not the panty type. Graduate to a larger size as soon as there is the least suggestion of snugness. If you feel more support is needed, ask your doctor to recommend a maternity girdle.

The best shoe during pregnancy is a low-heeled, broad-toed one. You'll have a tendency to a swaybacked and teetering posture since you are carrying so much extra weight in front. High heels would throw you even more off balance. However, if you are used to wearing high heels and feel uncomfortable in any other kind of shoe, medical authorities will allow you to wear a heel that is not more than an inch and a half high. Wedge-soled sandals are not considered advisable to wear during pregnancy.

MIRROR, MIRROR ON THE WALL . . . As you get larger and larger, you may be haunted by the fear that you're going to stay that way. Walking or other mild exercises prescribed for you will help keep good muscle tone. Your abdomen may sag for a time after your baby's birth, but that's a temporary condition, too. Good posture, attention to diet, and exercises as described on pages 74–79, if your doctor agrees, will bring your waistline into bounds again. Many of the lovely figures you see going up and down the street belong to women who have had one or more babies. This will be a pleasant, reassuring thought for you to keep in mind.

Follow instructions about not getting heavier than is necessary, and develop a strong determination!

TAKE PRECAUTIONS BUT CONTINUE TO LIVE NORMALLY Your pregnancy is exciting to you and if it's your first, it's even a little mysterious and awe-inspiring. That's as it should be. However, pregnancy is no excuse for making an invalid of yourself or for upsetting your normal life. Proof of this is in the number of women who have worked outside their homes all through their pregnancies, some up to the very day of delivery. They're well and happy the whole time, and their babies are fine healthy youngsters.

Common sense dictates that you take some precautions such as taking extra care to dress warmly to avoid becoming chilled. Otherwise, follow your usual daily routine. Here are the few precautions you need to observe:

1. Avoid anyone with a cold, and especially anyone with an infectious or contagious disease. Because many diseases are transmitted before definite diagnosis can be made, stay away from any person who seems to be coming down with an illness.

An infection, while it may not affect you at all, can be a serious danger to your baby. This is particularly true of German meases (rubella). This disease lasts but a few days, and may not make you very ill, but can have damaging effect on the fetus, especially if you contract the disease during the first three months of pregnancy. If one of your children has been exposed to German measles, turn his care over to another adult and stay well away from him.

2. You will require more rest and will tire easily. You should get eight and preferably nine hours of sleep every night, and a rest during the day. If you work and can't rest during the day, get an extra hour of sleep.

3. Pay particular attention to your doctor's diet instructions. Learn and use the foods which are best for good nutrition and religiously watch your weight for good health both before and after the birth of your baby.

4. Avoid violent exercise; activities that require jumping or sharp, jerking motions, lifting or pushing heavy objects, and running up and down stairs.

5. Avoid standing or sitting still for long periods.

6. Get as much fresh air and sunshine as possible.

7. Avoid becoming chilled.

8. Do not have intercourse the last month or six weeks before delivery.

9. Continue your outside interests, including seeing friends, as much as possible.

10. See your doctor at the regular times he has set, and report to him immediately any unusual symptoms.

Don't worry if a friend's doctor has recommended something different for her than your physician has for you. Your doctor knows your case best and has your welfare in mind. He has reasons for whatever instructions he has given you. Don't compare notes with other pregnant women, or veteran mothers. This only causes worry.

IF YOU'RE A WORKING WOMAN Your condition will become readily apparent by the fifth month. If your appearance is important in your work, you'll want to quit, or arrange to work at home after that.

Perhaps your pregnant appearance doesn't matter, but your work may keep you on your feet or be otherwise physically tiring. Then you should quit two months before your baby's birth. If yours is a "sitting" job and you enjoy it, follow your own wishes about discontinuing it.

Don't plan to return to work until your baby is at least 6 weeks old, and not then if you are nursing him. Unless it is absolutely necessary for you to work, think it over carefully before you leave your baby in the care of someone else every day. He needs you! And the job may not really pay after figuring out all the expenses.

ARRANGE WITH THE HOSPITAL Your doctor will probably recommend a hospital for you and may even make the arrangements. However, if he prefers that you make the arrangements, go to the hospital in person, learn the rates, and indicate your choice. Attend to this matter early and while there, inquire whether prenatal classes are offered. More hospitals are doing so.

Hospital rates are quoted according to the kind of room you get. They include board and nursing service, but there's an extra charge for the delivery room, medicines, and dressings. Also ask what you should bring for yourself and the baby.

ROOMING-IN Some hospitals have what is known as "rooming-in" programs. This means that the newborn baby, very soon after delivery, is placed in a crib at his mother's bedside. There he stays as long as his mother remains in the hospital. He is removed only if he is so noisy at night as to disturb his mother and other patients, or if either he or his mother becomes ill.

Rooming-in permits an intimate association between mother and baby almost from birth on. During the first twenty-four hours after delivery, the nurses take care of most of the baby's needs and, in the process, demonstrate to you the techniques of nursing and attending to him. After that, you perform the routine care yourself. This allows you to go home feeling very confident of your ability to take over your baby's care. Breast feeding seems to be established more easily with this system and babies tend to gain rapidly.

If you are interested in this arrangement, ask your doctor and your hospital if they have such accommodations.

ANESTHETICS OR NO ANESTHETICS The knowledge of pain and how to control it has become quite complex. Today a prospective mother and her doctor have a wide choice of pain relievers from which to choose.

Even if you have dismissed the idea of natural childbirth (delivery without the use of pain relievers), you can benefit from a community course on natural childbirth. This generally consists of instructional lectures and exercises by doctors and nurses. You are shown exactly what is going to take place and learn muscular techniques and breathing exercises to use during labor.

If such classes are not offered in your area or you would like additional information regarding natural childbirth, you can obtain the book, *A Way to Natural Childbirth*, by Helen Heardman, published in the United States by Williams and Wilkins of Baltimore, Maryland.

Pain relievers are classified in three groups—analgesia, anesthesia, and amnesia. These are terms you have heard frequently; however, you may not know the difference in their meaning.

Analgesia means relief from pain or discomfort without loss of consciousness.

Analgesics are given in many forms—pills, capsules, hypodermically, or by inhalation. Since you are conscious, they do not prevent you from doing your share during labor.

During anesthesia there is either partial or total unconsciousness. Anesthetics are administered hypodermically, rectally, or by inhalation. Some your doctor may select are: Ether, chloroform, nitrous oxide-oxygen, ethylene-oxygen, cyclopropane-oxygen, and sodium pentothal.

There are also amnesic drugs which allow the patient to remain conscious, but with little or no memory of discomfort.

CAUDAL ANESTHESIA Caudal anesthesia is a continuous injection of a drug at the base of the spine which blocks the nerves at the site of delivery. It eliminates discomfort, yet allows the mother to remain conscious during delivery. More important, however, it does not depress the breathing of mother or baby.

There are many individual circumstances under which caudal anesthesia is not advisable. Also, the administration of this anesthetic requires specially trained personnel which may or may not be available in the hospital you have chosen.

SADDLE BLOCK Saddle block is the most widely used form of anesthesia and, like caudal, is a local anesthesia which allows the mother to remain conscious and does not depress respiration.

The administering technique is brief and simple. While the patient sits over the side of the bed, a fine needle is passed through the spine between two of the lower vertebrae, injecting a small amount of anesthetic such as nupercaine. The needle is removed, the patient lies down, and discomfort disappears.

In a small percentage of cases, saddle block may cause moderate to severe headaches. If so, it will be relieved by bed rest for a few hours.

Many doctors feel that caudal and saddle block anesthesia have definite advantages over inhalation anesthesia. They are most useful in the second stage of labor, while analgesic and amnesic drugs are used during the first stage.

UTEROSACRAL AND PUDENDAL BLOCK Uterosacral anesthesia is a recent, but similar type of anesthesia. Its administration is followed, at the time of delivery, by a pudendal nerve block which blocks pain sensation in the vaginal area.

HYPNOSIS Some doctors, with special training in hypnosis, are instructing carefully chosen patients how to utilize hypno-anesthesia during delivery. Those patients suited to it are able to relax so greatly that they feel no discomfort during their delivery.

DECISION MAKING During one of your regular visits to your doctor, ask him what his usual practice is in regard to anesthetics. He will tell you his preference and explain the reasons for his choice of anesthetics.

Each doctor has many things to consider before deciding which anesthetic to give his patient. Remember whatever your doctor decides to do, he does because it is best for you and your baby. When the time comes, just relax and do what he tells you to do.

3

Routine and special tests during pregnancy

Probably on your first visit to your doctor, or as soon as it is certain that you are pregnant, your doctor will check on your pelvic measurements. This is to determine whether your pelvis (the bony structure between your hips) is of adequate size for the baby to pass through. He will record your weight and blood pressure at every visit, and sometime during your pregnancy, he will make an internal examination. This helps him determine the shape of your uterus, the construction of your pelvis and whether or not everything concerning your Fallopian tubes, ovaries, cervix, and the vaginal passage is favorable. During this internal examination, your doctor will also make a papanicolaou smear test. The "Pap" test is an invaluable screening test for cancer of the cervix and should be administered annually.

As your pregnancy progresses, your doctor will make regular external examinations of your abdomen to listen to the baby's heart beat and to learn the position of the baby and the size of your enlarging uterus.

In addition, he will make many other tests. To help you understand these tests, here are the most usual ones:

URINALYSIS At each visit to his office, your doctor will probably request a specimen of your urine. He may have you bring a sample in a small bottle, or he may have arrangements in his office by which a fresh specimen of your urine can be obtained.

This regular examination is to check for albumin, which could indicate a developing toxemia; sugar, which might be a sign of diabetes; and pus cells and casts, which may mean a kidney infection.

BLOOD PRESSURE Your doctor will check your blood pressure during your regular examinations. This is a precaution so that any unusual rise above your normal pressure can be detected and treated immediately.

BLOOD TEST FOR SYPHILIS Early in your pregnancy, your doctor will probably take a specimen of your blood to determine whether or not you may have syphilis. This test is compulsory in many states. The fact that your doctor has your blood tested does not mean that he suspects you may have the disease, although some women may have syphilis without being aware of it. If you should have the disease, your doctor must know it to begin treatment immediately. This is simply a precautionary measure to protect you and your child.

HEMOGLOBIN CONCENTRATION Your doctor will also have your blood tested for its hemoglobin concentration. This is done because many women have anemia, and a low hemoglobin estimation will show it. Your doctor can then treat the anemia to prevent it from causing any difficulty.

THE Rh FACTOR Another test which your doctor will make is for the Rh factor. Under certain conditions, he may also want to determine your husband's Rh factor.

Rh is the name given to a factor found in the red blood cells of most people. Persons who have this factor are called Rh positive. Those who don't have it are known as Rh negative. It was named for the Rhesus monkeys because it was first detected in experiments with these animals.

No complications for the Rh factor can arise where both parents are the same type. Only when the mother is Rh negative and the father Rh positive is there any possibility of trouble. This combination of blood types generally produces an Rh positive baby. At the time of delivery, some of the baby's Rh positive blood cells may pass into the mother's blood stream. This, in effect, gives the mother a small transfusion of Rh positive cells. The mother then produces antibodies which will destroy Rh positive cells. This process, up to this point, has caused the mother no harm nor has it produced any problem with the first baby. The mother, however, will continue to have the Rh antibodies in her blood stream. If during her next pregnancy, she has another Rh positive baby the antibodies from the mother's blood will cross the placenta and get into the baby's blood. There they will destroy some of the baby's blood cells.

In 1968 there was a monumental breakthrough in the treatment of people with potential Rh problems. A substance known as RhoGam was developed. This material given by injection contains anti-Rh antibodies. When this material is given in small amounts to an Rh negative mother, it will destroy any Rh blood cells she has in her blood stream. If this material is given within 72 hours after the positive blood cells enter the mother's blood stream, the cells will be destroyed before the mother has time to develop antibodies of her own. The injected material leaves the mother's blood stream within a matter of a few weeks and she is, therefore, prevented from developing Rh sensitivity. This material is given after a careful series of blood tests are done on both the mother and her recently delivered baby. As a result of this dramatic advance, it will be possible virtually to eliminate Rh problems in childbearing women of the future.

Mothers who have been made sensitive to the Rh factor by previous pregnancies unfortunately cannot benefit from this new development. In fact, to give a previously sensitized woman a dose of RhoGam would make her condition worse in succeeding pregnancies. If you previously have had babies with Rh difficulty or if your laboratory studies show a rapid rise in antibody titers, your doctor may elect to perform an amniocentesis (draw some amniotic fluid from around the baby in the latter stages of pregnancy). By examining this fluid he can quite accurately determine the extent to which your baby is involved. If the involvement is marked, he may elect to induce labor a few weeks before your expected delivery in order to prevent further destruction of the baby's blood cells by the Rh antibodies. In recent years, babies who are very severely involved early in pregnancy have been given blood transfusions while still in the uterus in order to protect the baby until it becomes large enough to deliver and have a good chance of survival. While not always successful, this dramatic procedure has materially improved the salvage of severely affected erythroblastotic babies.

In recent years, many other blood incompatibilities that can cause jaundice in the newborn have been discovered. The most common one is the major blood group incompatibility known as the ABO. In these cases, the mother is usually type O, and the father is type A or B. This makes the baby either type A or B; the method of sensitization is the same as in Rh incompatibility. The baby's A or B blood cells pass into the mother's blood which causes production of antibodies. When these antibodies cross the placenta and get into the baby's blood, they destroy some of the baby's blood cells. Usually the jaundice is not as severe as in cases of Rh incompatibility, but occasionally a baby will require a blood exchange transfusion.

The decision for transfusion rests on your doctor's evaluation of the many factors involved. The entire transfusion procedure is done with a very slight risk to your baby, and you can be assured that in all probability he will be quite normal.

SPECIAL TESTS To have a normal labor and a healthy baby, it is essential that the doctor detect any illness that might be present during your pregnancy and treat it promptly.

Special tests may be required to detect anemia, diabetes, heart disorders, tuberculosis, and thyroid malfunctions.

Although you may be reluctant to spend the money on any special tests, your doctor has your best interests in mind when he suggests them. Don't hesitate to follow his recommendations. The early detection and treatment of any illness is to your advantage and to the advantage of your baby.

4

If you
don't feel well

Many women go through the whole period of pregnancy feeling
better and looking lovelier than they ever did before. But you
may have various discomforts which can be lessened by proper
care. Serious complications sometimes develop, but these, too,
may be avoided if you follow your doctor's instructions carefully.

NAUSEA AND VOMITING The most common minor discomfort of pregnancy is "morning sickness," so called because
it usually occurs immediately after you get up in the morning.
However, you may feel nauseated at other times as well.

One-half to two-thirds of all expectant mothers have experienced nausea, especially in the first months of pregnancy.
To be nauseated is perfectly normal and physiological. To let
it grow into pernicious vomiting is not normal and may be
psychological.

However, if you're experiencing this discomfort, it would
be hard for anyone to convince you that you're imagining
things! But, unless you have pernicious vomiting (which requires constant medical care), you can obtain considerable, if
not absolute, relief by combining special diet with rest and
possibly a prescribed medication.

The idea of a diet to overcome morning sickness is to keep
the stomach full of solids. It calls for six meals a day, each
meal high in carbohydrates and low in fats. When you're on

the diet for nausea, you won't be able to keep your weight gain to a minimum as you would like.

When the nausea is overcome, or disappears, which usually happens at the end of the first three months, you may cut out the excess carbohydrates and lose some of the weight gained on the diet to overcome morning sickness. In this way, while you may gain a lot at first, you'll be able to keep your weight within bounds when it becomes necessary because of the baby's increasing size.

Since butter encourages the tendency to nausea, it should be used sparingly while the condition lasts. If you are taking cod-liver oil and it seems to upset you, ask your doctor about a vitamin D substitute.

In addition to the six meals a day prescribed for nausea, have a supply of crackers handy and eat them whenever your stomach gets uneasy. Keep some beside your bed at night, and eat one or two first thing in the morning before you've so much as raised your head from the pillow. Then rest quietly for twenty minutes or so. Follow the same course—lie down and eat a cracker—any time during the day that your stomach begins to act up. If you're working, keep some crackers in your desk and munch one when you feel a spell of nausea coming on.

After the first attacks have stopped, you may have a "regular" dinner at night of lean meat, green vegetables, potato, lettuce and tomato or fruit salad, and dessert.

Here's the high calorie diet (recommended *only* if you are troubled with nausea):

DIET FOR NAUSEA

7:30 a.m. 2 soda crackers.

8:00 a.m. Stewed prunes (6 large), or baked apple.
Cooked whole-wheat or enriched cereal with sugar or honey, and very small amount of cream.
Cup of chocolate with sugar (if coffee increases nausea).
2 slices of whole-wheat toast, spread with honey. No butter.

10:30 a.m. 2 slices of toast (with marmalade or jelly, no butter), or 2 crackers, 1 glass of milk, cocoa, hot malted milk, or tea.

12:30 p.m. Vegetable, cream of celery or potato soup, with crackers.

2 slices of whole-wheat or enriched bread.

Lettuce, ½ head.

1 cup of custard, cornstarch pudding, tapioca, or 3 ounces of gelatin.

4:00 p.m. Fruit juice, or tea with sugar.

2 slices of whole-wheat toast, honey or marmalade; no butter.

1 slice of sponge cake.

6:30 p.m. 1 cup of cream of pea soup, or other soups as at lunch.

2 crackers, or 2 slices of toast.

Baked sweet or white potato (large) or

3 ounces of rice.

3 ounces of stewed carrots, or beets.

Desserts as at lunch, 1 ounce of dates, or 1 ounce of raisins.

9:30 to 10:00 p.m. Toast or crackers.

1 glass of milk, cocoa, or malted milk.

Use this diet only when nausea is a problem. As soon as you're over it, change gradually to the diet on pages 32–33. Your doctor may advise medication to stop nausea.

REST RELIEVES NAUSEA If medication and the proper diet do not totally relieve your nausea, you will benefit from obtaining as much rest as possible. Surprising as it may be, rest is quite as important as diet.

As every nausea victim knows, the unpleasantness leaves as if by magic when the three months are up, although it may recur temporarily if there's too long an interval between meals or if you become overly tired.

OTHER DIGESTIVE DISCOMFORTS Gas, heartburn, indigestion, and the heart palpitation often felt are all largely caused by something in the diet. The first step in relieving them is to determine what food is causing the difficulty. Then eliminate it.

Heartburn can often be prevented by taking a tablespoon of cream one-half hour before meals. The cream shouldn't be taken at mealtime, however. If the heartburn persists, consult your doctor. He can give you something to relieve it. *Never take baking soda during pregnancy*, for heartburn or any other reason.

Rapid heart action, often experienced in pregnancy, may be due to indigestion or pressure of the uterus on stomach or heart. Paying close attention to diet and exercise usually helps correct the situation.

VARICOSE VEINS Sometimes certain veins in the legs become swollen and painful. This seldom happens in the first pregnancy, but may be a problem in succeeding ones. This condition should be called to your doctor's attention.

Varicose veins result from poor circulation. You were cautioned in the section about clothing never to wear tight garters or rolled stockings. In spite of these precautions, veins may still become dilated.

Proper bandaging with elastic bandages may give some relief. These may be purchased in any drugstore. In milder cases of varicose veins, relief may be obtained by wearing support stockings. Support stockings have been greatly improved in appearance and no longer have that bulky long-underwear look. Whichever you use, put them on the first thing in the morning, before getting out of bed. If you should use the elastic bandage, wrap it once or twice around the instep, around the ankle, and continue in an overlapping spiral all the way up the leg to just below the knee. The bandage should be snug and fastened with a safety pin, just below the knee.

Enlarged veins may be helped by lying down as often as possible during the day. Prop your legs up with pillows so they're higher than your hips. And when you're sitting, try to rest your legs on a high footstool.

HEMORRHOIDS Hemorrhoids have been called "varicose veins of the rectum." They are engorged veins at the opening of the rectum. They often itch and bleed and may be extremely painful. Generally, they result from straining over the hard stools of constipation. So the best preventive is to avoid constipation. Mention to your doctor any indication that you are developing hemorrhoids. A more laxative diet (see page 32) and a daily dose of mineral oil may be all that's needed to correct them. If the hemorrhoids become extremely painful, get in touch with your doctor at once.

Lying down frequently during the day and sitting with your legs raised level with your body is beneficial if you have hemorrhoids.

ITCHING OF THE BODY AND VAGINA Occasionally a woman who is pregnant complains that the skin all over her body itches. This may be helped by adding baking soda or corn starch to your bath water, but should be reported to your doctor as it may be a symptom of food or drug allergy.

Advise your doctor of any itching of the vagina so that he can determine the cause and treat it. Don't use any douches unless your doctor specifically orders them.

VAGINAL DISCHARGE In the latter part of your pregnancy, you may have a thin, pale yellow discharge from the vagina. This is normal and requires only the wearing of a sanitary pad and a thorough washing of the area once or twice a day. If the discharge is thick or profuse, or accompanied by itching, consult your doctor.

SKIN SPOTS AND BRITTLE HAIR You may notice brown spots developing on your face, particularly if you're a brunette. Occasionally, the brownish tinge spreads over the whole face. This "mask of pregnancy" disappears shortly after delivery.

In the latter part of your pregnancy, you may notice your hair becoming dry and breaking off. Don't be concerned if this happens. Your hair will return to its normal state after your baby is born.

Brush your hair and massage your scalp regularly. Hot oil scalp treatments before shampoos will be helpful, too. Permanent waving may not be successful at this time because of the brittleness of your hair.

MUSCLE CRAMPS Toward the end of pregnancy, you may have a tendency toward cramps in your thigh and leg muscles. This is associated with insufficient circulation of blood, and to the use of muscles not usually called into action.

It may also be the result of a calcium deficiency. Mention it to your doctor as he may want to prescribe additional calcium.

A good maternity corset and low-heeled shoes will help you avoid these cramps. If they occur, you may get relief by massaging your legs and by walking about the room without shoes. Stretching your leg out in front of you and pushing downward with your heel sometimes relaxes the cramped muscles.

Sometimes the baby's head presses on certain nerves and causes shooting pains down the legs. Changing your position may help.

SWELLING OF FEET AND ANKLES Toward the end of pregnancy, your feet and ankles may swell noticeably, particularly after you have been sitting or standing a long time. The swelling will usually disappear if you lie down and raise your legs with pillows. Check whether you may be getting too much salt in your diet. If your feet and legs are constantly swollen, get in touch with your doctor.

SHORTNESS OF BREATH As the baby grows and presses upon your vital organs, shortness of breath is to be expected. This is a normal condition and causes only minor discomfort. If it interferes with sleep, prop your head and shoulders up with pillows. Extreme shortness of breath, however, should be reported to your doctor.

During the ninth month of pregnancy, the baby's head begins to settle down lower into the hollow portion of the pelvis. When this "lightening" occurs, you'll feel less of a heaviness in breathing, and your heartbeat will become much easier. You'll know that soon your long wait will be over.

SERIOUS COMPLICATIONS In addition to the annoying symptoms described, more serious conditions sometimes develop. Your regular visits to your doctor will enable him to detect them.

Early symptoms of one or more of the complications of this type were described on page 47. Briefly, they are:

1. A constant headache that doesn't yield to ordinary headache remedies
2. Swelling of face or hands
3. Blurred vision
4. Bleeding from the vagina

5. Fever
6. Pain in the abdominal region
They should be reported at once to your doctor, as should vomiting which persists.

Bleeding from the vagina may indicate a threatened miscarriage or premature labor. Call your doctor at once, lie down, and don't take any medicine until you have talked to your doctor.

SACROILIAC PAINS (LOW BACK PAINS) You may have a pain or catch in the lower back. This is due to motion in the sacroiliac joint and can be relieved by wearing a good maternity girdle. It is sometimes an annoying discomfort, but doesn't harm health in any way and almost without fail will clear up following delivery of the baby.

Baby's nursery, layette are fun to plan

When your baby arrives, he'll not only need a layette, but various pieces of equipment as well. Fortunately, most items manufactured and advertised nationally for babies have been prepared with an infant's comfort and well-being in mind. The baby section of a good department store, moreover, is a service department where a special effort is made to give inexperienced mothers reliable information. If you'll tell the saleswoman how much you want to spend, she'll try to help you get the most value for your money.

BABY'S OWN ROOM—IF POSSIBLE A room of Baby's own should go at the top of your list. If you are not permanently located at the time, it may not be possible to have everything just as you'd like.

If you can give him a room that's exclusively his, by all means do so. A room of his own will help Baby build better sleeping habits and will also give you more rest. It may be ever so tiny as long as it's well ventilated and quiet so he can have his naps undisturbed. During the first weeks of his life, your baby should be in a room adjoining yours, so that you will hear him if he cries and can give him the attention he needs.

The furnishings should be easy to clean. A word of caution: if you're putting a fresh coat of paint on old nursery furniture, don't use a lead-base paint. Babies *do* get teeth, and they *do* gnaw, and if you use lead-base paint, there's danger of lead poisoning. A hard-surface floor covering like linoleum can be washed frequently.

If you can't provide a separate room for Baby, give him a corner where his clothes and equipment can be kept handy, and he can rest in peace and quiet. Should you have just one more bedroom, plan to put him in it for his naps. When you go to bed, wheel or carry his bassinet out into the room next to yours if it's warm enough.

HIS ROOM SHOULD BE WARM The room Baby uses should be easy to heat. A temperature of 72 to 74 degrees during the day provides adequate heat and an optimum humidity. Increasing the temperature much beyond 72 to 74 causes the humidity to fall, and the room feels no warmer.

Special care should be taken to keep the humidity at a proper level, so your baby's nose and mouth membranes won't dry out. Special devices which provide adequate humidity are available to attach to furnaces. Individual room humidifiers are available, too. Keeping shallow pans of water near the radiators or register in Baby's room is also a satisfactory means of increasing humidity.

In warm weather, Baby's room should be cross ventilated, but his bed shouldn't be in a draft. Ventilators or cloth screens in open windows will prevent drafts.

BABY'S FURNITURE The nursery may be furnished as simply or as elaborately as you wish. Soft pastel color schemes are ideal.

For your baby's first bed, a bassinet on wheels is very convenient, since it can be taken anywhere in the house and wheeled out on a porch for naps. However, a big laundry basket, well padded, does very well. The first bassinet should be at least 30 inches long. There is one shortcoming to a bassinet if this is your second or third child. The older youngster, in his eagerness to look at the new baby, may pull over a bassinet. A watchful eye will avert this kind of accident.

Whatever kind of bed you use, be sure it's long enough and wide enough to let the baby kick and squirm all he likes. When purchasing a full-size crib, choose the type with a side that can be raised and lowered. The latch which unfastens the side

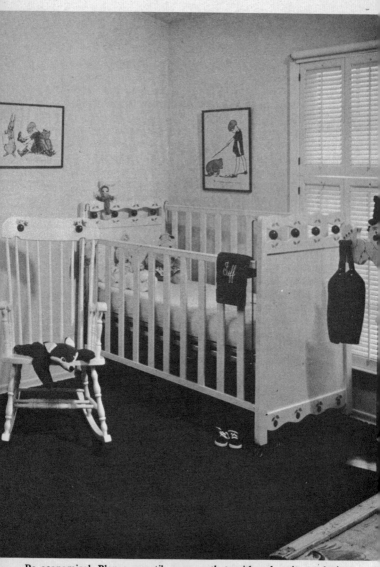

Be economical. Plan a versatile nursery that, with only minor substitutions, will grow with your child.

should be placed where Baby cannot reach it as he gets older.

Another convenience in a crib is an adjustable mattress base which can be moved up and down. The mattress should be at your hip height during the first months, so that you don't have to stoop low to lift Baby.

If you can't obtain a crib with this adjustable feature, raise the crib to the proper height by screwing wood doorstops into the legs.

HOW TO MAKE UP BABY'S BED It will make little difference to your baby whether his room is an elaborate nursery or a little corner, but the way his bed is made up will matter a great deal.

Mattress. First of all, the mattress must be firm; a baby's bony structure is soft, and needs good supports. High quality cotton or foam rubber are ideal materials for the mattress filling. Most mattresses today are waterproofed. If the one you buy isn't, you'll want to cover it with a protective waterproof sheet that's large enough to tuck well under the mattress.

Absorbent pads. The mattress pad for your baby's bed should be both soft and absorbent. You'll need 2 or 3 of these pads for changing when they become soaked or soiled. They should be large enough to tuck well under the mattress.

Sheets. Over the absorbent pad goes the sheet, which should be large enough to tuck under the mattress. Fitted sheets are now made with mitered corners, and slip over the ends of the mattress so they're held firmly in place, wrinkle-free. You'll want 4 to 6 sheets.

Small waterproof sheet or absorbent pads. For extra protection, and extra comfort for your baby, place a small waterproof sheet—these are made in several convenient sizes—in the spot where he'll lie, or use a small absorbent pad. This will keep moisture from soaking through the sheet to the mattress pad and will cut down the number of times it will be necessary to change the large pad and sheet.

Four cotton blankets. These should be long enough to tuck under the mattress. It's better to have several light blankets that launder easily than only one or two heavy ones.

Two heavier blankets.

WARDROBE AND CHAIR You'll want a wardrobe or chest

It's handy to have Baby's first bed on wheels. This bassinet, or an oblong-type bassinet, is good. You can use it for the first months, then switch to a baby crib.

A folding bath table where you can bathe the baby and change him is a convenient luxury, but if you're short on space, an ordinary table will do for changing Baby.

in which to keep your baby's clothes. If you're buying a new one, select one that will last through the teen-age years. Or you can repaint an old chest of drawers. It will be all the same to your baby.

A comfortable chair is indispensable in the nursery. Baby must be held in your arms for nursing and feeding. A good easy chair will make this your opportunity for relaxing comfortably. A footstool on which to rest your feet will be welcome, too!

You should have a small, steady table at the side of your armchair. This will hold the items needed during the feeding, and the bottle when baby needs "bubbling."

OTHER NURSERY FURNISHINGS You will need a place to change and dress Baby. This, like the crib mattress, should be your hip height to eliminate tiring strain to your back. The top of a low chest of drawers will do, if it's the correct height. It should be well padded, as should a wooden table. A bathinette which doesn't require padding can also be used.

Your doctor will weigh the baby each month during his

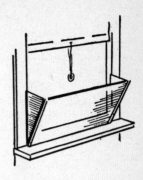

If you don't have a folding tub, a big plastic dishpan like this, roomy enough for all-over baths, is fine. Set it on the counter next to kitchen or bathroom sink.

Baby's room should be between 72 and 74 degrees, well ventilated. A deflector like this shields him from breezes, admits plenty of fresh air.

checkup, so a scale at home is more of a luxury than a necessity. Too, some mothers worry unnecessarily about weight when there is a scale in the home.

You will want a night lamp or shaded lamp to enable you to peek at Baby at night without disturbing his sleep.

A wastebasket, a 2- or 3-gallon covered pail, and a soiled-clothes hamper will be needed. The pail and hamper may be kept in the bathroom. If you intend to use a diaper service, the covered pail will not be a necessity as the diaper service furnishes the container for soiled diapers.

BATH ARTICLES Keep your baby's bath articles in his room or in the bathroom, whichever's more convenient. As the bathroom is usually warm, it's often the best place to bathe your baby.

Bath table. A bathinette is a convenience but *not* a necessity. Any ordinary table that's a convenient height is satisfactory. However, it will need thick padding to keep the hard surface from making the baby uncomfortable. A pad or folded blankets will do the job.

Tub. If you don't have a bathinette, you'll want a tub. A plastic tub is inexpensive and easy to keep clean. You'll find the long, oval shape the best. Or you can even use the kitchen sink—but scrub it out beforehand. If your doctor wishes you to give the baby a sponge bath when he first gets home from the hospital, a washbasin will do.

Bath tray. A handy tray or basket will be the most practical for this purpose. It should hold:

Bath thermometer (nice but not a necessity)

Mild, pure soap (Many doctors are now recommending soaps containing hexachlorophene.)

Baby cream or lotion

Shallow, covered soap dish or jar

Small jar (covered) of sterile water

Diaper pins (plastic heads)

Cotton swabs

Sterilized cotton balls in a covered jar

Then you'll need:

Washcloths—soft material for Baby

Bath towels, 4 to 6, large enough to wrap around Baby.

Bath apron—later on he'll SPLASH!

The bathroom closet or cabinet should contain these articles, ready for use when needed: Rectal clinical thermometer. (During the first four years at least, the temperature should be taken rectally.) Nasal aspirator with a bulb of two ounces or larger. (A syringe with a one-ounce bulb does not have a sufficient suction capacity to be of any value to clear the baby's nose. Hospitals find a two- or three-ounce ear syringe with a blunt tip more satisfactory for nasal aspiration.)

BABY'S LAYETTE Your baby's clothing needs are few, for his wardrobe has been simplified until it approaches the vanishing point. The basic dress, in summer or winter, is a shirt, a diaper, a gown, sacque, or a kimono, and a bath blanket. The old custom of swathing the tiny baby in wool and flannel, even in hot weather, has fortunately gone out. Most babies get along with no wool at all, except in outside garments, such as sweaters or other light wraps.

The warmth of your baby's clothing depends upon the climate where you live and the heating arrangements in your home.

Keep all of the supplies that you need for the
baby's bath in a handy bath basket or tray.

Keep in mind that the purpose of clothing him is to make
him comfortable, not to prevent colds or other infections.
These are contracted through germs carried to your baby by
some other person—not by the weather.

Of course, Baby should not become chilled. If your climate
and home heating arrangements are such that warm shirts will
be needed to keep him comfortable, get them. Fabric is still a
matter of choice.

Your baby should not be overdressed. Babies are more likely
to be too warm than too cold. Too many clothes will foster
sweating and rashes. Good sense will guide you.

If you have a warm, evenly heated house, shirts of cotton or
similar light materials will be adequate for a new baby's needs.

The suggested garments of your baby's wardrobe are:

3-6 shirts, side-gripper or side-tie for easier dressing (minimum size 2-6 months size)
2-4 kimonos
4-6 nightgowns
3-4 sacques
2 pairs of bootees
Sweater
Bonnet
4-6 receiving blankets
4 dozens diapers. One dozen if you're using a diaper service
4 plastic pants

A warm sweater or two and a snug bonnet keep Baby cozy during the winter months.

This cuddly cotton terry sleeper has fold-back mitten cuffs and attached feet.

2 treated cotton or silk waterproof diaper pants for special occasions

Safety pins

The first few months, when the baby is tiny and has to be changed frequently, sacques or kimonos can be used instead of nightgowns. As he gets stronger and more likely to kick off his covers at night, you'll want to pop him into a nightgown. Cotton knit gowns are comfortable and easy to launder. They should be long and have long sleeves, so Baby will remain covered even though he throws off his bedclothes. Cotton terry cloth sleepers are also grand for Baby, and they are absorbent and washable.

In these early months, too, a wool or orlon blanket is more satisfactory as an outer wrap than a baby coat or "baby bunting." These garments are usually too large for a tiny infant. And if they are the proper size now, he'll outgrow them very quickly. When he becomes more active, you may need a coat or bunting for him.

Quite a variety of materials and styles are available in diapers. The most common is an oblong shape, 20 or 21x40 inches. New, absorbent materials have been perfected that are easy to launder and quick-drying. The oblong shape can be folded in different ways as the baby grows, and the new materials are so soft that the 21x40-inch size isn't too large even for a tiny baby. Whatever material you select, bird's-eye, flannelette, or gauze, you'll need a minimum of three to four dozen diapers for convenience. You'll also want waterproof flannelette pads for crib and laps.

Adjustable, fitted diapers with built-in fasteners and prefolded diapers are also available. They are higher priced than standard diapers and may not fit a tiny baby even when adjusted to the smallest size; they're grand for an older baby.

In addition to these types, there are several brands of disposable diapers. Whether you want to use these all the time or not, it's smart to have a supply on hand just in case the washing machine breaks down or some other emergency arises. They're also a blessing when you're traveling with Baby.

Diaper liners, which go inside the cloth diaper, are especially convenient for a new-born baby as their stools tend to be messy. When you change the baby, just lift out the soiled liner and throw it away or dispose of it in the toilet.

Most communities now have diaper laundry services. These are a boon to many mothers. If you intend to use a diaper service, inquire about it several months before your baby is born. Otherwise, as it's very much in demand, you may not be able to get this service when you need it.

The doctor who will take care of your baby can advise you about diaper laundry services. Ask other customers, too, whether or not they've been satisfied with the service.

If you have a diaper service, it will supply the diapers, but it's a good idea to have a dozen of your own on hand for emergencies. Some diaper services will launder your own supply of diapers.

Hip-length sacques are a popular baby garment. The absence of skirts means less wet clothing. If the short garments are used, legs and feet are kept warm by wrapping Baby in an outing flannel square or a cotton flannel receiving blanket. These sacques are washable, need little, if any, ironing.

If Baby has any clothes that slip over the head, be sure the opening is large enough so they will go on easily.

6

Your part before and after delivery

The last month of waiting may seem longer than all the rest. You'll feel awkward and will have difficulty sleeping. But if you continue your regular routine and interests, you'll forget yourself and the calendar.

Keep on your diet and continue any exercise your doctor recommends. Soak up as much fresh air and sunshine as you can. Your doctor will give you your final checkup, and soon the great day will come.

Have your doctor's home and office telephone numbers by your telephone. Decide now how you will get to the hospital when the time comes. Also at this time, arrange the matters discussed under the next few headings.

DOCTOR TO SUPERVISE BABY'S CARE If the doctor who delivers you specializes in obstetrics, it will be necessary to arrange for a pediatrician to care for your baby. Get in touch with him now to make sure he will be available when your baby is born. Your doctor will call him after the baby is born and together they will examine your baby.

WHAT TO TAKE TO THE HOSPITAL At the beginning of

the ninth month, it's time to pack your bag and have it ready. You will need to include: A fresh gown or pajamas for each day; a bathrobe and slippers; cosmetics and toiletries; nursing bras; sanitary belts; and something with which to pass the time, such as books, stationery, or a radio. For any special items, consult your doctor or the hospital, but keep in mind, hospitals have limited storage space.

While packing, also lay out those things your baby will wear home from the hospital. Include a shirt, 2 diapers, safety pins, a waterproof outer diaper, a sweater and bonnet, and a wrapping blanket. Place these things where your husband can find them so that he can bring them to you shortly before you are to be dismissed from the hospital.

LAST-MINUTE DETAILS In addition to the things already mentioned, there are still other things to check. If you intend to use a diaper laundry, make sure their service will be available. Also make arrangements for someone to help you at home for at least the first week after you return from the hospital.

With all the forgoing details taken care of, relax with a free mind. Get out and see people, invite friends in, or go to a movie. All these things will make the time pass quickly and will enable you to think of something other than yourself.

LIGHTENING "Lightening" (when the baby sinks down and forward) may occur any time during the last month with a woman having her first baby. This forward movement of the uterus relieves the pressure on the abdomen, and you'll be able to breathe easier. With succeeding pregnancies, lightening may not come until the last week, or not until labor begins.

LABOR Labor is the physical process that makes the delivery of your baby possible. Although it is a continuous process, for the purpose of discussion, it is divided into three stages.

The first and by far the longest stage of labor is the period of time when the contractions of the uterus gradually push the baby through the cervix or mouth of the uterus. This pressure brings about a thinning and dilation of the cervix until the opening is large enough to permit the baby's passage. During this first stage of labor, the contractions are involuntary making additional straining on the mother's part unnecessary.

The second stage of labor begins when the cervix is fully dilated allowing the baby's passage through the cervix and into the vagina. During this phase of labor, you will be required to help push the baby down through the birth canal with your abdominal muscles. Generally, you will feel an almost compulsive desire to push at this phase. However, before this becomes an automatic process, you may be encouraged to push by the doctor or nurses. This will speed the delivery. Once the baby has descended to the floor of the pelvis, the doctor will then take over and supervise the delivery of your baby and the placenta.

The third stage of labor is the one in which the afterbirth or placenta separates from its attachment to the uterus as a result of the uterus contracting. Once the detachment has occurred, the doctor will express it by firmly pressing on your abdomen.

During the last several weeks of your pregnancy, you may experience lower abdominal cramps and upon examining your abdomen at the time they occur, will note that it becomes very hard. These cramps are known as false labor. Real labor, unlike false labor, is generally progressive and regular. Once the contractions begin, they increase in intensity and frequency.

SIGNS THAT LABOR IS STARTING As pregnancy nears its end, you will be naturally concerned about recognizing the signs of labor and getting to the hospital on time. At any one or all of the signs listed below, get in touch with your doctor. He will tell you when to start for the hospital.

1. Labor usually starts with a slight backache, often accompanied by weak abdominal cramps. These contractions last from 10 to 40 seconds, and will be from 10 to 30 minutes apart. Call your doctor when the contractions are five minutes apart if this is your first child, and 10 minutes apart for subsequent children.

2. The "show." This is a small amount of reddish or pink discharge of mucus streaked wth blood which passes from the vagina.

3. Breaking of the bag of waters. This is a rush of water from the vagina. It doesn't always occur by itself and may have to be induced by your doctor.

When you recognize the signs of labor beginning, do not eat

any solid foods. A full stomach at the time of delivery materially increases the hazards of whatever anesthetic you may receive. Once you think you are in labor, drink only clear liquids such as water, weak coffee, or tea.

AND NOW, THE HOSPITAL When you arrive at the hospital, you'll be taken to the "Prep" room. There you'll be prepared for delivery and examined by your doctor.

After you have been examined, you may be left by yourself in a "labor" room. Don't worry, though; you'll have a buzzer right at hand to summon the nurse immediately if the contractions become harder or more frequent. Also, a nurse or doctor will carefully watch and record your progress.

Many times after the first signs of labor, the contractions subside. If this occurs, relax and sleep if you can. Several hours may pass before they begin again.

FATHER'S WAITING PERIOD After your arrival at the hospital, your husband may be told that it will be many hours before delivery. Your doctor may advise him to go back to the office or home and keep in touch with the hospital. Some hospitals permit the husband to remain with his wife during labor. Others do not.

However, it isn't necessary for your husband to be there. You will be sleeping some of the time, and many doctors feel that you will relax more and rest better if your husband is not present.

But find out the hospital's policy regarding this beforehand. Always avoid last minute decisions. Hastily made decisions have a tendency to leave you upset.

YOUR TIME IN THE LABOR ROOM By the time your pregnancy has progressed to this point, you should have received some form of education concerning labor and delivery. If you did not attend formal prenatal classes, your doctor will have given you proper instruction and general preparation.

The important thing to note is that relaxation is the keynote to an easy delivery. By understanding the mechanics of labor, you will be able to relax. Then fear of the unknown will not intensify the pain. There is some pain, but because of its intermediate character, it is tolerable. Your attitude will determine if there is undue discomfort.

The labor period varies from 12 to 24 hours for a first baby, to less than 6 or 8 hours for subsequent ones. Much of this period is free from discomfort.

If the contractions are frequent enough to keep you awake, the nurse may give you a sedative in capsule form to help you sleep. You'll wake up a few hours later as the contractions become stronger and more frequent. At this time, your doctor may give you a hypodermic medicine to ease your discomfort. After this, you will sleep again between contractions. Periodically your doctor will examine you to see how far the cervix (the opening of the uterus) has dilated. If it is completely dilated, he knows that you are in the second stage and must stay awake to assist in the birth process. At this time, you will be moved to the delivery room.

IN THE DELIVERY ROOM This second stage of labor lasts from 30 minutes to two hours for a first baby, and five to 30 minutes in subsequent deliveries.

In the delivery room, you will be encouraged to work with your contractions to help push the baby down. The doctor or nurse will also instruct you how and when to breathe. These special breathing rhythms are excellent pain relievers as they give the mother a distracting and useful activity. Their primary purpose, however, is to help prevent injury to the mother's tissues as the head emerges.

During this period, you will probably be given light whiffs of an anesthetic (if you are receiving inhalation-type anesthesia). Just as the baby is about to be born, you may be given a complete anesthetic. If the anesthetic is of the inhalation type, such as nitrous oxide-oxygen, you will be unconscious, or nearly so, from then on. If you have a caudal or saddle-block anesthetic, you'll be conscious but will have no sensation in the birth area.

Your doctor may perform an episiotomy. This means that he makes a cut in the vagina to avoid any irregular tears which might be difficult to repair later. After the baby and the placenta have been delivered, he repairs the cut with absorbable sutures (stitches which do not have to be removed).

If you should lack the strength to push the baby out, the doctor will help you with forceps. There is no need to be concerned about a forceps delivery. It just means that the doctor inserts into the vaginal opening first one, then the other, of the separate blades of the forceps, and joins them so the baby's head is held with gentle pressure. Then he carefully draws the baby out. There is no danger to the child.

After your baby is delivered, contractions of the uterus separate the afterbirth, or placenta, and push it into the vagina during the third stage of labor. This happens anywhere from 3 to 5 minutes after birth, and if you have an anesthetic, you won't feel any sensation. Your physician will expel it from the vagina by applying gentle pressure on the upper part of the uterus.

After delivery is finished and the doctor allows you to see and hold your baby for the first time, you'll be eager to share the experience with your husband.

YOUR FIRST HOUR AFTER DELIVERY The first hour and a half following delivery is very important to your future health. During this period, you'll be carefully observed by nurses and doctors. You may be annoyed by their insistence on rubbing your abdomen and making examinations. However, this is important, particularly to prevent delayed hemorrhage following delivery.

HOSPITAL VISITORS Many hospitals allow only husbands to visit the maternity floor. If your hospital has this regulation, remember it's for the protection of you and the baby.

You are able to get the rest you need, and the baby is protected from possible infection which may be carried into the maternity area by visitors.

PREPARING TO GO HOME Before you leave the hospital, the nurse may show you how to bathe and care for the baby. In addition to this, your hospital may furnish a day's supply of formula. Take it home even if the baby is breast fed. Excitement of going home and the confusion of visitors may lessen breast milk for that day.

To avoid some of the last-minute confusion, send extra packages and luggage home the day before you are dismissed.

If at all possible, it is best for you and the baby if you have a minimum of visitors (even loving relatives), except the person who is to help with the housework and baby care, for the first week or two at home. You will rest better, and the baby will need to be protected from colds and other infections which visitors might bring in.

Your doctor will tell you what he wishes you to do to care for yourself at home. It might be well to write down everything he says so you will remember.

REST If you've made arrangements for outside help, take advantage of this time to regain your strength. Try to temper your natural eagerness to take over caring for your baby. You'll have this responsibility soon enough.

After you have taken over the full care of the baby, arrange your day so you can lie down for a half-hour twice a day. The best time would be when the baby is also sleeping.

If your budget can allow it, hire someone to do heavy cleaning and laundry for the next few months. If not, forget about unusual and seasonal house cleaning for the time being. A rested, well mother is the most important need right now.

THE BABY BLUES Often after a new mother returns home and the care of the baby becomes her responsibility, she develops a feeling of total helplessness and insecurity.

You may be utterly discouraged. You may suddenly burst into tears. Without any reason, you may worry about the baby. You may feel that you'll never look as attractive as you did before you became pregnant. You may fear that you and your husband will be unable to adjust to your changed life and its new roles. You may also feel that your husband is no longer as interested in you. Don't be alarmed by this "blue" feeling. Recognize it; accept it; and wait for it to pass as your strength and confidence return.

Remember, too, your husband is also going through a time of adjustment, the same as you are. The household where he was formerly the leading man now revolves around a tiny baby. He wants the baby to have your care and attention, but he needs to feel important, too. Help him to understand that he still comes first and always will. Include him in the care and the loving enjoyment of the baby, so he won't feel left out.

When you are feeling better, try to arrange an outing for yourself—in the evening with your husband, or downtown with friends during the day. If the baby is in good hands, getting away will relax you, leave you fresh and eager for the next day.

For a few women, the after-childbirth depression becomes so deep that medical help is needed—the sooner the better. Fortunately, these cases are very rare. Other mothers may have so little depression, they're scarcely aware of it. But knowing that it may happen, and it is not unusual, helps you to overcome it when it occurs.

BATHS Take either shower or sponge baths during the first month after your baby is born. At the end of that time, you may take tub baths, provided that you no longer have any blood-tinged discharge.

WHEN WILL MENSTRUATION REAPPEAR Generally, menstruation does not occur for several months after the birth of your baby. After it does appear, it may be irregular. It may be some time before your regular monthly cycle is reestablished.

Some mothers do not menstruate as long as their baby is nursing. If you should, don't discontinue nursing because of menstruation.

Sometimes breast milk is not as plentiful during these periods, or the baby may seem restless. If this occurs, give him a bottle for a few feedings. It is good to accustom him to an occasional bottle, anyway, after the first month or so even though he is entirely breast-fed.

Many women believe that they cannot become pregnant if they are nursing and have not resumed menstruating. This is not correct. Conception can occur during this period.

RESUMING INTERCOURSE Refrain from intercourse until your doctor has examined you a month or six weeks after delivery. Ask him then if it's all right.

Exercises
after delivery

You can do these simple breathing
and muscle-contracting exercises
safely in bed the day after birth.
Blow out breath as completely as
possible. At the same time,
pull in abdomen tightly. Relax.
Contract internal pelvic floor
muscles as if stopping bowel
action. Relax. Begin by doing each
exercise once or twice. Gradually
increase number and do at
regular intervals. Most doctors
insist mothers wait at least two
weeks after the baby's birth before
beginning any vigorous
calisthenics. When your doctor
gives the go-ahead, do the exercises
that are pictured on this page.

On hands and knees, swing hips like dog wagging tail. Turn head each time in direction of swing so waistline is tucked in on side to which you're looking.

On hands and knees, pull abdomen up toward spine, tightening hip muscles. Tuck head in to look at knees. Back should be completely rounded. Alternate with exercise at right. Repeat 5 times.

In same position as at left, lift head and look toward ceiling, hollowing back and letting hip muscles go slack. Repeat 3 times; then rest head on forearm. Repeat 3 times, 4 times daily.

Lie on back, knees bent. (a) Inhale slowly, expanding chest and abdomen. (b) Pull abdomen in, spreading ribs. Exhale. (c) Pull abdomen in, press lower back to bed. Hold; relax. Repeat each 10 times.

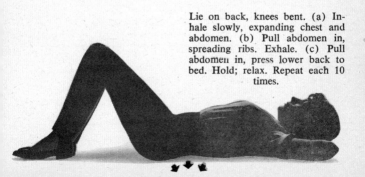

Exercises to
be started
after 6 weeks

"The Camel Walk." From standing position, bend over, rest palms on floor, feet 12 to 18" apart. Keeping knees, elbows straight, walk around on all fours. Repeat exercise 5 times a day.

Lie on your back, knees flexed on abdomen, hands clasping bent knees. Pull knees toward chest; hold; then lower legs slowly to floor. Relax. Repeat 6 to 10 times. Try to touch knees to chest.

Sit on stool against wall, back, buttocks, head touching wall. Keep chin in, feet flat on floor. Raise arms; pull tummy in so lower spine is pressed to wall, arms touching ears. Repeat exercise 5 times.

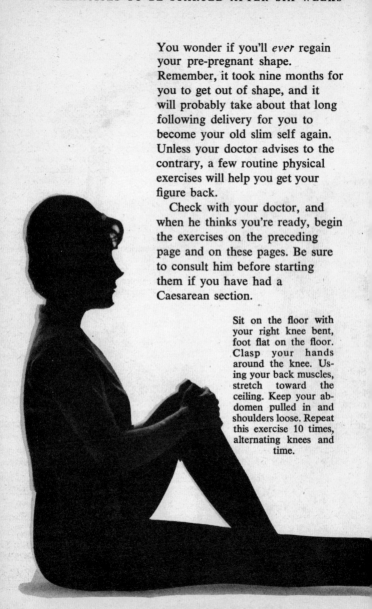

You wonder if you'll *ever* regain your pre-pregnant shape. Remember, it took nine months for you to get out of shape, and it will probably take about that long following delivery for you to become your old slim self again. Unless your doctor advises to the contrary, a few routine physical exercises will help you get your figure back.

Check with your doctor, and when he thinks you're ready, begin the exercises on the preceding page and on these pages. Be sure to consult him before starting them if you have had a Caesarean section.

Sit on the floor with your right knee bent, foot flat on the floor. Clasp your hands around the knee. Using your back muscles, stretch toward the ceiling. Keep your abdomen pulled in and shoulders loose. Repeat this exercise 10 times, alternating knees and time.

Lie on back, knees bent, feet flat on floor. Raise head and shoulders off floor. Reach forward with hands outside left knee. Repeat, reaching beside right knee. Repeat each movement 3 times. Rest.

Same position as left. With chin in, lift head off floor as far as possible, then lower it slowly. Repeat, stretching arms forward, raising shoulder off floor. Try to raise entire back. Repeat 5 times.

Same position as exercise shown, right. Swing the right arm under left side of body, reaching as far over back as possible. Turn head in direction you're reaching. Rest, and repeat 5 times with each hand.

On your hands and knees, swing right arm under the left side of body, then sideways and up toward ceiling, turning body and head to look up at hand. Swing each arm 5 times. Repeat exercise 5 times daily.

All of these exercises will improve muscle tone and help eliminate postpartum sag. However, if you should feel that stronger measures are necessary, see your doctor. There are only two sensible and natural ways to reduce: (1) eat less, to reduce calorie intake; or (2) increase physical activity, to burn up more calories. Avoid crash diets as they promote one nutrient at the expense of all others.

Your baby from birth to two years

The long wait has ended. The baby
is here. He is no longer a hope
or wish but a dream fulfilled—
your son or daughter.
Whenever you and your husband
look at your sleeping child, you
will be filled with wonderment.
At first this feeling may be
mixed with fear and anxiety.
Is he all right? Is he getting
enough to eat? What do I do now?
But, as your confidence grows,
this uncertainty will pass. In
its place will be love and
understanding, the cornerstone
in every happy family's foundation.

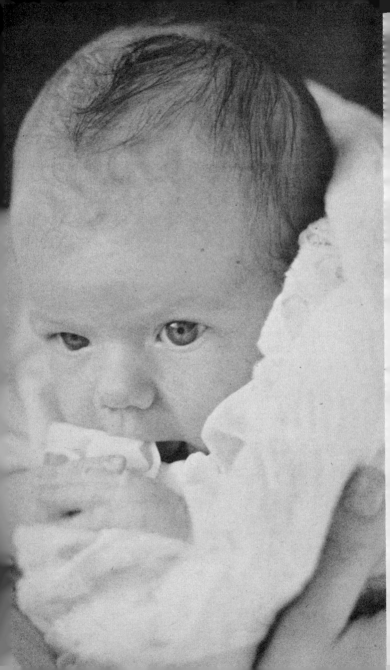

CHAPTER 7

Your brand-new baby

decisions you'll make in the hospital

If you've never seen a newborn baby, you're in for a surprise! Brand-new babies aren't as bright, alert, and handsome as picture-book babies. If you have not been given a general anesthetic at the time of delivery, you'll see your baby before the nurses have an opportunity to bathe him.

The first thing you'll notice is that his skin is a little blue. His color will improve as soon as the mucus has been adequately aspirated from his nose and throat, and his lungs have expanded. He'll also be covered with a white, waxy material—a temporary protective covering for his tender, sensitive skin.

If you do not see the baby until after the nurses have cared for him, you'll notice that his lips, nail beds, and hands are still slightly blue. His eyes will probably be closed, and chances are he won't take the slightest interest in what's going on around him.

His head may be misshapen with lumps or protrusions on one side or the other. But don't worry, by the time you leave the hospital, his head shape will have improved and will be a little more like you expected.

You'll also notice that your baby's feet and legs are in a peculiar position due to his position when he was in your uterus. His legs will also be quite bowed, but time takes care of all these "abnormalities." If there is anything that requires orthopedic care, your doctor will tell you.

Doting friends and relatives will be a big help at this time. After listening to everyone telling you how beautiful your baby is, you'll soon see it too. By the time you are ready to leave the hospital, you'll hardly even notice the tremendous improvement in your little one's alertness and general appearance. This is because it is terribly difficult to see any improvement in perfection!

BIRTH REGISTRATION Generally, your doctor fills out and files the birth certificate. In many states, it is compulsory this be done within a certain number of days after birth. Obtain a copy of the birth certificate and keep it in a safe place to insure its availability whenever needed. In most states, a copy of the certificate is mailed to the parents. Make sure all the information is correct. In the Record Section at the back of this book is space for a photostatic or certified copy of the certificate.

CIRCUMCISION If your doctor elects to circumcise your boy, it will probably be done between the 1st and 4th day. In circumcision, the moveable fold of skin which covers the end of the penis is clipped away. There are several reasons for this.

The first, and most obvious, is that it is an aid to cleanliness. The second reason is that it has been shown that men will not develop cancer of the penis if they have been circumcised at birth. Third, the incidence of cancer of the cervix of women whose husbands have been circumcised is less than those whose husbands have not been circumcised. Finally, as your son grows older, he will want to be like other boys, most of whom will have been circumcised.

However, some doctors are opposed to circumcision. This is usually because the incidence of cancer of the penis or cervix affects relatively few persons and, therefore, he feels surgery on every baby is unwarranted.

If a circumcision is not performed, your doctor will give you the necessary instructions for cleansing under the foreskin.

BREAST OR BOTTLE?

BREAST FEEDING IS DEFINITELY WORTH ESTAB-LISHING There are very few women who do not have suffi-cient breast tissue to produce an adequate milk supply; and the baby reared on breast milk has a number of advantages over the formula-fed baby. For these reasons, one of our country's foremost nutritional experts has said, "breast milk is for babies, cow's milk is for calves." To a degree this is certainly a true statement, although today, cow's milk is altered in such a way that it's now an acceptable food for a baby. And most pro-prietary formulas attempt to copy breast milk.

But, there are still many advantages to breast feeding. With the improved methods of preparing formulas, we can no longer argue that breast milk is safer, but most physicians will agree that there are fewer digestive upsets, less spitting-up, less diar-rhea, and no constipation with breast milk. Allergies don't develop with breast milk as they do with cow's milk. Certainly breast-fed babies have fewer skin rashes on an allergic basis.

Breast milk is the most convenient kind, too. It eliminates long hours of bottle washing, sterilizing, and formula prepara-tion. There are no refrigeration, warming, or transportation worries with your milk. It comes in the proper proportion and usually in the exact quantity needed for your baby's growth.

Breast feeding is also very convenient for fathers, too—they never have to get up in the middle of the night to feed the baby. Relief bottles are easily prepared (see Chapter 8), so if you decide to breast feed, you shouldn't feel that you're tied down and have to be home for each feeding.

Another advantage of nursing is that it's good for you, too. Fears that breast feeding will be detrimental to your figure are groundless. The organs involved in birth return to normal much quicker than those of a mother who does not breast feed her infant. Any changes in a mother's figure are due to the pregnancy and not to the breast feeding.

Perhaps even more important than all its physical benefits are the psychological values of breast feeding. Most mothers who successfully breast feed will agree there is a great deal of satisfaction gained in nursing. There is no faster way for you

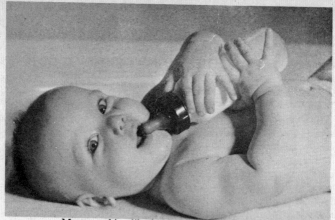
Master a thing like holding your own bottle and
they'll soon expect you to learn table manners!

and your baby to get acquainted with each other. And there's
nothing more reassuring to your little newcomer than the soft
warmth of your breast and the security of your embrace, as he
satisfies his physical hunger as well as his basic need to suck
and nuzzle and root for his food.

Mothers of today *want* to nurse their babies. But they need
help and encouragement.

Older people can help by keeping their opinions to themselves.

Doctors can help by telling the expectant mother how to
prepare for nursing. They can help most of all by convincing
her that there is no reason why she can't nurse her baby.

Hospitals, nurses, and doctors can help by giving the new
mother all possible cooperation in establishing breast feeding
while she is at the hospital.

Today, some doctors and nurses probably aren't too helpful
in encouraging the mother to breast feed, mainly because at
first it is a little more time consuming for them.

It's necessary for them to explain to the mother the techniques of breast feeding, to encourage her each day, and also
to assist her in seeing that the baby does nurse properly. Also,
many young mothers' efforts are being defeated in the early
stages because hospitals frequently offer a formula supplement
to the breast milk.

As a result, the babies aren't hungry when they're brought to their mothers, or they're spoiled from nursing at the breast because they've found it much easier to draw milk from a rubber nipple on a bottle.

When you and your baby get home, your husband can do a great deal to help you continue breast feeding. He helps by being especially considerate; by being enthusiastic about the nursing project; by lending a hand at housework and baby care; by overlooking a not-quite-immaculate house. And he'll help most of all by keeping you calm, relaxed, and free from worry —the most important factors in successful breast feeding.

Occasionally a mother who really wants to breast feed her baby, and follows the directions of her doctor who also wants her to nurse, just doesn't succeed. She has in no way failed her baby and shouldn't blame herself.

A word of caution to mothers who have been talked into nursing: Attitude has a great deal to do with success in nursing. Studies show that mothers who really don't want to nurse seldom have enough breast milk. If you do decide not to nurse, however, don't spoil your enjoyment of feeding your baby by feeling guilty. Plenty of mothering while you give him his bottle will provide much of what's best in breast feeding.

Today, cow's milk is prepared so that it's perfectly safe and disease free. Most of the proprietary formulas or a well-balanced formula prepared by your doctor will provide your baby with the nutrients that will allow him to thrive and grow in a manner equal to the breast-fed baby. With plenty of loving, cuddling, and fondling while feeding your baby, you will satisfy his need for emotional security—as important a need for proper growth as food is.

ESTABLISHING BREAST FEEDING Probably the most common concern that new mothers have while they're in the hospital is their babies' lack of interest in eating.

For three or four days after birth, a fluid called colostrum comes from the breast. It is yellow, and differs from the real milk which will usually appear on the third or fourth day. Most physicians will put the baby to the breast sometime during the first 24 hours after birth, and at regular periods from then on, as the colostrum is considered important by some for its nutritional value and possible presence of immunizing sub-

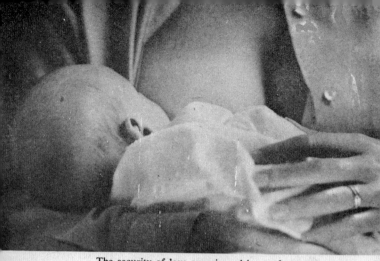

The security of love experienced by mother and child is just one rewarding element in nursing.

stances.

But Baby seems to sense that there's no breast milk, so he's really not very interested in nursing. Plotting or encouraging him to nurse longer than he wants is pointless. The formula-fed baby won't be interested either—it's a little difficult to tell him that he's going to get this milk from a bottle and should therefore gulp it down right *now*!

Actually, there's a good reason for this lack of breast milk and Baby's lack of interest. During the first two or three days after birth, many babies are bothered by a lot of mucus in the nose and throat. If you attempt to feed these babies, they may choke, gag, vomit, and are likely to aspirate or inhale milk into their lungs. Nature has no way of knowing which babies might have trouble. So it's for your baby's own protection that you don't have breast milk and that he not be forced to nurse during the first few days when the mucus is drying up. Within twelve hours after your breast milk comes in, whether you breast feed or not, you'll find your baby showing an increased interest in nursing.

However, what nursing Baby does do during the first few days helps stimulate the flow of milk. He's expected to lose about ten percent of his birthweight during this period.

Supplementary feedings should not be started during the first few days unless your doctor feels that they are absolutely necessary. Otherwise, what little appetite the baby does have will be satisfied.

Ask your doctor to leave orders at the hospital that your baby is *not* to get any supplementary bottle feedings, unless he has specifically ordered them.

If your baby is premature, he will not be brought to you for nursing. He'll be kept in a heated incubator and given special feedings. However, regular emptying of your breasts with a breast pump may maintain your supply of milk so he can be breast-fed when he graduates from the incubator.

HELP BABY TO NURSE WELL At first there may be difficulty in getting the baby to take your nipple. Ask the nurse to stay with you to help you. Baby has an instinctive rooting reflex. When his cheek touches your breast, he'll start looking for the nipple with his mouth.

Hold him so that his mouth can reach your nipple, and lift your breast from beneath, so the nipple is directed to his mouth.

Help him take the brown circle behind the nipple in his mouth, as well as the nipple. This keeps nipples from becoming sore.

While Baby is nursing, hold your breast away from his nose so that he can breathe comfortably. After he has finished nursing, remove the nipple gently by pressing his mouth open with thumb and forefinger on each cheek near the corners of his lips. Don't pull the nipple away abruptly when he's through, as this may injure it.

If he stops nursing, tickle him gently on the cheek. This will stimulate him to begin again, and soon he'll have the habit of sucking steadily until he has enough. Don't let him continue to hold the nipple in his mouth after he's had his fill, as he may chew and this makes the nipple sore.

It will hurt at first to have your baby tugging at your nipples. Don't let this discourage you, as they will soon become toughened. *Two to five minutes is long enough for each nursing period the first few days.*

Until the milk becomes well established, offer both breasts at each feeding, later one breast per feeding. Continue to alternate. However, your doctor may prefer dividing the time between both breasts at every nursing. If he does, follow his instructions.

A COMFORTABLE POSITION HELPS IN NURSING

Whichever position you find most comfortable and relaxing is the best position for nursing your baby. The more rested and relaxed you are, the better your milk supply.

Some mothers prefer to nurse their babies lying down—at least while they're in the hospital and the first few days at home. Lie on one side and, if necessary, prop yourself on one elbow, with Baby lying next to you. Once you're used to nursing and are completely relaxed, you may find yourself falling asleep, especially during the 2 A.M. or 6 A.M. feedings. There's a chance of obstructing the baby's breathing with your arm or breast, so it's best to give those feedings sitting up.

A rocker is a wonderful chair for nursing, but any low, comfortable chair with arms at a comfortable height will do. If resting your arm on a pillow and your feet on a footstool will help you to relax even more, go ahead and do it. Support the baby's head and back with your arm, holding him in a semi-upright position. In this position, he may not need bubbling as often as if he were lying down.

IF BREASTS ARE PAINFUL The coming of milk into your breasts may make them tender and sore. A breast binder or snug-fitting brassiere, which offers support, helps relieve this condition. A breast pump will help relieve pressure if the breasts are full and extremely painful. Use ice packs only if you're not breast feeding.

CARE OF YOUR NIPPLES IN NURSING Naturally, you'll take care to keep your breasts and nipples clean, as infected breasts or infections for your baby may result from carelessness. Wiping the nipples with soap, warm water, and sterile cotton once a day is sufficient. Between nursings sterile, absorbent nursing pads or a freshly laundered white handkerchief may be placed over the nipples to absorb any leaking milk and prevent irritation. Should nipples and surrounding skin become dry and chapped, lanolin cream helps.

TO AVOID SORE NIPPLES Your nipples may hurt a little at first from the suction Baby applies to extract his food. This soreness seldom continues after your nipples become accustomed to nursing. These precautions will help keep them from becoming painfully sore:

1. See that Baby takes in his mouth the brown circle (areola) behind the nipple as well as the nipple itself.

2. When first put to the breast, he will probably not nurse more than two to five minutes. This is long enough until your nipples become used to it. Gradually let him nurse for longer intervals, but until your nipples become quite hardened, 12 minutes is long enough for one breast at a time. After your nipples are conditioned, 15 to 20 minutes of nursing is sufficient for one breast at a single nursing.

3. When your baby has plainly had all he wants, remove the nipple from his mouth, so he won't sleepily chew on it.

4. Protect your nipples from soiling, infection, or injury by always washing your hands with soap before touching them. Wash your nipples at least once a day with soap, warm water, and sterile cotton. Then after each nursing, the nipple can be covered with a sterile nursing pad.

5. Wear a well-fitted nursing brassiere to support your breasts. The styles that open in the front or that have adjustable dropcups are the most convenient. If your breasts are very heavy, it's a good idea to wear a comfortable bra while you sleep.
   Many mothers like to attach a small safety pin to their bra to remind them which breast to offer first at each feeding.

If it becomes unduly painful to nurse, ask your doctor to examine your nipples. This will usually occur while you are still in the hospital. If they're cracked, he may want you to skip a few nursings or he may even suggest a nipple shield until the nipples have healed. During this time it will be necessary for you to empty the breasts by pump or manually expressing the milk by hand.

Tell your doctor immediately if any tender bumps or redness develop.

Newborn glossary

A glossary of physical characteristics in the newborn
which are normal or minor variations from the normal.

Acrocyanosis	Dusky bluish color to the hands and feet of newborns present soon after birth which persists for a few days. The circulation through the skin capillaries is not fully developed.
Bohn's Pearls	Small pearl white bodies toward the back of the palate of newborns which disappear in a few weeks. No treatment is necessary.
Birthmarks (*Hemangiomas*) Capillary Hemangioma (*Storkbites*)	Collection of superficial blood vessels seen on the back of the neck, forehead, upper eyelids, nose, and upper lip. Many fade or disappear. Some, like those on the back of the neck, may remain.
Cavernous Hemangioma	Involves both the skin and the underlying tissues. They are soft, compressible and bluish in appearance. Overlying the cavernous hemangioma may be a capillary or strawberry hemangioma. Some may resolve spontaneously and should be watched for a time before deciding upon treatment.
Strawberry Hemangioma	Bright red, spongy collection of blood vessels, elevated above the skin surface, present at birth or they may appear several weeks later. The majority regress completely.
Breast Engorgement	Engorgement of the breasts noticeable a few days after birth and due to maternal hormones which cross the placenta into the baby. Milk may be secreted (witch's milk). The engorgement lasts about 6–8 weeks.
Caput Succedaneum	The head is misshapen and lopsided at birth. A swelling is present over the part of the head which presented first. Small skin hemorrhages are frequently present. Common among the firstborn and when the head is large. The swelling disappears within a few days.
Cephalohematoma	Localized swelling along the side of the head usually to the back. Not present at birth but appears a few days later. Due to bleeding beneath the scalp. May be present on both sides of the head. It disappears in a few weeks. In some, calcium is deposited and the swelling may persist for several months.
Craniotabes	The sides of the head can be indented with the finger like a derby or table tennis ball. The indentation springs back into place quickly.

Erythema Texicum (*Newborn hives, Flea bites*)	Benign skin condition seen frequently in newborn infants lasting only a few days. Splotchy red areas on the trunk and extremities. Some contain a raised yellow blister in the center. Their cause is unknown.
Fontanel (*Soft spot*)	The anterior fontanel is located at the top of the head and to the front. It is a diamond-shaped opening covered by a tough thick membrane. It closes completely with bone somewhere between 12 to 18 months. The posterior fontanel can also be felt in the newborn and is at the top and to the back of the head. It closes by age 2 months.
Funnel Chest	Hollow-like depression at the lower end of the chest bone (sternum). The mild ones require no treatment. The more occasional severe cases may require surgical correction at a later age.
Harlequin Color Change	With the infant lying on one side, the upper half of the body may appear reddened and the lower half pale. There is a demarcation of color in the midline. When the infant is placed on his back the color changes disappear quickly.
Hydrocoele	A swelling in the scrotum due to the collection of fluid surrounding the testicles. It is fairly common in newborn males and disappears within a few months.
Jaundice (*Physiological*)	Yellow discoloration of the skin, eyes, and membranes of the mouth seen in over 50% of full term and 80% of premature infants. Due to the products released from the destruction of red cells in the newborn period and to immaturity of the liver. It appears about the second or third day of life and begins to disappear before the fifth day. It is usually gone before the end of the second week.
Lanugo	A fine downy growth of hair prominent over the back, shoulders, forehead, and face. It is more noticeable in premature babies. It disappears in the first few weeks.
Laryngeal Stridor	The infant makes a loud crowing noise on inspiration. It is common in infancy and is due to a flabby epiglottis or weak laryngeal structures. The condition disappears in 6–18 months.
Milia	Obstructed sweat and oil glands which appear as pinhead-sized white spots on the nose, cheeks, and chin of newborns and disappear spontaneously within a few weeks.
Mongolian Spots	Areas of bluish-gray pigmentation found over the lower back, particularly in babies with dark skin. In some cases they may be more widespread and found elsewhere on the body. They tend to disappear within 1–2 years.

Nipples, Supernumerary	An accessory nipple which is present just below the regular breast and may occur on one or both sides. They do not develop breast tissue and have no functional significance.
Periodic Respiration	Irregular, rapid, often shallow respiration for several seconds followed by periods lasting only a few seconds where there is no breathing. Common in premature babies but may be seen in some full-term infants.
Pilonidal Dimple	An indentation of the skin covering the lower end of the spine. In later life, these impressions may become infected.
Pseudoptosis	The eyelids in the newborn may operate independently. One eye may be open and the other partially or completely closed. This lasts only a short time.
Pseudostrabismus	The eyes give the false impression of crossing. The epicanthus, a fold of skin at the inner angle of the eye, may be prominent, and this results in the band of white in one eye appearing narrower than in the opposite eye, producing an illusion of crossed eyes.

Reflexes

Grasp reflex	Touching the palm of either of the infant's hands with a finger results in his grasping the finger vigorously.
Moro reflex (*Startle reflex*)	In response to loud noises or sudden changes in position both upper extremities are extended outward and together. With the infant on his back on a flat surface, raising him a short distance and suddenly releasing him, elicits the startle reflex.
Rooting reflex	When the cheek is stroked gently, the baby's head turns toward that side of the face with mouth open in readiness for sucking.
Sucking reflex	Vigorous sucking movements follow when the lips are lightly touched.
Tonic Neck reflex (*Fencing position*)	With the infant on his back the head is turned to one side, causing the baby to extend the arm and leg on the side the head is turned to and to flex the opposite upper and lower extremities.

Stools

Meconium	Term given to the newborn's bowel movements during the first few days of life. The stools are greenish-black in color and of a slimy consistency. About 70% of infants will have their first bowel movement within 12 hours and 95% within 24 hours.
Transitional	Thin loose yellowish-green bowel movement seen from the third to fifth day of life. They contain mucus, curds of milk and remnants of meconium.

Subconjunctival Hemorrhage	Small red spot of blood noticed in the white part of the eye due to rupture of a blood capillary during the birth process. It resolves spontaneously.
Sucking Callous	A small blister visible in the center of the upper lip of sucking infants. Condition lasts only a short time.
Undescended Testes (*Cryptorchidism*)	Normally both testes are found in the scrotum in the full-term newborn. Cryptorchidism is an inability to feel one or both testicles in the scrotum. No treatment is necessary in the newborn since descent may occur later.
Vaginal Discharge	A white discharge from the vagina common in newborns which lasts a few weeks. Vaginal bleeding may also occur. This is related to maternal hormones which cross the placenta into the baby.
Vernix Caseosa	Cheeselike material which covers the skin of newborns and is thought to protect the infant against superficial infections.
Umbilical Cord Vessels (3)	The cut end of the umbilical cord is examined carefully at birth for the number of blood vessels. The normal number is 3, 2 arteries and a vein. The presence of a single umbilical artery should make the physician suspicious of some congenital abnormalities, particularly of the kidney.

8

Baby's first six weeks

You have your baby. You and your husband are proud parents and suddenly it hits you. Soon you'll have to leave that safe, antiseptic, efficiently run hospital and go home. If this is your first baby, the thought of having complete responsibility of your newly acquired family can be a terrifying one. "Will I know when he's hungry? Has he had enough to eat? Too much? How should I pick him up? How do I diaper him? Is his room too hot—or too cold? Should I take him outdoors? Have company in? Is he dressed warmly enough?" All these questions—and more—run through a new mother's mind. These worries and concern for Baby, on top of being confronted with housework, make you feel as though you're facing an insurmountable task.

Try to remember this—babies don't break! They're remarkably sturdy little beings that thrive on common sense, care, and plenty of loving. Think of all the babies that are born to uneducated mothers in undeveloped countries. These mothers have little or no medical advice and few, if any, household conveniences, while you have the help of a good doctor and many timesaving appliances. Their babies do quite well—and so will yours!

Help yourself by learning as much as possible about child care before your baby arrives. Also, before you leave the hospital, take advantage of the nurses and doctors there. From actual experience, they can teach you how to feed, dress, and hold the baby.

Most important of all, you must have confidence in yourself and rely on your own good judgment. For the first few months, all your baby will want is to be warm, full, and dry. You can manage that!

FITTING BABY INTO THE FAMILY You're bringing your baby home to become a family member. Some adjustments, of course, will have to be made, but you should fit the baby into the routine family schedule as much as is possible.

Your home surroundings should be kept as normal as possible. You don't have to tiptoe around the house telling everyone "Sh-hh, the baby's sleeping," because household tasks carried on in usual fashion don't disturb him. Start out with a noiseless environment and every little noise will disturb Baby.

A HELPING HAND You might find it reassuring and helpful to have someone help you with the housework for a week or so after you leave the hospital. Make sure she understands that she's to do the housework while you take care of the baby. Otherwise, you might find yourself peeling the potatoes, and your mother-in-law or hired help looking after the baby.

Grandmothers are especially handy when there's a new baby in the house, although their older ideas on infant care may conflict with the instructions your doctor has given you. Be tactful but frank in telling Grandma that the doctor prefers you do it this way, and that's how you are going to do it.

THE NEW FATHER Your household may seem rather strange at first. It may have doubled in size with the new baby and Grandmother. If this is true, give special thought and consideration to your husband, the new father. Make certain that he doesn't feel left out of the excitement. You must remember, this is all new for him also.

Occasionally a new father may feel a little resentful over all the attention the mother must pay to the baby. Part of this feeling could be jealousy, but part of it may be because he would actually like to help you with caring for the baby.

If Father's willing, he might take care of Baby while you're busy fixing dinner or doing some of the household chores. Don't be alarmed if Father doesn't seem excited about caring for the baby.

At first, the new father may be reluctant to do any more than look at the new baby. Don't be pushy; just give them time to get acquainted. Don't forget, your husband hasn't been as close to the baby as you have all these months. He generally hasn't had as much experience with babies as you've had. Naturally, anything as tiny, fragile, and precious as your child is bound to frighten him a little.

Most of a new father's education in child care comes from watching you. So, be careful not to lose your patience when he seems to get underfoot while you're trying to change or bathe the baby.

Remember, with a bit of instruction, any father can give Baby a bottle, or a bath, or learn to change a diaper. However don't be surprised if he objects to changing when there's a stool in the diaper. His technique and feeding may be unique but more than Baby's basic needs have been met.

BRINGING BABY HOME When your doctor releases you from the hospital, try to plan the trip so that you, your husband, and the baby have a chance to be alone. It may be the first time. The peaceful mood will soon end as you may find throngs of well-wishing relatives and children waiting for you at home.

Children under the age of five often resent the new baby's presence, and you can hardly blame them. Especially if Johnny is an only child, he's had his mother's undivided attention up to now. Suddenly, he's forced to share the spotlight. That tiny little bundle that just eats and sleeps and cries is a very successful competitor for Mommy's time, and Johnny is bound to feel a little unhappy about this new, unsettling situation.

However, a great deal of this resentment can be minimized if you begin preparing him ahead of time for the new baby's arrival. Get across the important idea that once Baby's here, he'll belong to the whole family, not just to Mother and Daddy.

If you're going to move Johnny to a different room, do it far enough in advance so that he won't feel as though he's being booted out because of the new baby. Let him feel it's because he's a big boy and ready for his own room. Talk to him about names for his new brother or sister, but don't promise either one or the other. If you do, you run the risk of dis-

My getting a little sister instead of a little brother turned out to be kind of nice after all!

appointing him when Baby Brother turns out to be Baby Sister.

If at all possible, have the older children at home rather than camped out with a friend or relative when you come home from the hospital. When the children have been looking forward to the arrival of "their" new baby, they're tickled and happy to see him, and homecoming is a joyous occasion. Otherwise, if they haven't been told a new baby is coming and have been farmed out to Grandma, they'll come home, find a baby, probably wonder where he came from—and why!

Once Baby and you are home, you may notice a little regression on the part of the other children. One wants a bath when you're bathing the baby—followed by lotion and powder, too. Or, if Johnny is no longer taking a bottle, he goes back to wanting one. Go along with his requests with an occasional reminder that he's a big boy now and really doesn't need a bottle or whatever. He'll give it up without much fuss within a few weeks.

Toilet training often breaks down, and there's a period of pants-wetting and bed-wetting, but this seldom lasts long.

Resentment also diminishes if the older children help with the baby. Let one carry Baby's bottle while you carry Baby to your favorite feeding chair or hand you a diaper when you're changing the baby. Put a pillow on your toddler's lap and let him hold the baby while you stay nearby to make sure the baby doesn't fall off.

Naturally, you won't have as much time to devote to the older children, but spend as much time as possible with them. Both you and your husband should make an effort to assure your toddler or children that you love them just as much as the baby, but he requires extra attention because he's so small.

Discourage loving grandparents who rush in with "Where's the baby?" and unconsciously ignore the former apple of their eye. It's a sure way to make a little boy or girl feel unwanted and unimportant.

Constantly nagging the older children also leads to resenting the newcomer. If you continually tell them to hush, the baby's sleeping, or that they can't play in there because they will awaken Baby, they're going to wish that that intruder had never showed up.

It's fairly common for a toddler to show resentment by hitting the new baby, stealing his blanket, or pulling his hair or leg. Help him overcome this kind of behavior by reassuring him that you love him very much, but all the while letting him know that he must *not* hurt the baby.

Protecting the baby is also part of your job. Toddlers can accidentally pull over a bassinet, so it's safer to put Baby in a crib with side pads which will keep him from getting his head stuck between the bars. You may also find it necessary to keep the baby's room closed so the little ones can't get to him. If your little ones are playing around the baby, you'll have to be ready to jump in if it looks as if Baby might get hurt.

CONSIDERATION FOR YOUR DOCTOR Your doctor is always willing to help you as problems arise, but try not to take his time by asking him to perform services you can do yourself. He has many, many phone calls to make during the day which are time consuming and without financial compensation. Check your baby book first to see if the answer to your problem is there. If you find that the suggestions which are listed in the book are not giving you satisfactory results, then call the office and leave a message for the doctor to return the call. Write down whatever you think you should tell him and any questions you wish to ask him so that you will not forget them and have to make another call. Present your problems to the doctor in a short, concise manner and always have a pencil and paper available so you can *write down what the doctor tells you.*

The doctor will examine your baby thoroughly at birth. If there are any nursing or feeding difficulties, he'll tell you just what to do. Before you leave the hospital, you might ask the doctor what time of day he would like to have you call him if you find it necessary. Try to refrain from calling the doctor at night unless it's an emergency.

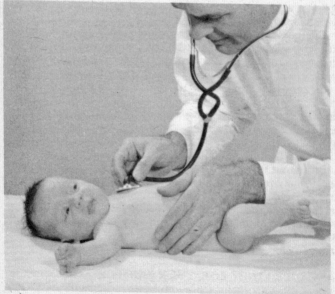

The first six weeks will go by so quickly. Before you know it, it will be time for you and your baby to make that first trip to the doctor.

BABY'S REGULAR CHECKUPS When your baby is a month or 6 weeks of age, take him back to his doctor for another checkup. Then be guided by his directions as to times for regular examinations.

These routine visits are important. They enable the doctor to know your baby and any problems you are having. At each visit, the doctor will outline an entire program for the baby's care until the next appointment. Follow this guide and you'll know you're doing what's best for both of you.

Feeding baby at home

A strict on-the-hour schedule is no longer considered good for babies. Allowing a hungry baby to cry for any length of time just because it isn't time for a feeding disturbs the baby *and* the mother.

So, have a schedule for your sake as well as Baby's, but keep it *flexible*. Let common sense and consideration for the baby's needs be your guide.

If the baby wakes ahead of time, crying and gnawing at his fists, feed him. Adults often get hungry and eat before their next scheduled mealtime, so why shouldn't Baby? Don't worry that he'll be set in bad habits.

Occasionally, when he wakes up like this, he may not want the full amount of formula. Allow him his freedom of choice and let him take as much as he wants. However, if Baby continues to cry ahead of time, try increasing the amount of formula or shortening the length of time between bottles.

A SCHEDULE TO FIT YOUR BABY Baby will quickly establish his own schedule, which will be the one best suited to him. This is called the "self-demand" schedule, which many doctors now recommend.

Let Baby have a hand in determining his schedule. Take things easy for the first week or two after you get the baby home, and get the feel of things. Find out when he seems to want to eat and sleep, and take this into account. At the same time, though, guard against letting him be disturbed, for this will throw both you and Baby off the track. For the first week after you're home, note the times when he sleeps, eats, is wide awake: This is his schedule.

Most newborn babies sleep the greater part of the time, except when being fed, changed, or bathed. There are a few, however, who seem to be awake much of the day. This is no cause for concern, but such a baby should be allowed to rest quietly without being disturbed, even though he's awake.

It's usually convenient to bathe him before the midmorning feeding, and it's a comfort after the night's sleep. But bathe Baby before you feed him, not afterwards. He's ready to sleep once he's nursed or had his bottle. If a later bath hour is more convenient for you, don't hesitate to change it.

By the time he's 3 or 4 weeks old, you'll have found the best time from Baby's standpoint for the various operations of his day and settled into a routine. His day may begin at 6 A.M., 7 A.M., or 8 A.M., according to his ideas and your convenience.

Once you've worked out a satisfactory routine, follow it consistently every day—not to the minute necessarily, but within 15 minutes, for instance. Baby will be better and happier, and he won't wear himself out crying. If an occasion arises, however, which you think is important enough to justify some rearranging, do it. Let your common sense guide you.

After you've had a chance to learn how smoothly things go when you follow a planned day, you'll be in a better position to decide whether or not something is important enough to disrupt it.

Take Dad's convenience into account, though. Arrange it so that he can have some of the pleasure of taking care of his baby.

THE RUSH HOUR At the time of day when there is the most confusion in your home, you may find that the baby will be fussy, cry irritably, and eat ravenously, as though he hadn't been fed all day. The rest of the day, when the house is quiet and peaceful, he'll sleep like an angel and go for three or four hours before wanting to nurse again.

So what's wrong with him? His formula isn't inadequate, because if it were, he'd be fussy throughout the day. It's illogical to think a pain develops every afternoon, precisely at five o'clock, for instance. Is a mysterious pain causing him to cry? Babies do have lots of gas when they cry—this is swallowed air. Many physicians doubt that this causes pain. (*Colic,* Chapter 8)

But, if these reasons are ruled out, why is the baby fussy and unhappy? In most homes, Mother's the busiest as the evening dinner hour approaches. She's preparing the meal, trying to straighten up the house a little, and squeezing out a minute to pretty herself before her husband comes home. If there are young children, they're probably adding to the general confusion.

By the time Daddy walks into the house, her emotional tension has reached a peak. Somehow, Baby seems to feel this tension and reflects it in his irritable crying, fussing, and hunger. In spite of frequent feeding and bubbling, he still isn't content. It doesn't seem to make any difference whether the baby is breast-fed or bottle-fed.

There's no ready-made solution to the problem. If you can cut down on the confusion surrounding the dinner hour and handle Baby as calmly as you do the rest of the day, he's less likely to be upset. Interest the older children in a quiet project to help calm them down after an active day. Feed the baby, bubble him, give him a little loving, then put him to bed and look in on him occasionally. And take heart, eventually he'll outgrow this fussy period.

You'll be more relaxed, too, if you can leave the baby in capable hands occasionally and get out of the house, even if it's just for coffee with a neighbor or friend.

BREAST FEEDING

If you've decided to breast-feed your baby, there are a few things you should know which will help you nurse successfully, once you're home from the hospital.

HOW LONG SHOULD BABY NURSE? Studies indicate a nursing baby will get 75 percent of all the milk that he's going to get out of the breast after five minutes of nursing. Considering this, it's probably not necessary to let the baby nurse longer than 15 or 20 minutes on one breast and 5 or 10 minutes on the second breast. *Prolonged* periods of nursing should be avoided because it's a waste of time and, at first, will make the breast quite sore and painful.

AMOUNT OF MILK The amount of milk you have will be determined by the amount the baby needs each day. If you offer frequent bottle supplements, your daily supply of breast milk will decrease by the amount taken in the supplement. When the baby takes twenty-eight ounces of milk from you today, you'll usually produce twenty-eight ounces of milk for him tomorrow. But, if you give a bottle containing four to six ounces of milk, then your milk supply will decrease by this amount the next day.

If you feel that your baby is still hungry and wish to offer water or a supplementary bottle, do it immediately after nursing—certainly not within two hours of next feeding.

Frequent nursing and emptying of the breast at each feeding stimulates the production of milk. For the first few weeks, offer the second breast after the first one has been emptied. Then start the next feeding with the unemptied breast. Usually after the first two weeks, it's unnecessary to use both breasts during each feeding.

HOW TO INCREASE YOUR BREAST MILK If breast milk is scanty, you may be able to increase it by the following measures:

1. Take extra fluid and foods. Every day you will need one quart more fluid and one-fourth more solid food than you ordinarily eat, or from 500 to 1,000 extra calories. A quart of milk will supply the fluid and 672 calories of food as well. So, one quart of milk a day, added to your ordinary diet will give you both the solids and the fluids needed for nursing Baby. Milk is valuable, because it's rich in calcium, which the baby needs to form bones and teeth. If you can't drink all of the milk as a beverage, use it in soups, custards, malt drinks, or cocoa. For weight watchers, skim milk is a suitable substitute for homogenized. Drink extra glasses of water and fruit juices daily.

   Continue the multivitamin capsules you took during pregnancy.

   Eat at least one generous serving of meat (beef, lamb, chicken, sea food, bacon, liver) a day—two servings are better; eggs; cooked cereal with sugar and cream once a day; potatoes and several servings of vegetables during the day; fruit twice a day. Limit your desserts to fruits, pudding, and gelatins. Skip the sweets.

2. Let the baby nurse frequently. The more milk the baby gets from your breast—or that you expel with fingers or breast pump—the more your breasts will produce. This is another example of the old supply-and-demand rule. So don't be too hasty about starting the baby on a relief or supplemental bottle, or you'll discover you've cut down your milk supply.

3. Get plenty of rest and don't worry. The more relaxed you are, the better your milk supply. Nap in the afternoon when Baby's sleeping and get 8 or 9 hours sleep at night (if at all possible). Try to avoid excitement and family arguments. Discourage visitors the first few weeks.

IS YOUR BREAST MILK ENOUGH? There's only one way to tell if you have enough milk for your baby—by his weight. If each week he gains between 4 and 8 ounces or more, it's ample. But if you're doing all the things just listed and he still fails to gain 4 ounces a week, weigh him before and after each feeding for a 24-hour period. Write down the amounts by which his weight increases after each feeding, and total them for 24 hours. This will indicate how much milk he is receiving from you each day.

Tell your doctor the amount. He may wish to examine the baby, or he may suggest giving formula to supplement breast milk.

If the baby appears to be receiving an adequate amount of milk, but still seems hungry, try offering a supplemental bottle after he has nursed full time at both breasts. If the baby consistently takes three to four ounces from the bottle, you probably don't have enough milk and should offer a bottle.

Breast milk is usually thin, floury-looking, and bluish. This often leads mothers to think it isn't "rich" enough. Don't discontinue nursing for this reason as that's the natural appearance of breast milk.

"RELIEF" BOTTLES Many mothers don't breast feed because they feel they will be tied down. If you are nursing, a "relief" bottle will keep you from feeling tied down. This supplemental feeding is easy to prepare with proprietary formulas as the milk source. (Instructions, page 121)

Breast milk itself is an excellent source of milk for the "relief" bottle. It can be expressed by breast pump or by hand into a sterile cup or bottle, then refrigerated for use in the next day or two.

Don't overdo the supplemental formula feeding. If you do, you'll cut down your supply of breast milk and eventually will have to stop nursing. Occasionally, a doctor will recommend that a bottle of milk be given each day. Although this usually works, some breast-feeding babies refuse to take a bottle.

WHEN YOU DISCONTINUE BREAST FEEDING When you decide to discontinue nursing, or when you no longer have enough milk, get in touch with your doctor. He'll prescribe medication to dry up your milk and will also give you a formula for Baby.

FORMULA FEEDING

If you've decided not to breast feed your baby, don't feel guilty about your decision. As long as he gets plenty of loving and cuddling while taking his bottle, he'll thrive and develop as well as the breast-fed baby.

This affection can't be given by propping his bottle, because then he's deprived of the sense of security so essential to his well-being. Propping bottles is also a dangerous practice. If Baby vomits or chokes and there's no one there to help him, he could aspirate the formula into his lungs.

FORMULAS FOR BOTTLE FEEDING For the first three weeks, the milk in a good basic formula is diluted as Baby might not be able to metabolize the excess of calcium and phosphorus. The kidneys are immature and require an extra amount of water to eliminate the metabolic waste products. The gastrointestinal tract is also immature.

The formula can gradually be increased in concentration as indicated in the charts until the third to fourth week. *Then continue the third week formula until the baby is four to five months old.*

In giving formula, consider the day you get home from the hospital as the beginning of the first week.

PLANNING A FORMULA PREPARATION CENTER A place for everything . . . and everything in its place. Never will these words be more appropriate than when applied to preparing Baby's formula.

Before the baby arrives, set aside space in a kitchen cabinet exclusively for the equipment and supplies you will need when preparing formula. A cabinet near both the sink and stove is ideal. This will conserve both time and energy and will eliminate many unnecessary steps.

Stock your formula preparation center with the following items:

Bottles, nipples, and caps.
Quart measuring pitcher.
Measuring spoons.
Long-handled mixing spoon, kitchen knife.
Can opener (punch type).
Funnel and tongs.
Bottle and nipple brushes.
Pint jar for storing extra nipples.
Sterilizer or deep kettle, saucepan.

KEEP BOTTLES AND NIPPLES FREE OF GERMS As soon as Baby has taken a feeding, rinse the bottle and fill it with cold water until you have time to scrub it with a brush in soapy water. One or two tablespoons of vinegar in the water will dissolve the lime deposit on bottles boiled in hard water when the aseptic method of sterilizing is used.

Immediately after each use, clean the nipple thoroughly, for the butterfat in milk causes rubber to deteriorate. Wash with warm soapy water and a small brush. Rinse thoroughly. A pinch of salt in the nipple cuts the butterfat, opens any clogged holes. Shake salt down inside the wet nipple to form a paste. Then squeeze and roll the nipple between your fingers to force the paste through the feeding holes. Rinse thoroughly. Until you are ready to sterilize them, keep used nipples in a jar separate from sterile nipples.

NIPPLE HOLES MUST BE RIGHT Amateur parents often

have difficulty making the right-size holes in nipples. Baby gets nothing but air for his efforts if the hole is too small. Or he may get tired before he gets enough milk and be uncomfortable from the air he's swallowed.

If the hole is too large, the milk will come out too fast and cause him to choke or have indigestion. The milk should come out in large drops, one at a time; not run out in a stream.

To enlarge a too-small hole do the following: Heat sharp point of a fine needle over flame. Stick needle into nipple; quickly pull out. Repeat the procedure if hole is still too small. The longer the hot needle is held against the nipple, the larger the hole will be, so it's best to enlarge it gradually, trying the nipple each time until the hole is just big enough, but not too big. Always sterilize the nipple before using it.

COW'S (WHOLE) MILK Cow's milk does not provide a balanced diet for an infant *unless it has been diluted and sweetened before feeding.*

Homogenized milk can be used for preparing infant formulas if it is properly diluted and sweetened. Formulas prepared from whole cow's milk (whether pasteurized or not) should definitely be sterilized so that all the bacteria are destroyed. Sterilizing also breaks down the protein in milk so it is more easily digested and less likely to cause allergy than if it were not treated.

WHOLE MILK FORMULAS

	First week	Second week	Third week *
Whole milk	16 oz.	20 oz.	26 oz.
Water	12 oz.	12 oz.	12 oz.
Corn syrup OR	2 tbsp.	2½ tbsp.	3½ tbsp.
Dextrin-maltose	5 level tbsp.	6 level tbsp.	7 level tbsp.

* Continue through four to five months.

PREPARED INFANT FORMULAS In addition to formulas prepared in the home using one of the available forms of milk,

Immediately after each formula feeding, rinse bottle, cap, and nipple with cold water. For easy cleaning, keep bottles filled with cold water until you are ready to wash them thoroughly.

Using bottle brush and nipple brush, thoroughly scrub bottles and nipples in hot sudsy water. Rinse with hot water and allow equipment to drain dry on clean surface or towel.

When ready to fix formula, put fresh cold water in teakettle or covered saucepan. Bring to boil, boil 5 minutes. Turn off heat, keep covered until needed.

there are a number of commercially prepared formulas (also called proprietary formulas). These consist of modification of cow's milk. Some are devised so as to achieve a composition and physical properties similar to human milk. Like evaporated milk and dried milk, the processing renders them easily digestible. They are available in liquid forms requiring dilution before feeding, and dried forms, which must be reconstituted with water for feeding. Most of the products include all the vitamins in the amounts required by the baby. An advantage of these proprietary formulas is the convenience in preparation and uniformity of composition and carefully controlled sterility and quality.

SPECIAL FORMULAS In case of allergy or an incompatibility to cow's milk, your doctor may prescribe a special prepared milk substitute. Evaporated goat's milk has probably been used the longest. Soybean milk and a meat base milk are also used for special formulas. Don't switch to these formulas unless the doctor suggests it.

There are also formulas using citrus or lactic-acid that he may prescribe if necessary. He'll tell you how to prepare these formulas.

TYPES OF FORMULAS

EVAPORATED MILK Evaporated milk is probably the most economical formula available today. This is cow's milk which has been concentrated to one-half its original volume, sterilized, and sealed in airtight containers. An unopened can keeps indefinitely. The addition of water restores it to the same consistency of ordinary cow's milk.

Evaporated milk, because of the treatment to which it is subjected, is a uniform, easily digested food which has been used with excellent success in feeding infants. The heat treatment makes the milk less likely to cause allergy. Evaporated milk can be prepared for infant feeding simply by adding the prescribed amount of water, corn syrup, or a dextrin-maltose powder.

EVAPORATED MILK FORMULAS

	First week	Second week	Third week *
Evaporated milk	9 oz.	11 oz.	13 oz.
Water	24 oz.	25 oz.	26 oz.
Corn syrup OR	2½ tbsp.	3 tbsp.	3½ tbsp.
Dextrin-maltose	5 level tbsp.	6 level tbsp.	7 level tbsp.

* Continue through four to five months.

PREPARED INFANT FORMULAS Proprietary formulas are among the most popular formulas today. They are quick, easy, and convenient to prepare. And most of them provide the daily vitamin requirement for a baby in an easily digestible form.

These commercially prepared formulas are actually a modification of cow's milk. And some of them achieve a composition and physical property similar to human milk.

They are available in liquid forms, requiring dilution before use, and in dried forms, which must be reconstituted with

Before opening, scrub top of evaporated milk can with hot soapy water. Rinse can with boiled water from teakettle. Open can with sterile opener.

Pour stated amount of hot boiled water into sterile measuring pitcher. Pour the water from the pitcher into sterilized 4-ounce bottles for drinking. Do not refrigerate drinking water.

To mix the formula, pour stated ounces of sterile water into pitcher. Add enough milk and sweetening to the water to equal the total amount of formula. Pour formula into sterilized bottles.

water before they are ready for use. Either form has the advantage of easy storage.

They are easy to prepare, and by requiring few utensils, they eliminate many chances of error. And because of the rigid processing standards, sterility and quality are carefully controlled and composition is uniform.

These formulas do cost slightly more than the completely home-mixed formulas, but the added convenience more than compensates for the higher cost.

POWDERS Most powdered formulas come in resealable cans and are usually supplied with a measuring scoop. Be sure to read and follow the manufacturer's directions carefully. In most instances, one level measuring scoop of powder is added to each two fluid ounces of water. In other words, 16 scoops of powder are added to each quart of water. For easy mixing always add the powder to the water.

PROPRIETARY FORMULAS

POWDER	First week	Second week	Third week *
Level tbsp. powder	9 tbsp.	13 tbsp.	16 tbsp.
Water	24 oz.	28 oz.	32 oz.

LIQUID	First week	Second week	Third week *
Liquid formula	9 oz.	13 oz.	13 oz.
Water	15 oz.	15 oz.	13 oz.

* Continue through four to five months.

CONCENTRATED LIQUIDS Concentrated liquid formulas are the most popular of all formulas. They are slightly more convenient than the powdered forms because they are already in the liquid form and, therefore, do not need to be dissolved in the sterilized water. And because of this liquid form, you can either add the concentrated formula to the water or add the water to the concentrated formula. Since they are both liquid, there will never be a mixing problem. The proportions are also simple. For normal dilutions, equal amounts of concentrate and water are used. This type of formula preparation is ideal for traveling.

Scrub bottles before sterilizing with hot soapy water. Rinse in hot running water.

If you don't sterilize bottles with water already in them, pour the prescribed ounces of boiled warm, not hot, water into the sterile bottles.

Add the prescribed amount of powdered formula to the water. Attach a sterile nipple to the bottle and shake.

If using liquid formula, scrub and scald can top before opening. Pour prescribed amount of formula into each of the sterilized formula bottles.

From teakettle or saucepan, add prescribed amount of boiled water to liquid formula in each bottle. Also pour water in bottles for drinking.

You may prefer to use another method. Add the prescribed ounces of liquid formula to the pitcher of previously measured boiled water and stir.

Pour formula into the day's supply of bottles. Fill one or two with cold tap water for drinking. Use the terminal heating method of disinfection.

Methods of bottle disinfection

TERMINAL

The terminal heating method is a simple way to prepare formula. You mix the formula, put it into clean nursing bottles, then sterilize the bottles and formula together as the final step.

The main advantage of this method of disinfection is that all the equipment, including bottles, caps, and nipples, do not have to be sterilized before the formula can be prepared. However, all equipment must be washed perfectly clean with hot, soapy water and rinsed thoroughly. Allow all equipment to drain dry.

Mix the formula according to your doctor's directions or if you are using one of the proprietary formulas, be sure to follow the manufacturer's instructions. Remember, if your formula requires the addition of water, tap water can be used. Previously boiled water is unnecessary when using the terminal heating method of disinfection.

Divide the formula by the number of clean bottles needed for the day's feedings. Fill one or two clean bottles with tap water for Baby's drinking water.

Touching only the nipple rims, place nipples on the bottles. Apply collars and caps, either disk or slip-on depending on the type of bottle, loosely so steam can get under them.

Place bottles on a rack or towel in the sterilizer or deep kettle. Add about three inches of water to the sterilizer and cover tightly with lid.

Gently boil exactly 25 minutes. Turn off the heat, but do not lift lid. Allow the sterilizer, still covered, to cool for 2 hours.

Remove bottles. Screw collars and caps tight and refrigerate immediately.

After pouring formula into the clean bottles, apply nipples, touching only the rims. Attach disk caps and collar rings loosely so that steam is allowed to pass under them.

Place a rack or washcloth in the bottom of the sterilizer or kettle. Stand bottles upright and add about 3 inches of water. Cover with lid and boil for exactly 25 minutes. Take sterilizer off burner but do not remove the lid.

Do not lift the lid until you can comfortably place your hands on the sides. By keeping the lid on until the bottles are allowed to partially cool slowly, no film will form on the milk and cause nipple clogging.

When sterilizer is cool (takes about 2 hours), remove bottles and screw caps down firmly. Place bottles in refrigerator until needed.

ASEPTIC

Another method of bottle disinfection is the simplified aseptic method. This simply requires that all equipment used in mixing the formula and feeding the baby must be sterilized before it can be used. Therefore, in the aseptic method, disinfection becomes the first step rather than the final step as it is in the terminal heating method.

Before you begin, assemble all the equipment you'll need for sterilizing and preparing formula. Everything should be thoroughly washed in hot, soapy water and rinsed in hot, clear water. It helps to have your special formula equipment in a convenient place, separate from other regular kitchen utensils. If you don't, you'll waste time looking for everything.

If using this method, make sure that all the equipment, not just the nursing bottles, are made of heat-resistant materials.

Put the bottles, bottom side up, into the rack and lower the rack into the sterilizer. If you are using a deep kettle instead of a sterilizer, place the bottles, bottom side up, on a clean towel in the kettle. Next, put the nipples in a jar, screw on a perforated lid, and place upside down in the center of the sterilizer. Then put in the plastic nipple collars, caps, tongs, punch-type can opener, and all the other equipment you will use to mix the formula. Add 2–3 inches of water to the sterilizer and cover with a tight-fitting lid.

Bring the water to a boil and continue boiling for five minutes. While you are doing this, also fill a teakettle or saucepan with tap water and allow it to boil for five minutes.

After the water has boiled for five minutes, turn off the heat and remove the lid. Unlike the terminal heating method, you do not wait two hours for the equipment to cool slowly. Using tongs, remove the items from the sterilizer and place them on a clean towel. Empty the nipple jar but do not touch the nipples with your fingers. Also, turn the bottles upright without touching the tops.

Using the sterilized equipment, mix the formula according to your doctor's orders, or in the case of proprietary formulas, follow the manufacturer's instructions. If the formula requires water, use only the boiled water in the teakettle. Pour the

Thoroughly wash all equipment in hot, soapy water and rinse in clear water. Arrange bottles, bottom side up, in rack. Put nipples in jar, cover with a perforated lid, and place in center of sterilizer. Next, put in all other equipment that will be used to mix the formula and feed the baby.

Fill the sterilizer with 2–3 inches of water, cover with a tight-fitting lid, and put on burner. Slowly bring the water to a boil and let it boil for five minutes. Also, fill a teakettle or saucepan with tap water and let it boil for five minutes. After the water has boiled for five minutes, turn off the heat and remove the lid.

With this method of disinfection, there is no need to wait for the equipment to cool slowly. Using tongs, remove items from the sterilizer and place them on a clean towel. Without touching the nipples with your fingers, empty the nipple jar. Also without touching the tops, turn the bottles to an upright position

Mix the formula using the boiled water and disinfected equipment. Fill the bottles with formula. Touching only the rims, place the nipples, disks, and collars on the bottles and refrigerate. Don't refrigerate drinking water.

prescribed amount of formula into each of the disinfected bottles. Fill two of the bottles with boiled water for drinking water. Touching only the rims, place the nipples on the bottles, add the collars, and refrigerate. Do not refrigerate the water.

Single bottle methods

The single bottle method of formula preparation is a boon to the busy mother. One bottle is made at each feeding, and this can be used as a supplement for the breast-fed baby, or as a time-saver by the mother who is traveling.

Any type of formula can be used. The most popular are the proprietary formulas, liquid or powder, or the ready-to-use formulas.

PROPRIETARY FORMULA When using the single bottle method with a proprietary formula, wash all bottles, nipples, and caps in hot soapy water and rinse thoroughly in hot running water. At each washing, use a bottle brush to insure the removal of all dried formula.

Add the prescribed amount of tap water to each bottle. Put nipples and caps on loosely. Place bottles in sterilizer or large covered saucepan. Pour in three inches of water. After water has come to a boil, cover, and sterilize for twenty-five minutes.

Remove sterilizer from heat. Remove bottle rack and cool

One single bottle method. Place bottle, nipple, and cap in a pan of water and boil for five minutes.

Remove equipment from pan with tongs. Cool until warm to touch. Keep pan of boiled water covered. Fix formula. Into bottle, pour prescribed

ounces of warm, boiled water from pan in which you sterilized the bottle. Add powder, shake, and it's ready to feed.

for twenty minutes. Tighten caps on sterilized bottles and store in any convenient location, at room temperature.

At feeding time, add prescribed amount of powdered or liquid formula to single bottle of water. Cap bottle, shake well, and feed. Usually no heating is required.

Or, at feeding time, wash a bottle, cap, and a nipple in hot soapy water and rinse thoroughly in hot running water. Place in a pan of water and boil for 5 minutes. Remove bottle, cap, and nipple with tongs. Pour prescribed ounces of water from pan in which bottle was sterilized into bottle. Add prescribed amount of powdered or liquid formula. Attach sterile nipple, shake, and feed.

DISPOSABLE BOTTLES Just as mythical product designers have worked to build a better mousetrap, so have designers worked to produce a better baby bottle. On the market today, there are several types of disposable bottles, specially designed with you and your infant in mind. Efficiency and convenience are now available in the form of a handy nurser kit.

One such kit comes complete with everything you will need, except the formula. The package contains pre-sterilized, disposable formula sacs, an automatic expander, an unbreakable, heat-resistant plastic bottle holder, and a soft, pliable rubber nipple.

Using the single bottle method of preparation, wash nipples with hot, soapy water and rinse. Turn nipples inside out to wash thoroughly. No brush is needed. Place cone-shaped automatic expander, bottle caps, and nipples in a saucepan of water and boil for five minutes.

Remove expander with tongs and place on flat surface to dry. After tearing the disposable formula sac from the roll at perforations, hold sac between thumb and forefinger and gently slide thumb back and forth until perforations break and the sac opens fully. *Do not put fingers inside formula sac.*

Slip formula sac onto expander and down to the ridge clearly marked on the expander. Next, place bottle holder over the sac and push down until the rim of the bottle rests on the base of the expander. Remove the bottle, fill with formula, and feed.

Another manufacturer has produced a bottle which is disposable in the truest sense of the word. It is a jar-shaped glass bottle which is pre-filled with formula and capped with a disposable metal cap.

To prepare a single feeding, simply unscrew the cap, attach any standard sterilized nipple unit, and feed your baby. Warming is a matter of preference—not necessity. Unopened bottles need no refrigeration.

Ready-to-feed bottles are ideal for travel.

A truly disposable bottle that comes filled with formula. What could be easier! To use, simply unscrew the metal cap, add a sterilized nipple unit, heat, if you wish, and feed.

After washing and sterilizing the expander, nipple, and cap, remove a formula sac from the roll by tearing along the perforated line. *Do not put fingers inside the formula sac.*

Open sac by sliding thumb and forefinger back and forth about 1 inch from perforated edge. Push the open end of the sac over the expander and push it down to the ridge of the expander.

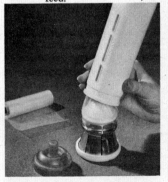

Push plastic bottle holder down over sac and expander as far as it will go. Hesitate before removing the expander. Turn the bottle right side up and it is now a complete unit.

Fill with formula. *Do not pour boiling formula or water into plastic formula sac.* Snap nipple on bottle firmly. Always push cap over nipple until you are ready to feed your infant.

Bottle feeding

Start with clean hands. Then take the formula from the refrigerator, shake, and warm the bottle to body temperature. Remove the nipple shield and turn the nipple right side up. Avoid touching the end of the nipple or the bottle rim.

Test the temperature of the formula by sprinkling a few drops on the inside of your wrist. It should feel warm, not hot. If the formula is too hot, let it cool a little or hold it under cold running water if you're in a hurry. This is also a test for the size of the hole in the nipple.

Always hold Baby in your arms while feeding him. He needs to feel the same security and loving warmth he'd have if you were breast-feeding him.

Bottle propping deprives him of the affection and companionship that are such an important part of his mealtime. Also, swallowing is difficult if a baby is flat on his back. He may choke and aspirate the milk into his lungs. If he loses the nipple, no one is there to help him—a frustrating experience.

Take formula from the refrigerator, shake, and warm the bottle to body temperature in a pan of water. Shake several times to heat evenly.

Test temperature of formula by sprinkling a few drops on the inside of your wrist. It should feel warm, not hot. If not warm, return to pan.

The nipple should be firm to encourage strenuous sucking. If the holes in the nipple are the proper size, it should take the baby about 20 minutes to finish a bottle, providing he sucks continuously. If it takes him longer, the formula probably isn't flowing smoothly through the nipple. Investigate.

First, check the cap—it may be screwed on too tightly. Loosen it, then retest to see if the milk flows properly. Bubbles will rise in the formula when the baby sucks if the cap is properly adjusted. If that doesn't do the trick, the nipple holes should be enlarged slightly by using a hot needle.

Tip the bottle to keep both nipple and neck of the bottle constantly filled with formula. Otherwise, the baby will suck air.

After a feeding, help Baby get up any swallowed air. He may need bubbling during the feeding, but only at a real pause in sucking. Don't interrupt Baby just to bubble.

When he is finished, place him on either his side or stomach. This will prevent him from drawing the milk into his lungs should he spit up while lying in his crib.

Do not reheat leftover formula. However, if the baby should awaken hungry within a short time, let him finish the bottle.

BUBBLING THE BABY Protect your clothing with a towel or diaper when you bubble Baby, for when the air bubble comes up, some milk may come right along with the bubble.

After Baby has nursed as much as he will, place him in one or a combination of the positions pictured on next page and help him get rid of any air in his stomach.

An air bubble may also cause your baby to stop nursing halfway through a feeding. If he's eating vigorously, don't interrupt his feeding to bubble him. Wait until he finishes or lets up a little.

Some babies need to be bubbled before a feeding as well as during or after. And other infants don't need it all. If yours is one of these, try to bubble him for a few minutes after each feeding, but don't worry if no air comes up.

After he's five or six months old, he'll be able to relieve himself without help.

HICCUPS, SPITTING, AND VOMITING If the baby swallows his food too fast, eats too much, or gets too much air,

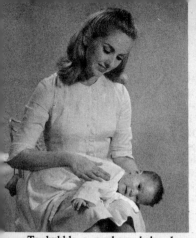

To bubble a newborn baby, lay him on his stomach in your lap. Turn his head to the side and support it by placing your hand under his head. Gently but firmly pat his back.

As Baby grows, you may find it easier to hold him against your shoulder. Let his head rest on your shoulder for support. Gently pat his back.

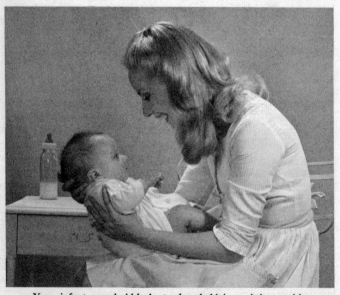

Your infant may bubble best when held in a sitting position on your lap. Use both hands to support his head and back. To bubble, gently pat his back or rock him back and forth.

he may hiccup. Usually this lasts only a few minutes and may be disregarded except to bubble him.

If it persists, however, give him a few teaspoons of lukewarm boiled water.

Spitting up, or regurgitation, is not the same as forceful, projectile vomiting. When the baby spits up, formula just seems to roll from his mouth without force. It's *common* and *isn't significant* as long as the weekly weight gain is made.

Spitting up may be caused by overfeeding, lack of bubbling, or incompatible formulas.

In many infants, spontaneous improvement of spitting up usually occurs when the baby is old enough to be placed on homogenized milk. This milk forms a curd which is larger and more difficult to get out of the stomach. If Baby continues to spit, try him on skim milk.

The condition usually stops when the baby spends more time in an upright position.

Continuous forceful, or projectile, vomiting is serious in itself, because it may lead to dehydration, but it's also an indication that something is wrong with the baby and should be corrected.

If it occurs continuously after more than two or three feedings, or if it occurs once or twice daily over several days, consult your doctor for his expert advice.

VITAMINS

Vitamins should be started shortly after the baby comes home from the hospital. Babies on certain types of formula and breast-fed babies require additional supplemental vitamins.

Some physicians feel that A, D, and C are the only supplemental vitamins required, and that milk contains enough B vitamins to prevent deficiencies from arising. Others feel it's essential to give B vitamins.

Some of the proprietary formulas contain a minimum amount of vitamins, so if the baby takes a full quart of formula, your doctor may feel he's getting adequate vitamins. He will tell you what vitamin program he prefers for your baby.

In recent years, studies have indicated that an excessive amount of vitamins can be detrimental. Don't assume that because a specific amount of vitamins is necessary for the baby, an increased amount will be more beneficial. Always give the recommended dose. When it calls for a few drops, give a few drops and not a teaspoonful.

The doctor will tell you how many units to give the baby. Check the package label to see how many units are in x number of drops or in a teaspoonful.

TIME FOR VITAMINS C AND D Cow's milk, while it is the most nearly complete food for babies—except for mother's milk—is lacking in vitamins C and D. It's also lacking in iron, a mineral which Baby has to have for health.

Baby comes into the world with enough iron stored up to last him for some time, but if he's formula-fed, he needs vitamins C and D added almost from the first. This is why they are now introduced in some form as early as the second or third week.

Human milk contains vitamin C in ample amounts, especially if the mother is getting vitamin C in proper amount in her own diet. But the breast-fed baby *does* need vitamin D.

SOURCES OF VITAMIN D For many years, cod-liver oil and other fish oils have been the main source of vitamin D. They also contain vitamin A. Because the taste and smell of these products is objectionable, they're no longer used extensively as a source of these vitamins.

Commercial preparations containing vitamins A and D are available singularly or in combination with vitamin C and the B vitamins. There are also flavored syrups and, for the older child, chewable tablets and capsules.

Regardless of the child's age, 400 I.U. (International Units) of vitamin D will fulfill all the needed requirements to insure superior skeletal development. Because certain illnesses are believed to result from overdoses of vitamin D, it is important that the daily dosage does not exceed 800 units a day.

The best natural source of vitamin D is sunshine. When your child gets older and is out in the sunshine a lot, it's probably unnecessary to give supplemental vitamin D.

Check with your doctor to see if there's sufficient sunshine in your area to warrant discontinuing vitamin D during the summer.

Fortified milk has 400 U.S.P. units of vitamin D added to the quart (in the case of fresh milk). In evaporated milk, 400 units of vitamin D are contained in the amount of milk which, when combined with an equal amount of water, will make one quart. Most babies won't take a full quart every day so a vitamin supplement is required.

VITAMIN C Until a few years ago, orange juice was the main source of the 30 to 50 milligram vitamin C requirement for bottle-fed babies. Vitamin C was not incorporated in vitamin drops because it would lose its potency.

Now, stable vitamin C is incorporated in most vitamin products, and it's no longer necessary to give orange juice or tomato juice.

Many doctors prefer that orange juice not be given until the baby is much older because of the high allergy incidence associated with it. Often, babies develop a rash, vomit, or have diarrhea after taking orange juice.

VITAMIN B$_1$ Vitamin B$_1$ is assuming more importance in the feeding of infants because there is a direct connection between energy metabolism and the requirement of thiamin (vitamin B$_1$).

Your baby is an energetic little fellow and needs his thiamin. Both the breast-fed and the bottle-fed baby get only the minimum requirement of vitamin B$_1$ in their food until wholegrain cereals and other B$_1$-rich foods are added to the diet. Therefore, many doctors recommend vitamins containing B$_1$, but there is some question as to whether extra vitamin B$_1$ is actually needed as there is no evidence of vitamin B$_1$ deficiency in the early infant stage.

VITAMIN A The Food and Nutritional Board of the National Research Council recommends an allowance of 1,500 units of vitamin A per day. A quart of cow's milk will supply this amount of vitamin A, and the equivalent amount of breast milk will supply even more. Therefore, supplemental vitamin A is not necessary. However, vitamin A accompanies the vitamin D in commercial preparations, so the baby definitely receives an adequate amount.

OTHER VITAMINS Also recommended by the Food and Nutritional Board are 6 to 7 milligrams of niacin daily for infants. Both human milk and cow's milk are somewhat deficient in niacin. However, we don't see symptoms of deficiency in the infant-age group, because most milks contain an abundant amount of tryptophan which meets part of this vitamin requirement.

Pyridoxine, or vitamin B_6, is another important B vitamin. The recommended dosage is 500 milligrams. Deficiencies are not encountered when breast and cow's milk are used.

Vitamin K is usually given to the newborn shortly after birth. Your obstetrician or pediatrician will handle it before the baby leaves the hospital.

HOW TO GIVE VITAMINS If you give the vitamins with a dropper, be sure it's placed in the cheek or on the tongue and squeezed. *Do not* squirt the vitamins directly into the back part of the mouth, because the baby may choke, gag, and draw them into his lungs. If the baby is taking most of his formula, it's all right to include the vitamins in the formula.

FLUORIDE The value of fluoride in the prevention of tooth decay is now well recognized. In some parts of the country, an adequate amount of fluoride is found normally in the drinking water. In other communities, the proper amount of fluoride has been added to the water. If you live in an area where the water contains an insufficient amount of fluoride, you may buy fluoride tablets or drops. Many manufacturers also combine fluoride with their vitamin supplements. Check your public health agency if you are uncertain of the fluoride content in your drinking water.

IRON Iron is essential if your child is to grow and develop. A lack of iron causes anemia, loss of appetite, increased irritability, and decreased activity.

The amount of iron in milk is inadequate. Therefore, you should begin feeding iron-rich foods to your baby at the third month. The best sources are infant cereals fortified with iron, egg, liver, and grain.

BOWEL MOVEMENTS

FIRST BOWEL MOVEMENTS During the first few days, a baby's movements are composed of a greenish black material known as meconium. Baby will pass these stools for the first few days when he's in the hospital nursery.

BOWEL MOVEMENTS IF BABY IS BREAST-FED Constipation, like thumb-sucking, is often a source of unnecessary worry to mothers. The breast-fed baby is almost never constipated, but ordinarily has frequent stools during the first month or six weeks. It is not unusual for him to have a movement after each feeding—from five to six stools a day is normal during this early period.

The stools are usually very soft and have an inoffensive odor. They may range from light yellow to yellow-orange, occasionally may be green and contain curds. (Green, because the bile hasn't had time to change from green to yellow, and curds because the milk curds have gone through the digestive tract undigested.)

As Baby's digestive tract matures and his utilization of food improves, the stools, especially the breast-fed baby's, will decrease in frequency. A baby may have only one stool in two or more days and still be perfectly healthy. Breast-fed babies often strain, groan, get red in the face while having a movement.

Your doctor will assure you that there is seldom cause for alarm over the bowels of the breast-fed baby. Always consult him, however, if you suspect something may be wrong.

BOWEL MOVEMENTS IF BABY IS BOTTLE-FED Depending on the type of formula, the bottle-fed baby's stools are firmer than those of the breast-fed baby. They're usually yellow, but may be brownish, and generally aren't as frequent during the first few weeks as the breast-fed baby's. Baby may have from one to four movements a day at first, then, as he grows older, cut down to one or two a day.

IF BABY IS CONSTIPATED As long as Baby's stools are soft and smooth, he isn't constipated, no matter how far apart movements may be. But when the stools are so hard they're passed with straining and difficulty, your baby is constipated.

The formula may not contain enough water, or it may not have enough carbohydrate (sweetening). Check water content. An increased amount of sweetening may help. Begin with an increase of a tablespoon of sweetening each day; work up to two or three of the powdered sugar (dextrin-maltose), *or* one and a half of syrup.

Offer Baby cool, boiled water between feedings. Also, one or two teaspoonfuls of prune juice or prune pulp may be given each day. Should you feel it necessary to further alter the formula, consult your doctor.

Be slow to use suppositories or enemas, without the doctor's advice, as the Baby might come to rely on them.

Sometimes stools are so hard to pass there is blood on the outside. If this is just an occasional occurrence, there is no reason for undue concern, but the formula should be altered to soften the stools. If the condition persists, consult the doctor. Illness and fever, with resulting lack of appetite, may be cause of temporary constipation.

DIARRHEA? CALL YOUR DOCTOR If the baby's stools have been of the same consistency—whether soft and smooth or firm—and then suddenly become loose, watery, frequent, greenish, or contain mucus, this is an indication that your baby has diarrhea.

Your baby may not tolerate the usual amount of sweetening in his formula. Reduce the sweetening to see if this is the cause. If the condition continues, stop all food, especially fruit juices. Give Baby small quantities of cool, boiled water at frequent intervals or dilute, boiled skimmed milk. Diluted skim milk given in small quantities will frequently help to control milk diarrhea.

If this simple measure doesn't correct the condition, *call your doctor.*

The danger of diarrhea lies in its rapid draining of the water from the tissues. Dehydration of body minerals may result.

DIAPERS

WHEN TO CHANGE DIAPERS If diaper rash is to be prevented, change diapers before and after a feeding, after a bowel movement, and whenever he seems to be uncomfortable because of a wet diaper.

Unless his skin is extremely sensitive or he has a diaper rash, don't disturb his sleep just to change him. Rest is more important. Baby won't be cold because of a wet diaper, if he's warm enough otherwise.

If he wakes and cries, change him, but check to see if there is some other reason for his crying. He may be too warm or too cold. Or a gas bubble may be bothering him.

The buttocks and genital area must be thoroughly cleaned each time the diaper is changed. If the baby has only urinated, cleanse the skin by wiping with plenty of warm water and cotton. Dry thoroughly with more cotton or a soft towel. Then apply lotion or cornstarch before diapering if needed.

After bowel movement, gently wipe off with soft toilet paper or tissues any feces that may be clinging to the skin. Then use cotton balls moistened with warm water to wash. Dry thoroughly. Then apply lotion or cornstarch if needed. If you use powder, don't shake it around loosely in the air.

DIAPER CARE The automatic washer has lightened the seemingly endless task of diaper care. Even the pre-soaking once so much a part of diaper care is no longer an absolute necessity when you use an automatic washer, but your doctor may recommend you pre-soak diapers if the baby develops certain types of diaper rash.

In some convenient place, probably the bathroom, keep a covered 2-gallon plastic diaper pail (half-filled with water in which 2 tablespoons of borax has been dissolved if your doctor suggests it). Plastic diaper pails are more satisfactory than metal containers because they won't rust. You may also pre-soak soiled diapers in a solution made from one of the commercial powdered products.

If diaper is soiled, shake or scrape stool off into toilet. Then flush it and rinse stained place in the clean water which refills the toilet. Drop the diaper into the pail.

It's a good idea to run the diapers through the rinse cycle of your automatic washer first. Then wash them in *hot* water and detergent and rinse in the washer's long rinse cycle.

A fabric softener in the final rinse cycle will add extra softness to the diapers, but must be used with caution as it may cause a rash on some babies.

The heated circulating air of an automatic dryer helps reduce air-borne bacteria and adds to the softness of the diapers. Line drying in the sunshine is satisfactory, too.

An older baby's diapers may develop a strong ammonia smell. The reaction of bacteria on the diaper and buttocks with the urea contained in urine causes this strong smell. There are several ways of handling this.

If an ammonia rash develops, boil all diapers, 10 minutes every time they're washed *or* use a diaper antiseptic in the final rinse water.

It is usually necessary to do this only to the night diapers, because the day diapers are not in contact with the baby's skin long enough to cause trouble.

In most cities and large towns, there usually are diaper services which lessen the burden of diaper care. They do an excellent job of supplying diapers that are properly washed and dried. Skin problems seldom develop from using diapers washed by their methods.

DISPOSABLE DIAPERS Using disposable diapers is the ultimate method to end diaper drudgery. Today, more and more mothers are discovering the everyday convenience and time-saving qualities of the throw-away, flush-away diapers.

Disposable diapers are only used once, thus preventing a buildup of ammonia, a prime cause of diaper rash and odor. Therefore, your baby is rash-free and odor-free and you are free of washing and folding diapers.

These diapers are layers of soft, cloth-like material sandwiched between a waterproof back-sheet which takes the place of plastic pants and a special lining which serves to keep the baby dry. The moisture is sealed from skin and clothing in the absorbent layers below.

To assure a proper fit, disposable diapers are available in various sizes and thicknesses. They are more expensive than using diaper service, but this is relative to how highly a young mother values her time.

DIAPER RASH This condition, which can make Baby extremely uncomfortable, results either from ammonia formed by the action of bacteria on urine-soaked skin and diapers, from acids in diarrheal stools, food sensitivities, bacterial infecitons, cosmetic applied to skin, or preparations used to wash or soften diapers.

An ammonia rash is usually seen in older babies and is more widespread than a diarrhea rash, often affecting the buttocks, groin, and lower abdomen.

If your baby shows any indication of a rash, change his diapers as soon as they are wet or soiled, even during his sleep, unless this disturbs him so much that he can't go back to sleep afterward. Don't use plastic or rubber pants. Put a soaker pad under Baby.

The next step, if no improvement is noted, is to remove the diaper entirely and expose the whole diaper area to the air. Remove his diaper, wash and dry the skin, but don't apply any ointment. Put several diapers, an absorbent pad, and a waterproof pad under him.

Let him lie like this, in his shirt and a short sacque, an hour or so several times a day in a warm room. Change the diapers under him if they become wet or soiled. Remove his diaper whenever he is taking a sunbath, too, but don't let him get sunburned.

If the baby has an ammonia or pustular rash, in addition to caring for the baby's diapers as directed, washing Baby's little behind with a soap containing hexachlorophene tends to cut down the bacterial flora that's present. There are also commercial lotions and ointments (use after washing diaper area) for these types of rashes that have the same effect as the hexachlorophene soap.

Another method of clearing up diaper rash is to stop using regular diapers and switch to the disposable diapers—at least until the rash is healed. By then, you may be too spoiled to return to your old diapers.

If pustules appear on the diaper area or the rash fails to respond to treatment, it may be due to a yeast infection. See your doctor.

How to diaper your baby

New materials and ways of folding make it possible to have just one size of diaper for the entire time your baby will wear them. Moreover, this can be made to fit him at every stage of his development. Some methods of diapering are the panel fold and the kite fold, shown on opposite page. These put the extra thickness in the middle where it's needed, while fitting Baby's dimensions quite comfortably.

As Baby expands, you will have to change from either of these folds, and adopt the triple fold for oblong diapers or a double fold for square diapers.

Besides the square and oblong diapers, there are fitted ones which fasten with tapes or gripper-type fasteners, and also several types of disposable ones. As well as for use at home, these make trips and outings easier.

Also available are paper diaper liners. Placed between Baby's buttocks and the diaper to catch the bowel movements, they prevent hard-to-remove stains.

Waterproof outer diapers should be used only for outings or dress-up occasions. They may chafe Baby's skin if used continuously. And there is also a tendency not to change the diaper as often as necessary. These diapers should be made of a porous, washable material, or else be loose enough so they won't be airtight. Neither kind should bind.

BABY'S BATH Most babies love their bath. They coo and giggle, kick and splash. Some babies, however, fear water. If your little one is afraid, don't be alarmed. Take extra care, though, that bathtime doesn't become even more frightening to him by keeping his head above water always. Be especially careful that you don't get soap and water into his eyes.

Is it necessary to give Baby a sponge bath until the cord falls off and the navel heals? Ask your doctor about this. Some doctors prefer a sponge bath for babies at this age while others feel you can give a tub bath.

A plastic tub works as well as the specially designed bath tables, is easy to keep clean. If there is an adjoining counter, a thoroughly clean kitchen sink is also satisfactory.

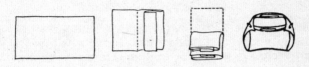

1. Panel fold for oblong diaper. Bring right end over to about 8 inches from left end. Turn right end back upon itself to about 3 inches from fold. Now bring the left end over even with first fold on the extreme right.

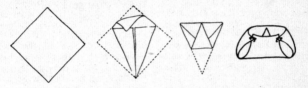

2. Kite fold for square diaper. Fold in two sides to make a long V. Turn down the remaining flap, forming triangle. Bring point of V up to the straight edge of flap. Makes thick center panel.

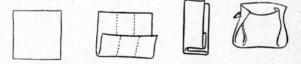

3. Fold over one-third of end of square diaper. Then fold to three thicknesses. Extra thickness in front for boys, in back for girls if they lie on their backs. Fits the infant comfortably, but not adjustable as the baby grows.

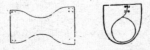

4. Fitted diapers are available or can be made. Double row of fasteners makes the diaper adjustable as Baby grows. Extra thickness is provided in the center where it's needed. This diaper can also be fastened with pins.

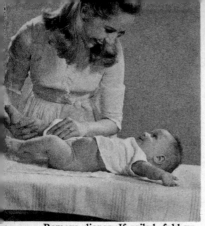

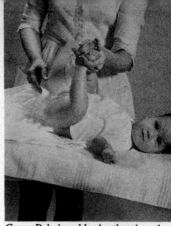

Remove diaper. If soiled, fold under as you unpin. Place pad under Baby's hips to catch moisture. Wash genitals and buttocks with cotton moistened in warm water. After bowel movement, wipe with tissue, sponge with water, rinse. Wash from front to back. Dry thoroughly with cotton or clean, soft cloth.

Grasp Baby's ankles by thumb and middle finger, inserting index finger between his ankles to keep from pressing them together. Raise his legs and hips off the table, slide folded diaper under him. Bring diaper up between legs, extra thickness in front for boys, in back for girls if they generally lie on their backs.

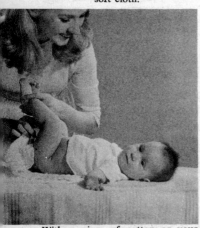

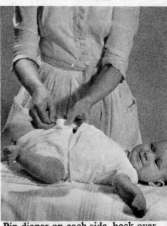

With a piece of cotton or your hand, apply lotion to genital area and buttocks if needed, taking care to reach all folds and creases or powder lightly with cornstarch. If you use powder, don't shake it in the air or Baby may breathe it in. Have clean diaper at hand, folded to fit. Keep pins out of Baby's reach.

Pin diaper on each side, back overlapping front. Keep finger next to Baby when pinning to avoid pricking him. Pin shirt at sides between front and back fold of diaper. Smooth shirt down over diaper in front to keep his tummy warm. Pin if you wish. Do not pin shirt in back. Fold it up to keep it dry.

Many physicians are now recommending soap containing hexachlorophene which is helpful in destroying harmful skin bacteria. Most babies' skin will tolerate the hexachlorophene soap well without very great incidence of sensitivity and allergy.

If a hexachlorophene soap is not used, a mild soap or any one of the soaps specially prepared for babies is perfectly all right.

HOW OFTEN DOES BABY NEED BATHING? The weather and the season determine how often the baby needs bathing. In warm localities, most babies can be bathed every day without drying the skin. On excessively hot days, you can give the baby a sponge bath several times a day to keep him comfortable.

During the winter, when the heat is turned on in a home, the humidity falls. With this low humidity, daily bathing often dries and chafes the baby's delicate skin. If the humidity is low in your home, a bath every other, or every third day is sufficient.

A good rule to follow: if Baby's skin is dry, skip a bath. If his skin is nice and soft, bathe him every day. Although you don't give Baby a daily bath, you can certainly wash his face, hands, and diaper area whenever necessary.

HEAT RASH The best way to treat heat rash is to prevent it. Overdressing the baby is the surest way to start it. If Baby does develop heat rash, cooling sponge baths with lukewarm water, several times a day, will help to make the baby more comfortable.

Cornstarch or commercial products containing cornstarch and menthol are also soothing treatment for heat rash.

OIL AND POWDER Today, most physicians are advising parents to use baby lotion or cream rather than oil if the baby's skin is dry. Oil plugs up the skin pores and is the source of many rashes.

Cornstarch is one of the best preparations which you can use as a powder substitute. It is soft and nonirritating to Baby's skin.

If a little cornstarch gets into the baby's eyes or if he accidentally breathes it into his lungs, no serious damage will result.

A number of baby powders now available have cornstarch as their base. Check the ingredient information on the can.

If plain cornstarch is used, a kitchen salt shaker is a handy container.

Powder made of talcum powder is harsh and frequently responsible for skin rashes. Inhalation of it is dangerous.

CARE OF THE NAVEL It's important for you to keep the navel clean and dry. Clean it once, or even twice, a day, if necessary.

So that all of the secretions can be washed away, first wash the navel thoroughly with soap and water using a cotton swab. Then apply rubbing alcohol. The alcohol will have a desired drying effect.

If the little stump that remains is kept clean and dry, it will not become infected and it will drop off sooner.

Occasionally, the stump drops off shortly after the baby leaves the hospital, but it may take three, four, or even five weeks.

When it does, you'll notice a little blood spotting on the baby's diaper or undershirt. This is normal and is nothing to worry about. Just go on cleaning the navel as if there'd been no spotting.

If the navel continues to bleed or spot beyond a week, it may start to look a little lumpy. This is granulation tissue. If this occurs, ask your doctor if he feels the navel needs any specific attention.

A dressing or a band is no longer considered necessary. Most doctors feel that a band will not prevent a small rupture which many babies will have during their first year or so.

CARE OF THE PENIS Caring for the circumcision is quite simple. Generally, a bandage or gauze pad won't stay in place and is really unnecessary. If the wound has a tendency to stick to the diaper, apply a little vaseline to the cut edge.

During the first two or three weeks, it's important not to forcibly pull back the foreskin, because the cut edges of the wound might pull apart. However, after three weeks, retract the foreskin with each bath to prevent it from adhering to the head of the penis.

If the baby is not circumcised, your doctor may tell you to retract the foreskin with each bath. Be sure you pull it forward again after washing the head of the penis. If you can't pull the foreskin forward again, and the penis begins to swell, call the doctor immediately.

SWOLLEN BREASTS Both boys and girls may have swollen breasts and little girls may also bleed from the vagina. Both occurrences are due to the mother's hormones which pass through the placenta and into the baby's bloodstream.

The baby's breasts and the little girl's uterus undergo the same changes as the mother's. There's no need for alarm because the occasional blood-tinged discharge is certainly normal. It is not a flow of blood.

When you bathe her or change her diaper, use moist cotton to clean the vulva. If the baby has swollen breasts and milk runs out, don't squeeze them in an attempt to express the milk. Just leave them alone.

DRESSING YOUR BABY Grandma used to bundle up the babies no matter what the temperature, and today there's still a tendency to overdress them.

During the summer, adjust Baby's outfit to the temperature. If the temperature is somewhere between 70° and 74°, the infant's basic clothing should be a diaper, undershirt, kimono, and a receiving blanket. Remove the blanket when the temperature climbs to 75°–78°. From 80° to 85°, you can skip the kimono, and if the temperature goes above 85°, the baby needs just his diaper.

During the winter months when the temperature of the house can be maintained at a constant level of 72° to 74°, the basic dress would be a diaper, undershirt, kimono, and receiving blanket. If you turn the thermostat down or cool your home to 68° to 70°, add a heavier blanket for added warmth.

When you get out the articles for his bath, lay his clean clothes arranged in the order in which you'll put them on him where you can reach them. You won't want Baby to become chilled and he shouldn't be left unattended.

The clothes should slip on and off freely and quickly and

should never interfere with his exercising. If your house is cool and you put more clothes on him, they should be loose enough so that he'll be comfortable and free to move around.

Most babies wear a nightgown over their shirt and diaper until they're about 6 months old. After that, a nightgown and diaper are usually adequate.

Baby's nightgowns should be long, open all the way down the front or back, and close with either a tie or gripper snap. This makes changing Baby's diaper a relatively simple matter. If he sleeps on either his tummy or his back, the nightie can be spread open and won't get soaking wet.

Sleeping bags will prevent Baby's getting uncovered, but they should be roomy.

During early infancy, you may use short sacques and nightgowns, and wrap Baby in outing-flannel squares or receiving blankets. Spread the blanket on a table diamondwise. Lay him on it with his head near the upper point and lap one side point over his tummy. Fold the lower point over his feet and tummy, followed by the other side point.

This is usually enough covering for him, even in bed, if your house isn't too cool. Place another blanket over him if additional cover is needed. A waterproof pad inside the blanket will keep it from getting wet.

Knit terry sleepers are ideal for a tiny baby, keep him comfortably warm, and are ready to be worn right out of the dryer.

Baby girls look extra sweet in a pretty dress on special occasions. However, skip overlong, starched, fussy dresses that make Baby uncomfortable. Topper sets, with plastic-lined diaper covers, which come in styles for boys or girls, and no-iron dresses make dandy dress-up outfits. A pair of booties will keep tiny toes warm, but they'll probably fall off if he's a kicker.

A cardigan sweater is a must for breezy summer weather. Add a sunshade hat to keep the sun out of his eyes. In really cold weather, bundle a tiny baby up for outdoors in a pram suit or extra-warm sweater, cap, mittens, and booties, topped off with a wool blanket.

How to give baby a sponge bath

Until the baby's navel or circumcision is healed, your doctor may prefer that you give Baby a sponge bath. Or, if your baby is particularly tiny and delicate, or has dry or irritated skin, your doctor may even recommend that you give him a sponge bath for the first month or six weeks.

Choose a quiet time that's convenient for you. Many mothers find it simplest to bathe their babies before the midmorning feeding. But if it's more convenient for you just before his 6 P.M. feeding, do it then. Don't, however, give a bath just after a feeding. This is the time your baby should be kept quiet to enable satisfactory digestion.

Choose a warm room, preferably one that's sunny. Be sure there are no drafts in the room. The temperature should be from 75 to 80 degrees. Probably the most convenient place for you will be either the bathroom or kitchen, which are usually warm rooms and where the warm water is handy.

Before you begin, assemble all the equipment. You can't bathe a baby properly if you have to stop frequently and hunt for various items. On a low table, place 1 or 2 pans of warm water, cake of mild soap in a soap dish, cotton swabs, large pieces of cotton or a soft washcloth, a large bath towel for

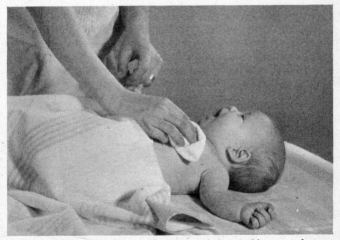

If your baby is very tiny, or has dry or irritated skin, your doctor may suggest a cleansing lotion rather than a sponge bath. Place Baby on a table and follow the directions shown for a sponge bath.

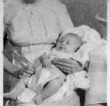

Sit on low chair with Baby in a big towel in your lap. Unpin the diaper but do not remove it entirely. Take the soiled diaper and shirt off as you go along.

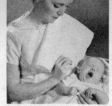

Use moistened swabs to clean only outer section of nose and ears. Take care to avoid penetrating too deeply. Gently clean face, avoiding eyes, with cotton or soft cloth dipped in warm water.

Shampoo scalp three times a week with soapy water. Rinse well, supporting head and back over basin with your hand and arm. Pat head dry. Apply oil if scales form on head.

Remove shirt. Keep rest covered with big towel. Soap his chest, arms, and hands with a mild soap. Pay special attention to folds and creases in his skin.

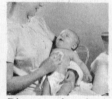

Rinse neck, chest, arms, and hands with clean, warm water. Be sure to get all soap out of the creases and folds, or the skin may chafe. Then pat him dry with a soft towel —don't rub his tender skin.

Gently turn him over on right side to reach the back and buttocks. Be sure to support his head with your hand. With a soft washcloth, soap and rinse the back area, then dry.

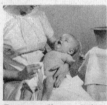

Remove diaper. Wash and rinse abdomen, genitals, legs, and feet. Work gently when you sponge the navel. If unhealed, wipe with alcohol on cotton.

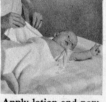

Apply lotion and powder if you wish. Now put on Baby's clean clothes which should be right at hand and assembled before you start the bath. Dress the baby gently but quickly on your lap or table.

All clean and sweet-smelling. Baby reminds you that it's time for his meal and bed. You should warm his bottle at start of bath, so it's ready to pop into his mouth.

covering the baby, small towel with which to dry him, baby lotion if it's necessary, cornstarch or powder with a cornstarch base, nursing bottle of warm sterile water, diaper, safety pins, shirt, kimono or nightgown, and a bath apron for you. Have a few toothpicks on hand to clean the baby's nails if they need cleaning. Use the blunt tip. A bath thermometer is a convenience but is certainly not a necessity.

Before you begin Baby's sponge bath, scrub your hands and nails with hot, soapy water. Keep your nails short and round so you won't scratch the baby's delicate skin.

Fill pans with water that registers 95 to 100 degrees on the bath thermometer, or which feels comfortably warm to your elbow. No water softener or commercial toiletries should be added to the water because of Baby's delicate skin. These preparations are often responsible for skin irritations and rashes.

Sit down, with the baby in your lap, and you're ready to begin. If you use a bath table, sit beside it on a stool of convenient height. Use the photographs as a guide. While it looks like a time-consuming project, it really takes no more than ten minutes or so and soon becomes routine. Work out your own bath routine and follow it each day. Your baby will expect it, become accustomed to it, and learn to cooperate step by step with you. Baby will enjoy the water, so enjoy it with him.

If Baby's finger- or toenails are long, they can be cut best when he's asleep. Use a clean, sharp pair of blunt tip scissors that have been wiped off with alcohol. Never use manicure or other sharp scissors for this job as you might easily hurt your child.

Pay special attention to cleaning the genital organs. If your baby is an uncircumcised boy, ask the doctor how to clean under the foreskin. For girls, separate the folds of the vulva, and clean. Always wash and wipe from the front toward the back in this area.

How to give a tub bath

By the time the baby's navel and circumcision have healed, he's ready to graduate from a sponge to a tub bath, unless your doctor advises otherwise.

His first tub bath should be a pleasant experience. It's his introduction to the good feeling and enjoyment he'll find later in water play. Bathe him at a time when he's not ravenously hungry, hold him securely, and use the right temperature water, so that bathtime becomes a happy new ritual.

Use the same arrangements as for the sponge baths, except to substitute a small tub or bath table for the basin or pan.

A bath table is convenient but a plastic tub that's large enough is also satisfactory and easier to keep clean.

The first few times you give the baby a tub bath, use no more than 3 inches of water in the tub so he will become accustomed to the water gradually.

Before you begin the baby's bath, scrub your hands and fingernails with warm, soapy water and a brush. Have all sup-

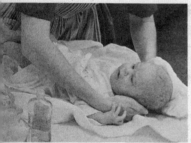

Susan's had her face rinsed with a soft cloth, clear water. Now Mother's lathering her scalp with baby shampoo.

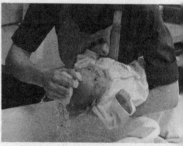

Football-carry, described above, is a safe way to hold the baby securely while you rinse the head. Dry immediately. Remove Baby's

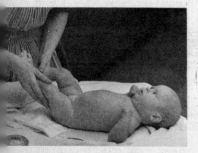

The diaper comes off so Mother can soap tummy, groin, sturdy legs, feet. Wash carefully the genital folds and between the tiny

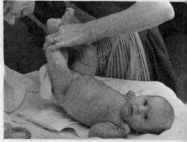

toes. Use your hands or a soft washcloth to lather these areas. Mother lifts Susan by holding her ankles with forefinger between ankles.

plies that you'll need laid out within easy reach.

Test the water with either your wrist or elbow. It should feel comfortably warm. If you don't trust this method, use a bath thermometer. Keep a pitcher of hot water handy to warm the bath water.

Lift Baby onto clean towel on table. Keep a firm grasp as he is lowered into the water so he will feel completely secure.

As in a sponge bath, use cotton swabs to clean only the outer ears, nostrils. Don't poke in nostrils or inner ears.

Before washing the baby's hair, rinse his face with clear water, no soap, using a soft washcloth. Then pat dry.

Baby's hair needs a shampoo about 3 times a week. Use clear water other times. Soap his scalp well with a baby sham-

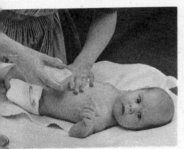

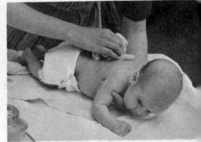

shirt and soap chest and tummy. Or undress Baby, transfer him immediately into the tub, soap him there. Susan gets soaped on the table.

With your hand under armpit, thumb clasping arm, turn Baby over on his tummy to soap his back, buttocks. Keep firm grip.

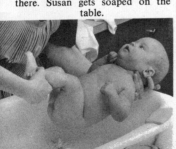

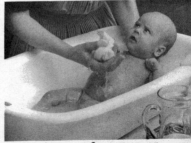

Support Baby's head, shoulders with left arm, hand, and grasp legs, forefinger between ankles as you lower Baby into the tub.

Mother keeps a firm grasp on Susan's arm with one hand, supporting her head and back as she rinses with a washcloth in the other. Susan looks dubious!

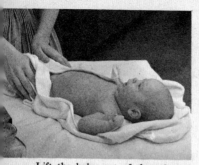

Lift the baby out of the tub and wrap immediately in a large towel. Pat dry. Then apply lotion or powder.

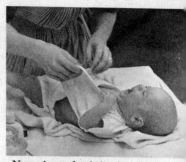

Now dress the baby in a clean diaper, shirt, and kimono or nitie. Clean clothes should be at hand on the bath table.

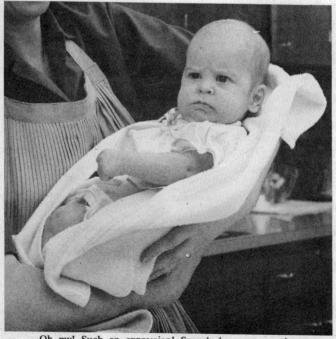

Oh my! Such an expression! Susan's been very patient, and now, clean and cuddly, she's about to insist on bottle.

poo, using your hand. Hold his head over the tub and rinse his scalp with washcloth. Support his back and hips with your arm, your hand supporting his head, his legs tucked under your arm.

Leave Baby in his shirt and diaper, covered by a towel or cotton blanket, while you wash and dry his face and head. Remove the shirt first, then the diaper, when you're ready to soap those areas. When he's all soaped, he goes into the tub to be rinsed. Work quickly on soaping, so lather doesn't dry on his skin.

Lift him out, wrap him immediately in large towel. Dry navel, creases and folds first to make sure they're dry. Then dry all over.

DRESSING YOUR BABY

FRESH AIR FOR BABY Most parents are eager to start taking their babies outdoors as soon as possible. By the time your baby is 6 weeks old, he's ready to go for a buggy ride, or to snooze in a sunny spot, well protected from the wind. The temperature should be at least 60 degrees. Don't put him outside in wind, dampness, or extremely cold weather.

Today's automobiles are well-heated, so there's no reason why you can't take short trips with the baby, regardless of his age or of the outside temperature. Of course, he'll be reasonably dressed for the trip from the house to the waiting car.

BABY NEEDS HIS SLEEP There are almost as many different sleep patterns in the early weeks as there are babies. Some babies will sleep most of the time they aren't being fed, changed, or bathed. And some, from birth on, seem to sleep only fitfully and have long periods of wakefulness. This shouldn't cause any alarm. Let him rest even though he's awake.

In the section on arrangements for Baby before he arrived, the right sort of sleeping provisions are described.

The baby should have a comfortable bed, and if at all possible, a room to himself, or at least a spot of his own, partitioned off from the rest of the room. Put him in his bed with the door closed and lights out.

Don't waken him to show him to people. There's no harm, though, in letting relatives or friends slip in for a look while he's sleeping, provided they don't disturb him.

At this age, Baby can't move himself, so you'll have to shift his sleeping position from time to time, from abdomen to one side, and then to the other. Just after a feeding, lay him on his side. He'll be less likely to spit up. To keep him on his side, roll up a blanket and prop it against his back.

As he approaches five weeks, he'll probably sleep five hours at night, and when he's six weeks old, six hours at night. Although night feedings are hard on parents, in many cases they're desirable. If the baby is very small or his weight gain

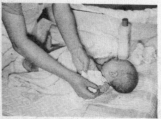

1. Baby's shirt goes on one arm at a time. Put your fingers up sleeve, grasp his fist, guide it through. Sleeveless closed shirt is pulled over feet.

2. Fasten shirt, fold up in back so it doesn't reach below hipline. Put diaper on and pin it. Take care it isn't too snug or too loose.

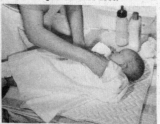

3. Kimono or nitie goes on next. Long-sleeved shirt, kimono may go on together. Place shirt sleeve inside kimono sleeve, gather them together in one hand. Reach through for Baby's arm.

4. Many mothers prefer to tie kimonos in back, so Baby's hands don't catch in ribbon or tape ties. Spread lower back of kimono open to keep it dry. Front opening is also satisfactory.

is slow, an extra night feeding or a feeding every three hours during the night is necessary if the baby is to grow normally.

TONIC NECK REFLEX Why does Baby seem to hold his head to one side all of the time: During their first few months, babies will always turn their heads to the same side, either right or left. This is perfectly normal behavior and is called the tonic reflex. This reflex disappears when the baby is about three months old, and from then on, he'll hold his head midline or turn it to the other side. Therefore, it's pointless to try to turn his head to the other side before he's able to do so by himself.

WHEN YOUR BABY CRIES When they cry hard, all babies draw up their legs, get red faces, hard tummies, and wave their arms. Every muscle in their bodies tightens as they cry or scream. Crying is the only way the baby can tell you when he's uncomfortable or hungry.

Soon you'll learn to distinguish the hunger cry, which simply means that it's getting toward dinnertime; the fretting of a tired, sleepy baby who needs to be left alone so he can go to sleep; the cry of pain or discomfort.

It's always best to investigate thoroughly and be sure he's as comfortable as you can make him. Maybe he has a bubble in his tummy that's making him uncomfortable. Try bubbling him. Or if it's been an hour and a half or two hours since his last feeding, he *might* be hungry again. Try nursing him or giving him his bottle.

If he wakes regularly, crying from hunger, make a 24-hour check of the amount of milk he's getting from you. If he's formula fed, ask your doctor about increasing the amount of formula the baby usually receives.

Maybe he has a wet or soiled diaper and is uncomfortable. Investigate and change him if necessary. Once you've done everything you can to make him comfortable, he's better off by himself. If he's still crying hard after ten or fifteen minutes, he may just want to be held for a few minutes and comforted. But then put him right back down and leave him there. Constant holding, jostling, walking the floor, and bouncing may turn him into a demanding little fellow who has to be held to be happy.

Practically every baby has a regular crying period at about the same time each day. The severity and duration of the crying is usually directly proportional to the tension, confusion, and turmoil that exists in the home.

Many people refer to this distress period as colic. What causes it? There are many possible explanations.

Some physicians feel that colic is due to cramping of the intestines, but why would the intestines start cramping during just that one period each day? Something is wrong with the formula? No—because then he would cry all day. Possibly, the baby is sick? This is unlikely, because a sick baby cries continuously, not at a specific time each day.

If an easily excited, nervous mother has a colicky baby, they're involved in a vicious circle. The more the baby cries, the more nervous the mother gets, and the more nervous she gets, the more the baby cries.

A calm atmosphere and a composed mother ease the situation, but it might be necessary for the mother to receive the sedative rather than the baby. Fortunately, especially for the parents, this colicky period usually disappears after the third to the fourth month.

It is certainly important to have your physician give the baby a thorough examination if he seems happy and content, then suddenly begins to cry continuously rather than at a specific time each day. Probably the most common cause of a previously happy baby who all of a sudden begins crying and becomes ravenously hungry is an ear infection. By carefully examining the baby's ears, the doctor can quickly determine if this is the cause.

Another cause of prolonged crying is an inguinal hernia. If you should notice the presence of a hernia, consult the doctor immediately. He'll examine the groin to see if it is bulging. The swelling, or bulging, may also travel into the baby boy's scrotum.

An overly-concentrated formula will cause irritability, fussiness, so a formula change may help. Allergy or food incompatibility is recognized as an occasional cause of fussiness. Changing to one of the hypo-allergenic milks (a soybean milk or meat base milk) will quickly tell you if this is the cause of the baby's crying.

Urinary tract obstruction is another important cause of continual crying which is frequently overlooked. Constant crying is seldom without a cause, although the cause may be difficult to determine.

THUMB-SUCKING Sooner or later during these early weeks, you're going to find your baby with his thumb in his mouth. There was a time when a mother would have beamed and said, "A baby that sucks his thumb is a good baby."

But some 20 years ago, thumb-sucking among babies came into much ill-repute. It was held responsible for crooked teeth and other complications. Parents tried to eliminate the habit with various mechanical aids. They even resorted to mild torture, with the result that their child sucked his thumb even harder than he previously did.

You must consider thumb-sucking as a normal reflex. In a study by the Harvard Pediatrics Department, seventy healthy babies were observed. Sixty-one of these babies showed that they enjoyed sucking their thumbs even though they weren't fatigued, hungry, or uncomfortable.

The study points out that finger- or thumb-sucking began between birth and three months. Intensity gradually increased to reach a peak by seven months, and then, as the babies' motor development occupied the baby more, finger and thumb-sucking decreased. By twelve months, except during periods of stress or tension, most of the babies had ceased sucking their thumbs.

This study definitely indicates that finger- or thumb-sucking is normal in babies and usually disappears in most infants.

Unfortunately, Baby is often singled out and actually picked on for attempting to satisfy his oral gratification. Cigarette and pipe smoking, gum chewing, and chewing on toothpicks and straws are actually the adult's substitute for thumb-sucking. Even though medical authorities point out the potential danger in cigarette smoking, more attention is directed to the little baby or small child who enjoys sucking his thumb than to the adult who smokes too heavily.

It's quite common for an older child, or the child past one year, to continue to suck his thumb when he's tired and sleepy, bored, or unable to keep up with the adult world in which he finds himself. He temporarily returns to early infancy when sucking made him feel safe and secure. So instead of fussing, remember that if the child is well nourished, comfortable, and happy, the thumb-sucking will eventually stop by itself.

Thumb-sucking, nail biting, blinking the eyelids, fidgeting with the hands or other types of fidgeting, or nervous twitching may indicate a psychological problem in the child four years old or older. A pediatrician should carefully evaluate the child's behavior, and, if severe, a child psychiatrist or psychologist should be consulted.

Parents, grandparents, and well-meaning friends often make the thumb-sucking itself the problem. They constantly nag the child, pull his thumb from his mouth, put bitter substances on his fingers and thumb in an effort to stop him—all without trying to find out what's really bothering him.

Any child with any spunk will rebel against this constant domination and settle into knowingly sucking his thumb in earnest and in sheer defiance. Then, of course, the thumb-sucking becomes a real problem.

There is still a great deal of disagreement among doctors and dentists about the results of thumb-sucking on the child's teeth. Most authorities agree, however, that there is no permanent damage until after the child is past five years of age. The growing mouth and face will compensate for any minor changes made by the thumb-sucking.

"BLANKET-CARRYING," BANGING, AND ROCKING

In the same category as thumb-sucking are head banging, crib rocking, and "blanket-carrying"—and they're all perfectly normal in the infant and small child.

What mother hasn't tried to pry away from her little one a disreputable looking blanket, or stuffed animal, badly in need of a bath, only to be met with terrible resistance.

For some reason, the child gets great comfort and security from his old rag and doesn't want to part with it for even a few short hours. He tucks it under his arm and constantly rubs it between his fingers or under his nose while sucking his thumb. This, too, he'll eventually give up as he leaves babyish ways behind him.

Many babies will bump their heads against the crib or rock from side to side instead of sucking their thumbs. This is the same type of rhythmic activity as thumb-sucking. Even though you think Baby is knocking himself silly, he really can't do much damage, but you may want to get a four-sided bumper pad to soften the blows.

The little fella that likes to get on his hands and knees and rock back and forth can send his crib scooting across the room into the wall. Rubber bumpers, available at most hospital supply stores, protect crib and wall, lessen the wear and tear on your nerves.

These rhythmic activities may occur for just a short while before the child goes to sleep, or they may go on periodically throughout the night. Perhaps these bouncers and bangers are trying to relieve tension before dropping off to sleep. Just be patient, and don't try to stop the baby or scold him. He'll only get more tense.

PACIFIERS There's a good deal of disagreement over the use of pacifiers. Those who don't favor them feel that the thumb is cheaper, is the proper shape, doesn't fall on the floor, and doesn't look as though someone jammed a plug in the baby's mouth. If you do have strong objections to their use, then don't give one to your baby. You'll only upset yourself.

There are many parents, however, who do favor using a pacifier. They view it as a satisfactory method for correcting the problem of thumb-sucking. Usually, by the end of the sixth or seventh month, the baby will begin to lose his interest in the pacifier, and you can begin to eliminate it.

Many times the so-called "cure" turns out to be as much of a problem as the original thumb-sucking itself. It can be just as difficult to break Baby of his pacifier habit, so all you've done is replace one problem with another equally as vexing.

A WORD ABOUT WORRYING Some mothers worry themselves sick when their babies really are doing beautifully.

But let's say that the doctor has found your baby perfect in every respect—a fine, healthy fellow. Then what's your role?

Given loving care, warmth, and proper food, your healthy baby will continue to be all right. You can always reason that as long as he's happy, eating his food, and making his weight gains, there can't be anything much the matter with him.

He may skip a meal, have small appetite for it, or even lose it without anything serious being wrong. For such mild upsets, you can afford to wait until the next meal or two before you start worrying. If he takes his next meal voraciously (as he probably will) and keeps it down, be assured all's well. It isn't necessary to bother your busy doctor. And don't bother a perfectly well baby by taking his temperature every few hours.

INFANT ILLNESSES NEED A DOCTOR'S CARE There are, however, conditions which need your doctor's attention at once. Listed in the last chapter are the more common conditions which could—not necessarily will—lead to something serious unless you take steps in time.

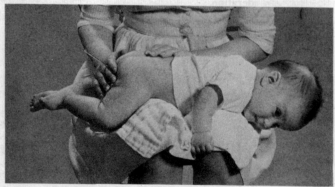

Hold Baby on lap in either of the positions shown. Grease end of rectal thermometer with petroleum jelly. Holding thermometer loosely, insert it into anus, leave for two minutes, clean, and read.

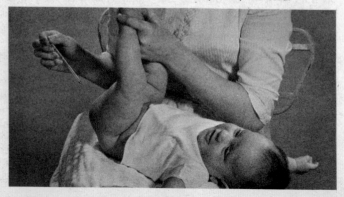

Babies are born with immunity to certain childhood diseases. This immunity will last from four to six months. The most important childhood disease that they are immune to is the red measles. They are also immune to polio and mumps during this early period.

They are not, however, immune to whooping cough, chicken pox, and scarlet fever. It is extremely important that the baby not be exposed to anyone who is ill, although it may be difficult to tell people who have obvious infections not to come and visit the baby. The baby's health must always be your foremost consideration.

If you should develop a respiratory infection, wear a surgical gauze mask when you take care of the baby. You certainly don't have to stop nursing if you have a cold, but your breast milk may decrease a little in quantity. This is only temporary.

If the baby refuses to nurse several times in succession, seems listless and lethargic, starts crying continuously when ordinarily he's a happy baby, then take his temperature rectally to see if it's higher than 100.4 degrees. Rectal temperatures are normally about one degree higher than those taken by mouth, so if the reading is one degree above the line for normal (98.6°) on your thermometer, Baby's temperature is as it should be. If these signs and symptoms develop, consult your doctor.

Use a special rectal thermometer that has a large, round bulb. Shake the thermometer down until it registers not more than 96 degrees; then grease the bulb with petroleum jelly or cold cream. Hold the baby flat on your lap or bath table, face down. Spread the baby's buttocks apart with thumb and finger and insert the thermometer one-quarter its length into the anus. Leave it in for two minutes, holding it all the while. Then clean it with a piece of toilet paper and read the recorded temperature. When you're through, wash the thermometer thoroughly with soap and warm water—hot water will break it.

When you describe Baby's symptoms to the doctor over the telephone, it will be helpful to him to know this temperature reading.

If Baby shows any sign of illness, keep him quiet in his own bed and away from family or visitors until the doctor can see him or advise you what to do.

Your baby
from six weeks to
three months

DEVELOPMENT By the time he's passed the six weeks mark, your baby will probably: . . . hold his head well off the bed when he's placed on his abdomen . . . start to smile.

Between the ages of 6 weeks and three months, your baby may: . . . follow a moving person with his eyes . . . stare at a bright object . . . lift chest a short distance when placed on abdomen . . . lie awake for longer periods at a time . . . kick feet or push with legs in bath.

PHYSICAL DEVELOPMENT Your baby's weight gain at 6 weeks should be from 2 to 3 pounds over his weight at birth. Depending on his size at birth, a baby usually gains from 4 to 8 ounces a week during the first four months. However, if your baby was premature or small to begin with, his weight gain may be slightly less.

FEEDINGS By now, the baby has usually dropped one feeding and is nursing or taking formula 4 to 5 times a day. Many pediatricians omit the 10 P.M. feeding if the baby is gaining well and takes a sufficient quantity in 4 bottles.

However, if a fifth bottle is necessary, it is better to wait until the baby wakes up. You wouldn't want to be awakened if you really aren't hungry and neither does Baby.

It's not necessary to alter the formula at this age. The breast-fed baby doesn't suddenly get a change in breast milk which still contains the same amount of proteins, carbohydrates, and fats. Also, the total calories per ounce are unaltered. Therefore, the formula-fed baby doesn't need a change either.

SLEEP SCHEDULE Your baby will sleep in the position in which you put him to bed. He lies that way unable to rotate his body during the first three months. During this time, it is best to encourage the baby to sleep first on one side, then the other, or on his stomach. Alternate after each feeding if you wish. Lying on his stomach may soothe him if he is restless because of unburped gas.

By the time the baby is 6 weeks old, he should be sleeping 6 hours at night, but this isn't a hard and fast rule. Some babies will sleep longer, and, unfortunately, some babies will sleep their longest during the day or early evening and demand a feeding every 4 hours at night.

These little night owls are too young to tell time, and you can't very well tell them when to sleep and when to stay awake.

In an attempt to rearrange his offbeat schedule, you might try awakening him after he's slept four hours in the morning or afternoon to feed him. But do this only when the baby has his days and nights mixed up.

SLEEPING BAGS Many mothers have found a sleeping bag helpful, because the baby can't get uncovered. If you do use a sleeping bag, it should be long so his feet won't get cramped. It should not bind around the neck or confine the baby too much, and it should be made so that he can't get tangled up in it.

SPLASHY TUB BATHS Bath time is becoming the highlight of the baby's day, and you've probably been giving him tub baths for several weeks. Although the navel has healed, it is still important to clean the recesses of the navel during each bath.

Remember, if Baby's skin is very dry, skip the daily bath and bathe him when the condition of his skin permits.

CARE OF THE GENITALIA If your baby is a girl, separate the folds of the vulva and clean with a little cotton which you've dipped in clear water.

Even though your little boy has been circumcised, the foreskin may adhere to the base of the head of the penis. If the fold falls onto the head of the penis, retract it gently and clean gently with soap and water.

CARE OF THE SCALP At about 6 weeks, a crust, called "cradle cap," may form on the scalp. The simplest way to control it is to massage a little oil into the scalp; leave it on overnight, brush the hair thoroughly in the morning, and then shampoo. Use a brush with medium-texture bristles. If they're too soft, they're useless, and if they're too firm, they'll scratch the baby's scalp.

Shampoo with hexachlorophene will also control "cradle cap."

Frequently a crust forms because Mother is afraid to touch the "soft spot" on top of Baby's head. Touching it won't hurt the baby. In fact, it is almost essential.

SUNBATHS In suitable weather, the baby will certainly enjoy being outside. "Suitable weather" will have to be interpreted by your own good judgment. Even in many localities with severe winters, a baby can be uncovered to the sun on a south porch, protected from the wind, around the last of March. The warmth of the baby's flesh can be your criterion as to his comfort. If he feels warm to the touch, he's all right, even though the day may seem a bit chilly to you.

At first, he shouldn't be left in the direct sunlight for more than a few minutes. As he becomes more and more accustomed to the sunshine, you can increase his period in the sun to 30 or 40 minutes daily. When he's on his back in the sun, shield his eyes with a peaked cap. On extremely hot days, he should get his sunbath early in the morning or later on in the afternoon.

CARE DURING HOT WEATHER During hot weather, keep the house cool and well ventilated. By all means, keep the windows open and use a fan, but it's not necessary to put the baby in the direct flow of air from either fan or window.

When the temperature hits 85 or 90 degrees, remove the baby's shirt—his diaper's plenty of cover in hot weather. A bath in lukewarm water several times a day will certainly help make the baby feel more comfortable.

The best treatment for heat rash is prevention. If the baby is reasonably dressed, your home is kept as comfortable as possible, and the baby is bathed occasionally during the day, heat rash won't be much of a problem.

If it does develop, short periods in the early morning or late afternoon sunshine will be very helpful in clearing the rash. Cornstarch or one of the commercial products for heat rash also give some comfort and seem to improve the rash.

Don't get alarmed if the baby's appetite seems to decline a little during hot weather. Yours does too! Offer him cooled boiled water several times during the day. If his body needs the water, he'll take it. If he refuses it, don't force it on him.

DISCIPLINE BEGINS AT BIRTH When does discipline, in the sense of learning, begin? It starts when your baby is born.

He learns that all his needs and legitimate wants receive attention. He feels the love in your voice and hands. Your job is to continue to train and teach him in the future as you have done up to now.

Don't rush Baby's bath time. Every girl needs an opportunity to be a big duck in a little puddle!

It isn't necessary that you follow the advice in this book to the letter. Much latitude is safe as to when you should begin some new phase of training. Some of the suggestions may have to be altered a bit to fit you, your home, and your baby. Most important of all—be as consistent as you possibly can.

Try to look at things through your baby's eyes. What a strange, perplexing world this is into which he has come! How much he has to learn! How much is expected of him!

So be gentle and patient. The tense way in which some parents go at teaching a new skill often defeats their purpose. A punishing attitude on your part will bring out all the power of resistance your baby possesses. On the other hand, he'll enter happily into a learning situation which you've made as pleasant as possible.

YOUR BABY AND HIS DOCTOR By now, both you and the baby have had your six weeks' checkup. The doctor will discuss many of the points discussed in this chapter. If opinions differ, follow the advice of your own physician.

Remember, good doctors are always busy, but they will take time to help you if there's a problem. If you have questions, make a list of them. The doctor will probably answer most of them in his discussions with you about the baby. If not, he'll be glad to answer them before you leave his office.

PHENYLKETONURIA Phenylketonuria, occurring about once in every 10,000 births, is a hereditary disease which results in mental retardation.

This disease is transmitted by a recessive gene which is carried by one in a hundred people. Such a person is called a carrier and may be identified by a specific laboratory test. Both the mother and the father must be carriers in order for the baby to be born with phenylketonuria.

The disease is suspected if phenylpyruvic acid is found in the urine after running a simple test. The diagnosis is established by finding an increased amount of phenylalanine in the blood.

The condition can be diagnosed before the baby leaves the nursery by doing a blood PKU test. This should be a routine procedure in every hospital where babies are born.

Your baby
from three to
four months

DEVELOPMENT Between 3 and 4 months, your baby may:
. . . begin to grasp a toy in his hand. . . . raise himself up
by his arms. . . . coo and gurgle with pleasure. . . . roll
from his back to his side. . . . be quieted by a voice or by
music. . . . begin to play with his hands. . . . turn his head
freely to watch activities and objects around him. . . . smile
and respond to friendly overtures. . . . hold his head erect.

FORMULA CHANGES Formula changes are unnecessary
unless your doctor should feel they are needed. He'll tell you
what the new amounts should be.

SOLID FOODS A difference of opinion exists over the best
time to introduce solid foods into the infant's diet. Because
this difference exists, we turn to an authoritative source of information—the committee on nutrition of the American
Academy of Pediatrics. We quote from their report:
  "Solid foods are being introduced into the infant's diet
at an increasingly early age. Justification for individual
practices appears to rest on opinion, rather than on demon-
strated proof of benefit or of harm. . . . No nutritional
advantage or disadvantage has yet been proven for supple-
menting adequate milk diets with solid foods in the first
three or four months of life. No harmful results have been
reported thus far, but potential danger exists that early

supplementation of milk diets of infants with solid foods of inferior nutritional content may, because of satiety, result in decreased intake of milk.

"Normal full-term infants can be expected to thrive for the first three months of life on human milk or on properly constituted cow's milk formula. Supplements of a minimum of 400 units of vitamin D and 30 milligrams of ascorbic acid (vitamin C) should be provided."

The belief that the early introduction of solids hastens the onset of sleeping through the night is completely erroneous.

A study conducted by the Child Research Council, University of Colorado School of Medicine, points out clearly that infants are not ready to accept solid food until at least 2½ to 3½ months of age.

This timetable closely follows their need for additional nutrients. At 2½ to 3½ months, cereal was accepted, followed in the next two months by vegetable, and finally by meats.

Following these recommendations, here's a tentative schedule for starting solids:

> Cereal: 3 months
> Fruit: 3½–4 months
> Vegetables: 4 months
> Meat: 5 months
> Egg Yolk: 6 months

CEREAL Cereal can be started quite readily at 3 months. It is a good source of carbohydrates, in the form of starch, protein, and iron. It is a bland food which the baby can easily digest. You have a wide range of cereals from which to choose. Special precooked baby cereals are available on the market. All you have to do is mix them with warm formula, milk, or water and they are ready to use.

When the doctor says you can begin solid foods, ask him with what cereal he'd prefer to have you start. You'll probably begin with rice—the least allergenic.

OFFERING THIS NEW FOOD For the first week, give cereal at the morning and evening feedings—usually at the 10 A.M. and 6 P.M. feedings.

Initially it is perhaps better to offer the milk first and then

A girl has to master the plain cereal before
switching to the snap-crackle-and-pop kind!

the cereal. The baby is accustomed to the milk and may balk at taking solids. Later, in a few months, cereal and other solids may be offered with or before the milk feeding.

HOW TO FEED BABY Place a tablespoon of precooked baby cereal in a clean dish and moisten it with the baby's formula or with sterilized milk. Some babies like their cereal mixture thin, others seem to prefer it a little thicker. Trial and error will show you the consistency your baby likes best, although most babies blow or spit out the first few feedings. Eating foods of this consistency is a new experience for him, and at first he may spit them out because he doesn't like the feel of the food in his mouth.

Hold the baby in a semi-sitting position, with his head cradled on your arm, or use one of the little seats especially designed for infants. Place a very small amount of cereal on a teaspoon, or after-dinner coffee spoon.

At first, he'll squeeze most of what you give him out on his chin. You'll have to shovel it off and scoop it back in more than once, but with a few more feedings, he'll get the hang of eating this new way.

If this is your first baby, you're probably wondering how to tell when he's had enough. It's impossible not to know! The baby will turn his head, refuse to open his mouth, or definitely spit out the unwanted food. Don't worry, it doesn't take a mind reader to tell.

Never coax or force a food down your baby. If he refuses a specific food, repeat the same food the next day. Once vegetables and meat are introduced, he may not like one or two of them. If this happens, drop the offenders for the time being. The baby may change his mind in a month and accept them.

This can be a messy business, especially if Baby should sneeze, so protect yourself with a plastic apron and the baby with a bib.

VEGETABLES You can begin vegetables at four months. Offer the vegetable for his noon meal. It makes little difference which one you give first, but do not give more than one kind each week.

If the baby becomes fussy, irritable, develops a rash, spits up the vegetable, or has loose stools, you know it's the vegetable he's getting that week that's causing the trouble. Stop giving him that particular one and proceed to the next vegetable.

However, if no difficulty develops, start a new food each week. Once a food is tried and proves acceptable, you can give it any time.

MEATS At five months meats can be started. Introduce them one at a time at weekly intervals as you did with the vegetables. The meat adds protein, iron, and vitamin B complex to the diet.

ALLERGENIC FOODS Highly allergenic foods, such as wheat, eggs, and orange juice should be postponed to the latter part of the first year. This is especially important if there is a family history of allergy. Discuss this with your doctor and start these foods at the ages he recommends.

EGG YOLK Egg yolk is a good source of iron along with the cereal and meat. It is recommended to be started at six months of age.

FRUITS What about fruit? Infants are willing to accept fruit at an early age. Should the baby balk at taking cereal, one can try adding a little fruit to his cereal. If this does not work, stop the cereal and continue with the fruit. In a few weeks, offer the cereal again. The baby may take it more readily now.

Fruit provides a source of carbohydrates, vitamin A, and vitamin C. They may be added to the baby's diet between 3½ and 4 months of age.

The addition of fruit to the baby's diet will also help minimize the problem of constipation when you switch the baby from formula to regular cow's milk.

VITAMIN C If you are giving vitamins containing vitamin C, orange juice is unnecessary; because so many babies are allergic to orange juice, give it only if the doctor recommends it.

CHANGE IN THE BABY'S STOOLS As soon as solid foods are started, you'll notice a change in the appearance of the baby's stools. They'll resemble the type of solid food you're giving the baby.

Most mothers accept this change without alarm, but once beets are started, and the stools are red, they start worrying that the baby is bleeding. There's no cause for concern, if you'll just remember that the red is from the beets.

As a general rule, the consistency of the stool does not change markedly when solids are started. In many cases, the stools do become a little pastier.

TIME TO CHANGE BEDS Baby will soon outgrow his bassinet; now is the time to shop for a regular baby bed. Select one that's at least large enough for a 4-year-old. It will last as long as the baby bed is needed, and there'll be plenty of room for him to stretch and exercise.

If you have limited bedroom space, and it's neccessary for the baby to sleep in your room during the day, consider buying a portable crib so that he can be moved from your bedroom into another room or the living room for the night. A small portable crib can be used until the baby is about two years old.

You may continue to use the bassinet for his waking hours, or for short naps, but he'll need a bed for long naps. A bassinet is fine for airings on the porch or under a tree after he's outgrown it as a bed. If insects are a problem during the summer months, put a mosquito netting over the bassinet.

BABY'S GETTING ADVENTUROUS At three months, Baby's muscles are growing much stronger and larger, and he'll be able to twist and squirm about quite freely.

Although it shows good physical development if he does roll over or start scooting, it's a signal to you that he can no longer be left alone on his bath table or your big bed where he can roll off.

And, when you hold him in your lap, don't restrict his movements, but do be sure he can't wiggle away from you.

GIVE BABY A PLAYPEN Three months is a good age at which to begin playpen periods. At this age, the baby is beginning to enjoy being in the family circle and, if he gets accustomed to his pen at this early age, he won't object to being put in it when he's older.

There are several types on the market. One model has a platform raised a few inches above the floor. This places Baby above floor drafts indoors, and above damp or cold ground outdoors. A collapsible type is also very convenient for moving in and out of doors. The collapsible playpens with steel frame and mesh sides are very lightweight and sturdy. You should have a waterproof pad for his pen.

HE SHOULD HAVE TOYS When Baby begins reaching for things and trying to grasp them, it's time to place one or two toys within his reach—a rattle, or a bright-colored cotton doll which he can easily hold. Hang toys on strings to the sides of his playpen, so he can hit at them whenever he wants. Skip the stuffed or wool toys. Select toys that move or react to Baby's movements.

PROGRAM OF IMMUNIZATION Here are listed the ages at which the normal baby or youngster may be immunized

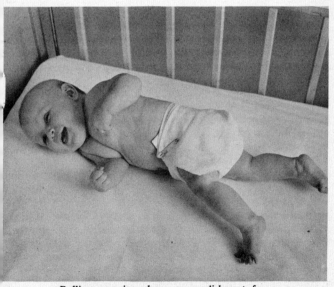

Rolling over is a huge accomplishment for a little boy. No wonder he looks proud of himself.

against the various preventable diseases, and circumstances under which immunization is advisable.

Acquaint yourself with the immunization programs, but your doctor will decide when and what to give your baby. Some physicians feel immunizations should be started slightly later because of a better antibody response in the infant.

A combination of three toxoids in one injection is now in general use to obtain simultaneous immunization against diphtheria, pertussis (whooping cough), and tetanus (lockjaw). This multiple vaccine is called the "triple antigen" or "D.P.T." (for diphtheria, pertussis, tetanus). In addition to the D.P.T. injections, the baby will receive the oral polio vaccine immunization.

Immunization injections should not be given if the child is ill in any way. It's quite common for a youngster to be fussy and irritable or even to run some fever following an injection. If they do react this way, advise your physician at your next visit.

In 1966, the American Academy of Pediatrics recommended the following program of immunization. However, your doctor may have special reasons for varying these times.

Triple antigen (D.P.T.)
2 to 3 months . . . . .1st injection
3 to 4 months . . . . .2nd injection
4 to 5 months . . . . .3rd injection
(The injections should be given at intervals of not less "than one month and preferably not more than 3 months apart.")
15 to 18 months . . . . .1st booster injection
(about a year following the original injections)
3 years . . . . .2nd booster
6 years (D.T.) . . . . .3rd booster

SMALLPOX VACCINATION It is best to give the smallpox vaccination during a relatively cool season. The time recommended by the American Academy of Pediatrics is 15–18 months. It should not be given to a child who has a rash, and particularly to those children with eczema or where there are members in the family with eczema. Your physician is familiar with the situations in which vaccinations are inadvisable.

Smallpox vaccinations should be repeated every five years.

POLIOMYELITIS Oral polio virus (Sabin) is the immunization procedure most widely recommended.

Routine immunization against poliomyelitis may be carried out using either the monovalent or trivalent strains. With the former, type I is given first, type III, 6-8 weeks later, and type II is administered last, 6–8 weeks after the second dose. On the other hand, the trivalent form of the vaccine contains type I, II, and III of the same material. The child is given a dose of the trivalent type three times at 6–8 week intervals.

The schedule recommended to give the polio vaccine is as follows:

2 months ....1st oral dose
4 months ....2nd oral dose
6 months ....3rd oral dose
15–18 months ....1st booster
5 years ....2nd booster

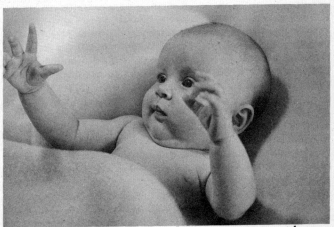

At this age your youngster is still too young to accurately reach for things with his hands. Accurate reaching aim—who cares? Fat little fingers are very fascinating to him.

Your doctor will set up an immunization program for your child. Report any illness or reaction your child has during the program.

MEASLES Baby should receive his measles vaccine at 12 months or as soon thereafter as possible. Active immunization against measles with live attenuated measles virus vaccine should be given routinely to all children who have never had measles.

PERTUSSIS Infants under 2 years of age who have not been immunized and have been exposed to pertussis (whooping cough) should receive an injection of pertussis immune gamma globulin. This is also given to infants who contract whooping cough and have not been immunized. This is expensive but it may save your baby's life, so it is well worth the expense.

Whooping cough is extremely serious in small infants. Although immunization against it may not give complete protection as do immunizations against tetanus and diphtheria, it does offer very valuable protection.

After the 4-year booster, it's unnecessary to continue with the whooping cough immunizations. But if there's exposure to whooping cough at any time during the next two years, a booster should be given. When children who have been immunized contract whooping cough, it's difficult to recognize because they usually don't whoop. Your doctor, however, can make a fairly definite diagnosis.

TETANUS All children and adults should be immunized against tetanus with tetanus toxoid. If your child sustains an injury in which the skin is lacerated, punctured, or torn, or is bitten by a dog or cat, some type of protection against tetanus or lockjaw is definitely needed.

In situations where a child has not been previously immunized or where information is lacking about previous tetanus immunizations, a tetanus antitoxin injection is given. The antitoxin should be made from human immune globulin rather than from horse serum. The latter is frequently associated with severe allergic reactions. Immunization with tetanus antitoxin is only temporary and must be followed by active immunization with tetanus toxoid.

Keep an accurate record of all tetanus immunizations. In the event that your child is injured, you will be able to tell your physician the date of your child's last booster. If it has been within 12 months, probably another booster is unnecessary.

If it has been more than a year since your child has received a tetanus booster, a booster at the time of the injury will adequately protect the child.

DIPHTHERIA If your child has received his D.P.T. immunizations, a Schick test to determine susceptibility to diphtheria is unnecessary.

TYPHOID Routine immunization against typhoid is not advisable.

However, if you should be traveling outside the United States to a country where typhoid is endemic or should there be an outbreak of typhoid in your community, immunization against typhoid is recommended.

PROTECTING THE BABY Although the 4- to 5-month-old baby is no longer a tiny infant, he's still susceptible to infectious diseases and is therefore highly dependent on you for protection. Don't expose him unnecessarily around other children or adults who may be ill. This protection is also part of the job of being a mother.

Your baby from four to five months

DEVELOPMENT Between 4 and ·5 months your baby may: . . . laugh out loud. . . . hold his head steady when carried. . . . hold his toys. . . . splash with his hand when in his bathtub. . . . raise his hands when lifted. . . . reach for objects. . . . make a noise when he hears a voice. . . . turn his head to follow objects removed from his sight. . . . play with his hands. . . . lift head and shoulders and roll over. . . . lift himself by hands or forearms when lying on stomach.

FORMULA CHANGE Doctors differ over when to change the baby from formula to homogenized milk. Your doctor may suggest you do it now, or he may wait until the 5th or 6th months. If he does change the baby to homogenized milk now, several things may happen.

Babies often become constipated, because they're no longer receiving as much carbohydrate or sugar as they did in their formula. The protein in homogenized milk has not been altered by evaporation and forms a much harder curd than that formed by altered protein. This may also contribute to the firmness of the stool.

To minimize this problem, start fruits at the same time homogenized milk is started. If fruits have already been started, increase the amount you're giving. Prunes are especially effective in softening stools.

If starting fruits or increasing the quantity doesn't solve the problem, add dark corn syrup or sweet molasses to the homogenized milk. This usually helps.

Occasionally, a baby develops diarrhea or vomits when he starts taking homogenized milk. Simmering the milk for five minutes breaks down the protein curd and makes the milk more digestible.

If this doesn't correct the condition, your doctor will probably suggest that you return to the formula you've been using. Constipation, diarrhea, and vomiting are usually temporary problems which resolve themselves within a short time.

Many physicians recommend reconstituted evaporated milk or some form of heat-treated milk if there is an allergic reaction to homogenized or whole milk or if there is an allergic family history. The proper proportions are 13 ounces of evaporated milk to 15 ounces of water. This reconstitutes the milk to a full strength of twenty calories per ounce.

When you switch to homogenized milk, it's no longer necessary to sterilize as long as you're using a good grade of pasteurized milk from a reputable dairy.

All bottles, nipples, and caps should be washed in clean, hot, soapy water before the rest of the family dishes are done, then rinsed thoroughly in hot water, capped, and set aside until they are used. Dishwashers do a satisfactory job, too.

SCHEDULE FOR SOLID FOODS During this period, most babies will eagerly accept three feedings of solids a day— morning, noon, and evening. Their need for iron contained in solid foods is now *greater than* their need for an abundance of milk.

ADDING NEW FOODS Your doctor may already have started the baby on vegetables at 3½ months. If not, 4 months is the time to add them to the baby's diet. You can buy strained vegetables prepared especially for babies, or you can mash and strain, if necessary, the vegetable you prepare for the

Let's see, today on Zoo Parade I think I'll
be a lion. Now, what do lions do all day?

So near and yet so far! A baby's tiny world is often
full of many major setbacks—like a short reach!

rest of the family after cooking and before adding the seasonings.

Green beans, carrots, beets, peas, asparagus, and squash may be used or any of them combined if first tried individually.

Beginning with just a teaspoon of the warmed vegetable, gradually increase the amount until he's taking 2 or 3 ounces. You can cover and store the unused portion of a can or jar of vegetables *in the refrigerator*. It will remain safe for as long as 2 or 3 days.

You'll probably find that Baby dislikes the flavors of some of the vegetables. Don't force him to take any he doesn't like. In a month's time, offer the disliked foods again. He may take them then.

OTHER FOODS Your doctor may now suggest giving one of the strained meats commercially prepared for young babies. These are very good for the baby and may be added to his cereal or vegetable once daily. These should be started one at a time as you did the vegetables.

Every proud father knows that it's never too soon to begin man-to-man talks with his son.

Playpens can be fun for short periods if both
Mommy and favorite toys are close at hand.

BUILD GOOD EATING HABITS Now is the time when
your baby will build his food habits for years to come. He can
learn now to take and like almost any healthful food.

Your own calm reassuring manner is an important factor in
introducing new foods. The baby's acceptance of each strange
eating experience may be slow since almost all babies resent
changes. Be content if he merely tastes the new food at first.
Never force a feeding of any food!

If the baby becomes slightly ill or develops a cold, he'll
probably not want to eat as usual. At such times, allow him
to eat only what he'll willingly take.

Watch your own attitude toward the food you're giving the baby. He's a little copycat, and if he senses that you dislike peas or carrots or some other food, he'll probably put up a fuss about eating them.

HE'LL LIKE A BALL Now you can add a soft rubber or woolly ball to his toys. Put him in the playpen, give him a rattle, soft doll, and ball. Then leave him alone except for necessary care.

A BUSY BABY By now your little one is beginning to reach for objects, and everything he picks up goes into his mouth. This is your signal to remove and put in a safe place things like safety pins, coins, or buttons—anything that might be left within his reach. Caution the older children not to leave objects around or to give objects to the baby on which he might choke.

And keep an eye on your little wiggleworm. Now that he's rolling over, you can't leave him alone on his bath table, your bed, or a sofa for even a minute.

DON'T RUSH NEW ACTIVITIES You'll probably notice now when you hold your baby that he is beginning to push with his toes. This doesn't mean that he wants to stand up, so don't rush him. It's simply his way of exercising muscles that he'll use later in pulling himself up.

He might begin sitting up at 5 months, but this usually doesn't happen until 6 to 8 months. Let him do this at his own speed. If he can control his head, and if he's well supported, you can put him in a semi-sitting position, but then if he slouches over, it's too early for even supported sitting.

This doesn't mean that you can't set him up in your lap or pull him up to a sitting position, but be sure to keep his back straight whenever you do. A better practice, however, is to put him in his playpen and let him sit and stand whenever he gets ready.

TEETH ON THE WAY The average baby cuts teeth between the sixth and eighth months. The earliest teeth to appear are those in front—the central incisors. There are wide variations in the ages at which first teeth come through—all the way from 4 to 14 months so don't worry if he teethes later than other children his age.

If he's getting the proper foods and vitamins, and is developing normally, then his teeth will take care of themselves. There's also a tendency for the babies in a family to cut their teeth at about the same age.

Many babies will cut their teeth without their parents being aware that they're teething. Some will be fussy and irritable, and drool a lot for a few days. Occasionally they will have loose stools and may spit up.

As a relief measure, offer him a teething ring made of hard rubber or plastic and cooled in the refrigerator.

Teething is rarely associated with any illness. However, your physician should be consulted if there is a high fever, rash, or if your baby does not act well.

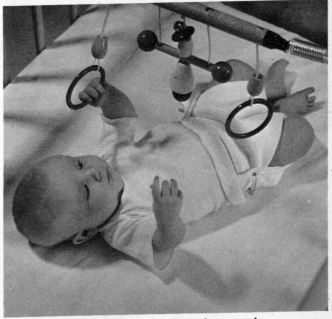

Looks easy to you . . . but trying to reach those rings at my age is an all-absorbing task.

CHAPTER

12

Your baby from five to eight months

DEVELOPMENT Between the ages of five and six months, your baby may do the following: . . . roll from his back to his stomach. . . . turn his head at the sound of a hand bell, or voice. . . . sit up with some propping. . . . object noisily when an object is taken away from him. . . . recover a rattle if it falls within easy reach. . . . reach for paper. . . . cough artificially and know he's cute. . . . play in bath water. . . . discriminate between a stranger and a familiar person. Between the ages of six and eight months, your baby may: . . . sit up well without support. . . . bang spoon or pat table in play. . . . be more active with a little help. . . . pick a cube or block up off the table, or hold a block in each hand. . . . show his temper if things don't suit him. . . . show pleasure by cooing or crowing. . . . reach for objects he sees. . . . get a tooth—maybe two—in the middle of his lower jaw.

From now on you'll find this lusty little chap of yours a force to consider in family affairs. Six months represents completion of half that all-important first year during which your child grows and develops faster than at any other time.

FORMULA CHANGE Many doctors find it best to change the baby from formula to homogenized milk at this age rather than earlier. The switch can now be made because the digestive tract and kidneys are mature. (See Chapter 10.)

SOLID FOODS Some doctors prefer to wait and start fruit at 5 months. They've been delayed until now because these doctors feel that if fruits are the first solid given, babies tend to refuse other solids when introduced. Giving fruits which have a tendency to loosen the stools (prunes, apricots, peaches) prevents constipation when homogenized milk is started. Applesauce and bananas may cause stools to form a little.

If there is a tendency to allergy in your family, your doctor may prefer to postpone giving the baby orange juice, egg, and the wheat containing cereals. He may also suggest continuing with formula feedings rather than changing to homogenized milk.

If egg yolk is given, here's a sample of the baby's menu.

> Morning—egg yolk and cereal
> Noon meal—vegetables and pudding or fruit
> Evening meal—meat and fruit or vegetables

Milk from a cup or bottle should accompany each meal. A bottle may also be given at bedtime or early in the morning.

NEW FOODS ON HIS MENU At the half-year mark, stewed fruits and simple desserts made with gelatin or milk can go on the menu. Introduce him to vegetable, liver, lamb, or beef soups, or soups which have a cream base. The mixed meat and vegetable products have a low meat content; they should not replace his regular meats.

FINGER FOODS As most babies approach their seventh-month birthday, they're able to eat "finger foods" without choking on them. Small round dry cereals, toast, baby cookies, and graham crackers can be picked up with the fingers. If the baby consistently chokes on any of these, stop giving them to him.

Some babies have more sensitive gag reflexes and will have a tendency to gag and vomit if coarse foods touch the back of their throat. If your baby has difficulty with these finger foods, try them again in a few weeks.

DRINKING FROM A CUP During this three-month period, offer the baby milk and water from a cup. A small cup which his mouth fits easily is good, and one with a lip is best of all. There'll be considerable spilling and leakage at first. Put a long, moisture-proof bib on the baby and hold a towel under the cup while he's learning.

In the beginning, Baby will take only a swallow, and you must remember to take it slow and easy. He's used to the milk coming from a bottle or breast, and it'll be quite a few months before he's completely ready to give up his bottle or breast feeding. If cup feedings are introduced in this way, however, he will be less likely to balk at milk from a cup when he's ready to be entirely weaned.

About this time, many mothers find that their breast milk begins to diminish in quantity, or they decide to discontinue

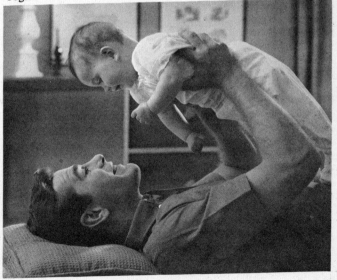

The highlight of Daddy's day is to play silly games with me. He lifts and I laugh.

breast feeding. If this happens, offer the baby some milk from a cup when he takes his solid food. You'll have to supplement this amount with a bottle. If the baby is 4 to 5 months old, you can offer homogenized milk. But if the baby is younger, formula is required.

THE AMOUNT OF MILK BABY TAKES *Milk intake will decrease during this period.* The baby has doubled his birth weight by the time he's four to five months old. His rate of weight gain during the next seven months will be cut in half. He no longer needs as much of the high caloric food—milk.

When formula is discontinued, a supplement of 400 units of vitamin D will be needed. If the baby still doesn't get orange juice, he needs 30 milligrams of vitamin C a day. He needs the substances contained in solids more than ever, which accounts for solids intake remaining the same or increasing while his intake in milk drops to twenty or twenty-four ounces a day.

TIPS TO MAKE EATING GO WELL Feed the baby before the family mealtime in his chair at his own little table. After that he may, if you like, join the family circle by playing in his pen while the family eats. Don't give him food from the table!

In the evening you may wish to put the baby to bed immediately after his supper and before the family sits down to its meal. This will be convenient for you, as well as good for the baby.

Introduce any new food at the beginning of the meal when your baby is hungry. Give only a little at first, gradually increasing the amount until he takes the required quantity. If he shows a disinclination for a particular food, try to get him to take a small amount, but do not make an issue of it. Urging will only make him balky.

Also, if he's very hungry, he may violently rebel at new foods.

If he spits out the food several times or just won't try it at all, give up on it for a few days or a week. He may feel differently about it later. If you try to force it down him now, he may develop a permanent dislike for that food. And any unpleasantness at mealtime may lead to resistance to all foods.

Usually, it's advisable to give his milk last, after the solid foods have been taken. With some babies, however, milk is the least-liked food. If he takes less than 20 to 24 ounces of milk a day, offer milk first.

Sometimes it's difficult to strike a balance between milk and solid foods. You don't want Baby to get into the habit of filling up on milk at the expense of other foods, because he will develop milk anemia.

Milk doesn't contain iron. If too much milk is taken, the baby won't eat enough iron-containing foods and will become anemic. In spite of the fact that he's plump and sassy, he may be anemic.

If a baby of this age absolutely refuses solid foods, your doctor may prescribe iron drops. They'll prevent anemia from developing, and usually the baby will begin taking solids within a short period of time.

Try offering the various solid foods at the beginning of the meal as has been suggested. After he's taken a reasonable amount, offer the milk. One time he may refuse milk altogether, then at the next meal drink two cups.

As long as his daily intake of milk, including what is used in cooking for him, is approximately 20 to 24 ounces, there's no need to be concerned. But if he consistently refuses milk, begin offering it at the first of the meal before the solid foods.

If your baby stubbornly refuses to take any milk over a period of several weeks, talk it over with your doctor.

If the baby refuses food he has been in the habit of accepting, take it away from that meal without fuss or emotion. If he has good eating habits otherwise, and refuses most of a meal, it may be a sign of indisposition, and the best treatment is to let him go without until he's ready to eat again.

If the baby has been taking solids, then refuses them for a period of several days to a week, he's probably ill so call your doctor. If there is nothing or apparently very little the matter with him, he'll probably make up for his fast at the next meal.

How much food should your up-and-coming eater be taking? Individual babies utilize food differently so an exact amount can't be stated. As long as your child is growing normally and has a lot of pep and energy, he's getting enough to eat.

When he's getting several familiar dishes at a meal, alternate in feeding them. Give a spoonful of vegetable, then one of dessert, and then go back to the vegetable.

Babies who eat their full helpings of one food first, then clean up the next food, are inclined to continue the habit. No great harm is done, so don't worry about it.

GRADUATES TO OVERALLS Now that the baby is entering into a more active phase, there will necessarily be some changes in his wardrobe.

The shirt and diaper remain his basic dress, but when he's on the floor and outdoors, little overalls or coveralls should take the place of dresses or kimonos.

If he's outgrowing his nightgowns, he's ready for sleeping garments with legs, feet.

In warm weather, a sleeveless cotton shirt or sunsuit, and a diaper are enough. A diaper alone may even be sufficient. In cooler or cold weather, a sweater or coat, cap, mittens, and leggings may be needed in addition to the coveralls. Make him as comfortable as possible. Clothe him as lightly or as warmly as is necessary for this purpose. A well-nourished baby is more likely to suffer from too much clothing rather than too little. Here you will have to use your own judgment and check indoor and outside temperatures.

FREQUENT PLAYTIMES He's very active now and needs space to play. Put him in his playpen both indoors and out (the same pen can be used) for regular playtimes with his toys —rattle, cloth or knitted doll, and a soft ball. A porch is ideal for his outdoor play, or in warm weather, the pen can be put on the grass. Be sure it's in the shade if the weather is hot.

A SAFE CHAIR FOR SITTING Between five and seven months, most babies begin to sit without support. Some can also pull themselves to a sitting position. When he does this of his own accord, he's ready to leave your lap and arms, and sit alone for play and eating times. Don't hurry the sitting process. The baby will do this himself as soon as he's ready.

You'll need a safe chair in which he can eat his meals. If it's a highchair, it should have a wide, sturdy base with safeguards to prevent the baby from tipping it over. There should also be a means of strapping him into the chair to keep him from standing up or sliding out when you're not looking.

A low table, with an inset seat, is very satisfactory and serves the baby until he's 2 years of age or older. The table top around him serves the double purpose of keeping the baby in and giving him something to eat or play on. Don't place his chair or table near a stove, adult's table, electric fixtures, or draperies. He's grabbing at everything now.

HE GETS A SOCIAL LIFE It's good for the baby to see some outside people, but his eating and sleeping schedule should on no account be disturbed. Visitors may play with him during his social hours. *Don't be too concerned if he shows fear of strangers.* As Baby develops an awareness of his surroundings, it is perfectly natural for him to react in such a manner when confronted with unfamiliar persons and even objects.

It's also nice for him to join the family circle while munching on his zwieback and for a time before the evening meal, but he should not be overhandled.

As the baby widens his contacts, shield him from people with colds or infections.

IT'S FUN HELPING BABY LEARN If you've followed the suggestions thus far, your baby has probably established habits of eating what's set before him, sleeping well, and amusing himself. Each month or two from now on will bring some new

The well-dressed baby wears sturdy washable coveralls or overalls for busy play periods.

Popular arrangement is a chair set in Baby's table. Plenty of room for eating or play.

phase of training to build upon this foundation.

If you deal with each phase of learning at the proper time, you'll be astonished to see how easy training is. Psychologists who have studied babies and small children for years in the Normal Child Development Clinic at Columbia University, say that there is a "critical time" in a child's life for learning each different habit and skill.

Many parents have found from experience, too, that at a certain age, a child seems to be willing to tackle a new learning situation. This doesn't mean that he can't learn them later, but it will be harder for him, and harder for you to teach him, too.

Children indicate by signs when they're ready for a new type of learning. For instance when the baby is five or six months old, he needs to touch and feel things. When he reaches out to grasp and tug, he's ready for hanging or dangling toys, bead dolls, rattles, balls, and floating bath toys.

Children differ in the age at which their muscles and nervous systems have developed sufficiently to permit a certain type of learning. It's better to rely upon signs, as indicated above, rather than upon chronological age, to determine when it's time to start a new phase in his training.

As his mother, you'll soon become adept in detecting these signs if you're on the lookout for them. Study your baby, work with him, and play with him. When he shows he's ready for the next step in training, start.

Always remember to keep this training easy and fun. Expect him to fail many times before he masters a skill. He isn't failing deliberately; he simply has to learn, as you have had to learn something new to you. Crossness and punishments don't help when the baby doesn't understand, or isn't ready yet to grasp the lesson. Know your own baby; then be gentle but firm in working out the things necessary for his development.

The times at which Baby might be ready for training are suggested in this book, so you can be on the lookout and prepared to provide the training indicated. If your baby isn't quite ready for the training suggested at a certain age, let him take his time. If he beats the gun, sneak a look into the pages ahead and help him along.

The period approaching right now is that of "sitting up," when your baby is going to be ready for a whole series of new experiences and a certain amount of independence. Independence is definitely something you want to build. Get any equipment your baby will soon be needing to develop his new abilities.

HOW TO HANDLE FEARS Baby's big enough now to be a member of the family, and to be around everyday-living processes which may frighten him at first. The noise of the vacuum sweeper, the radio next door, or the swirling of bath water down the drain may bring forth sudden screams.

Although you can head off many frightening experiences before they happen, these are things he'll have to get used to. Instead of shielding him from contact with them entirely, show him by your cheerful matter-of-fact handling of the situation that there's nothing to be afraid of.

Pick him up in your arms and hold him while you show him how the vacuum works. Watch with him as the water runs out of the tub and laugh about it as though it were fun. Make your manner extremely reassuring, but not comforting, for no hurt is involved.

If any sudden, loud noise, such as thunder, badly frightens your child, pick him up and talk to him. Let him feel your physical strength and protection. Once you're sure he feels calm and safe again, start him off on a new line of interest. However, stay at his side until a storm is over. After a while, he'll realize that the thunder and lightning aren't going to hurt him, and he'll conquer the fear himself. Remember, he'll soon learn to take frightening experiences in his stride if he knows you are near.

FEAR OF STRANGERS Up to about five months, babies are willing to go to anyone—parents or strangers, but around five months, they begin to regard unfamiliar faces with fear and apprehension.

If the stranger reaches for the baby and picks him up, there're bound to be tears. Grandparents are often greeted with this reaction, but much as they love their grandchild, they're still strangers to him.

The baby's doctor gets the same treatment. This fear has nothing to do with the immunizations the doctor is giving him. Up to now, the baby's probably been unconcerned about his regular examinations, but now the doctor is a seldom-seen face, a stranger, and your little one cries when he visits the doctor. Eventually he will mature to the point where strangers are no longer frightening.

HE'S LEARNING TO UNDERSTAND SPEECH Your baby's bubbling, gurgling, and cooing sounds are all part of his learning to talk. At the same time, he is detecting differences in the tone of your voice. He can tell whether it's cross, comforting, or approving.

At this age, he babbles sociably and even surprises you with inflections and intonations that resemble adults' speech—even to the rising inflection of a question. About this time, too, he begins to understand and recognize some of the words you say to him.

By the time he's a year old, he'll understand a good many words, even though he can't say them. This is known as his "passive vocabulary," and it will always be made up of more than his active vocabulary, or the words he uses in everyday speech.

Since he's picking up the words you say, it's important to talk to him a lot in short, simple sentences, and pronounce words correctly and distinctly. Don't use baby talk!

HOW HE'LL SLEEP NOW About now, many mothers become alarmed because they feel their babies aren't sleeping enough. It's quite natural, however, for your baby to sleep less during the daytime. Many babies take only a short nap between breakfast and their noon meal, and may stay awake for the entire interval between their afternoon nap and bedtime.

At about nine months, some babies start dropping out their morning nap, while some children may take two naps a day until they're fourteen or fifteen months old. Even though the afternoon nap becomes very short in comparison with the morning nap, the morning nap is usually the first to go.

The need for sleep varies between children. Some youngsters don't seem to need an afternoon nap and will start dropping it around 3 to 3½ years of age. Insist, however, that your child continue with a rest period during the afternoon even though he doesn't sleep. A quiet activity such as looking at books or coloring will keep him from becoming restless.

On the other hand, if he wants to sleep, let him. If Baby

gets fussy and irritable, or sleepy at any time, put him in his bed for a nap. Close the door to his room, so he won't be disturbed by family activity.

NIGHT WAKEFULNESS During this five-to-eight-months period, it's common for babies to awaken and cry at night. Parents often think hunger is frequently associated with this night crying, especially because the baby's milk intake has now decreased. But in most cases, hunger has nothing to do with this wakefulness.

It's more likely that the baby awakes at night, looks around at the dark room, doesn't see his mother or any other familiar figure, and starts to scream. The minute the mother walks into the room and says a word or two or picks him up, he immediately stops crying.

One explanation offered by a psychiatrist is that up until he's five months old, the baby feels he is a part of his mother. After the five-months period, he begins to realize that he is an individual but that he needs his mother for protection.

If the baby does awaken at night, don't immediately rush to him with a bottle or a drink of water. Feed him one night, and he'll expect it the next night, and the next, and pretty soon you'll have a nightly problem on your hands.

When he does cry more than momentarily at night, check on him. He may have an arm or leg caught, may be uncovered and cold, or he could be ill. Pick him up for a minute and comfort him, but put him down again.

Rocking, walking the floor, or taking him to bed with you (which is a dangerous habit) may soon become a nightly event —one you'll wish you'd never started!

LEARNING ABOUT HIMSELF At this age, the baby will discover his genitalia. If you'll recall, when the baby was between 3 and 3½ months, he found his hands and spent a great deal of time watching and playing with them. About a month later he found his feet, and was fascinated all over again by his feet and toes.

Now, he will find his genitalia and will show as much interest in it as he did with his hands and feet. This normal curiosity helps the baby learn about himself and should not be a reason for concern or alarm.

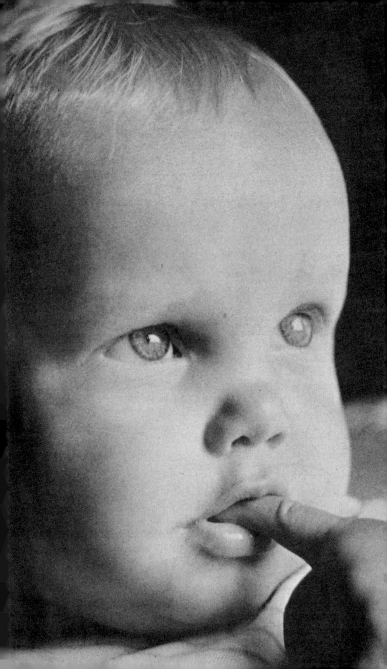

Your baby from eight to twelve months

DEVELOPMENT Between the ages of 8 and 12 months, your baby will probably: . . . sit up strongly with no support. . . . play with his image in a mirror. . . . creep and pull himself up. He may even walk, but don't hurry him. . . . pick up large and small objects in his hands and examine them carefully. . . . understand many things you say to him. . . . wave bye-bye. . . . have two teeth, cut four more. . . . co-operate in rhythmic nursery games. . . . begin to use one hand more than the other. . . . make sounds, such as da-da and ma-ma. He may say several words. . . . show an interest in throwing things. . . . enter a shy stage toward end of first year.

BEGIN CHOPPED FOOD Between 8 and 12 months (depending on what your doctor says), introduce chopped foods in the same gradual way you did solids. Baby will accept chopped foods more readily at this age. Later he may reject "lumps."

The makers of strained baby foods also have a line of

chopped ones in many appetizing combinations. Or chop or mash with a fork, fruits and vegetables you serve the family.

Take the baby's portion out before seasoning to adult tastes, for he requires only about half as much salt and sugar and should have no spices at all. The vegetables in canned vegetable soup are also the proper size and soft enough for the baby.

Add a small amount of a chopped food to a serving of strained, preferably a strained food which your baby particularly likes. Gradually increase the chopped food, until the baby's taking his whole serving in this form. Then do the same with another food.

Until he's about 3 years old, chop or grind the meat you give your youngster. Broiled hamburger or meat loaf that's not highly seasoned is satisfactory. Soft, mealy lunch meats are also a good choice.

Or you can buy the excellently prepared diced meats for juniors which come in several varieties suitable at this age. In this form, he'll eat it better, and you'll avoid the danger of having a chunk of meat breathed into his windpipe. Skip stringy meats, hard to firm vegetables, and fruits with peelings for the same reason.

At this age, the baby will enjoy feeding himself. Give the baby the freedom to enjoy touching, tasting, and handling food. At nine months, let him hold a spoon and teach him to use it in spite of the messiness. Observe his hand preference. Let him use whichever hand he wishes.

If you're busy, put a small amount of finger food on a small plate or his high-chair tray and he'll be content feeding himself. The small amount is important, because whatever you give him will be divided into three parts—one-third will go in him, one-third on him, and the remaining one-third will land on the floor. Newspapers under his chair will cut down on the cleanup job.

TIME TO THINK ABOUT WEANING The *earliest* age at which you would want to wean the baby *completely* from the breast or bottle would be about nine months. Weaning takes significantly longer when begun *before* nine months than after. By nine months, the baby is taking some milk from a cup, but is still too young to be taken abruptly off the bottle or breast.

Weaning a baby early is far too time-consuming for a busy mother because it takes time to give the baby all of his milk from a cup.

WEANING YOUR BREAST-FED BABY If you wean the baby from the breast before he's nine months old, a bottle should be given. If the baby is older than nine months, offer the cup at all his meals and gradually increase the amount of milk he receives from a cup, but continue to breast-feed him at the end of each meal.

Then, leave out the daily breast feeding that he shows the least interest in and offer only the cup. The following week, if he seems willing, omit another feeding, and the next week, omit the last daily breast feeding.

He doesn't like to be rushed, so don't force weaning if he hits a period of unwillingness. Teething or a cold may set him back a little. His own inclination is your guide in weaning.

Inquisitive little fingers are eager to learn everything, including how a bear's nose feels.

Don't worry if he's slow to change over or measure his readiness by the time some other baby was completely weaned. Some formula-fed babies don't lose their liking for milk from a bottle until they're 18 months or older. Unless your doctor advises it, weaning a sick baby should be avoided.

CARE OF BREASTS DURING WEANING Gradual weaning should cause little discomfort, but if you are uncomfortable, a fairly tight-fitting bra will help give you relief. However, the bra should not put pressure on the nipples. You can decrease your milk supply by cutting down on your intake of liquids. It's a good practice to discuss this matter with your physician; he may prescribe something to dry up your breast milk, especially if you have to suddenly stop nursing.

WEANING YOUR BOTTLE-FED BABY Weaning from the bottle should also be a gradual process. Some babies who especially love sucking may not want to completely give up their bottle. There's certainly no harm, if he's a late weaner, in letting him have a bedtime bottle, even if he's 18 months or a little older. A single bottle a day is not going to prolong infantile behavior.

By nine months, he should be familiar with the cup, even if he's only taking a few sips. Continue offering the cup and avoid fussing if he doesn't want more than a sip or two on some days. Eventually leave out the bottle that he shows the least interest in, often the breakfast or lunch one. If he's progressing, omit the second bottle, then the third.

That last bottle is the hardest to give up and is usually his supper or bedtime bottle. The bottle-fed baby backslides too when he's feeling miserable from a cold or teething, so just be patient.

Some mothers prefer to wean a baby abruptly, especially if the baby is taking just one bottle—usually the night bottle. This is also a satisfactory method.

The baby's milk intake will drop after he's been weaned, but remember that this is about the time he derives most of his calories and nutritional needs from his solid foods. The need for a large quantity of milk is no longer as necessary.

WHEN HE STARTS TO CREEP For some time you've been

putting the baby in his playpen both inside and outdoors for playtime. Besides getting him used to amusing himself, this has given him full opportunity to develop his muscles, which he couldn't have done if he had been kept in a bed or buggy all the time.

Around the seventh or eighth month, he'll be able to pull himself over the floor, and soon make good speed. Babies creep in various ways: some sitting up, some on all fours, and some on their knees. The method doesn't matter—any one serves the purpose and gets him where he wants to go. There's also a fair number of perfectly normal babies that *never* creep! They just get up and walk when they're ready to walk.

Whenever he can be watched, let Baby creep about the house while you keep an eye on him. This gives him more freedom and stimulates his mental development. Remember, though, that once he has a heady taste of this new freedom,

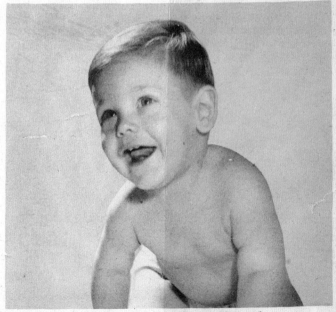

Take a tip from Christopher Columbus and me: The key to exploration is transportation.

he's going to be reluctant to accept the confines of his playpen.

The baby of an allergic family probably shouldn't be permitted to crawl about on a carpeted floor. Carpeting is a good dust catcher and Baby's constant exposure to this dust could cause sensitization to develop.

CLOTHES FOR CREEPING The shirt and diaper remain his basic dress, but when Baby creeps, he'll need something over his knees, if he hasn't had it before. The preferred garments for this period are overalls or coveralls. These are roomy enough to make diaper-changing fast and easy, and are available ready-made in many styles for boys and girls. You'll need several pairs, for the creeping stage is perhaps the dirtiest and messiest of all.

TOYS AID CREEPING Soft, washable toys which Baby can grasp are still best for him at this age. Balls of various kinds—soft rubber which can be grasped readily; woolly balls; bright-colored balls—will help in the first stages of creeping by giving the baby an incentive to go after them. Knitted or rubber dolls and animals are easily kept clean, and he can't hurt himself on them.

Toys on low shelves will encourage creeping.

Babies are tempted by everything in sight.

GIVE YOUR BABY A CHANCE TO EXPLORE Any time after about the ninth month, Baby may start pulling himself to his feet, holding to furniture, or to the sides of his playpen. Don't hurry or urge him, though. When his muscles are strong enough for this type of exercise, he will begin doing it.

Now you'll be confronted with your first problem of management. As soon as the baby reaches the stage where he can creep and move at will, then pull himself up, objects on tables are within his reach; and you can depend on it, he'll reach for them. Baby's curiosity, however, is proof of his alertness and growing independence.

Some of your housework can be combined with baby-watching. You can dust the floor or furniture, or make beds while Baby roams around the room. He'll probably investigate the contents of the wastebasket, tug at bed-clothes, or play with the shoes in the closet, but he won't be doing a bit of harm.

Whenever the weather permits, take your small chores outside, so you can let him wander about the yard while you work.

ELIMINATE HOME HAZARDS During this phase of your baby's growth, clear out of the house or yard anything on which he might hurt himself. He'll need to be protected, of course, from falls which might injure him. All doors to stairways must be closed. If there is no stairway door, put a gate across the open doorway.

Any poisons or medicines that you must keep should be locked up far beyond his reach. This applies to cleaning materials, dyes, cosmetic preparations, hair oils and tonics, cough drops, aspirins, or other remedies of any kind. Don't ever allow the baby to play with a full or empty can of talcum powder, since the powder, if inhaled, can cause severe inflammation of the lungs.

If you let him play when you're working in the kitchen, watch out for boiling liquids, hot coffeepots, and buckets of scrub water. And now starts the job of teaching the baby that the hot range, burners, or switches, and electrical outlets are dangerous and must not be touched.

Breakable objects should be put out of reach—at least until he's a little bit older. At this age, he's just too young to know what will and won't break. If you don't put breakables away, you'll constantly be saying, "No, no" and "Don't touch" until your cautions no longer have any significance because they're used so often.

To prevent falls and other accidents, disconnect the lamps in the living room and wind their cords around the bases. Tablecloths that hang over the edge of the table are also dangerous. One good tug and everything will come tumbling down.

Keep all instruments with sharp points or ragged edges out of Baby's reach. Dry beans and peas should be stowed away high, because they swell and cause real trouble if the baby sticks them up a nostril or into an ear. Small objects such as coins, marbles, corn, jacks, and seeds are also dangerous and should always be kept away from him.

GIVE HIM A PLAYROOM Before your little fellow reaches the place where he's getting everywhere, he should be given a playroom, or play corner in a family room, where he can touch anything he likes. This should be where he'll be near you as you go about your work. An older child would be content to play alone in another part of the house, but your youngster at this age is still too young.

A little gate or his playpen across the doorway will keep him safe and still not give him the sense of being shut in that a closed door would. If he's given this room or area where he can have perfect freedom, Baby will obey the rules of the rest of the house without too much fussing.

His playroom may be anything from a cubby hole or breakfast room to a large, luxuriously furnished nursery. Your circumstances must, therefore, dictate the furnishings.

The room shouldn't have a polished floor on which the baby might slip, or a nice rug which would have to be protected. The ideal floor-covering is linoleum or tile, for either provides a safe footing, a good surface for play activities, and is easily cleaned.

The playroom should have an open cupboard or set of shelves (made from boxes, if you like) where Baby's toys can be placed within his reach. These are the essential furnishings of a playroom. Add to them as your purse and desires dictate. Any furniture you buy, such as small tables and chairs, should be strong and durable.

BABY NEEDS YOUR COMPANY Even though the baby will now be interested in his toys, he still needs the reassurance that you're near by. But you don't have to play with him every minute of the day. He needs to learn how to amuse himself.

Put him outdoors in his playpen if the weather permits. If he fusses a little after a while, go to him. Sometimes, if you give him something new to play with, he may be happy for another hour. If he's still dissatisfied, give him the attention he needs and play with him for a while.

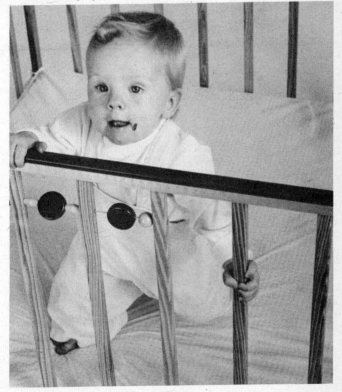

Playpens are for babies. This young explorer needs a chance to discover the new world.

HE JOINS THE FAMILY CIRCLE In addition to the lesson of amusing himself, Baby also needs social contacts. He can have these in his journeys of exploration about the house, and there should be a period each day when he joins in family activities.

Whenever strangers come to visit you, give him every chance to get used to them. Don't be concerned if he's reluctant to go to them.

If you take him with you when you do your marketing, he'll soon become accustomed to unfamiliar surroundings. And at times along the way, stop whenever he wants to watch other children at play.

BEGINNING TO TALK By 10 or 12 months, your baby will probably say an honest-to-goodness word. Sometimes this first word will go completely unnoticed for a while simply because

Mirror, mirror on the wall, who's the fairest of them all? For heaven's sake, it's little me!

it doesn't sound like the word Baby is trying to imitate. But, after he has used a certain sound several times to indicate a certain thing, you will catch on to what he's trying to say.

Usually the first thing that the baby will say is "da-da-da." He'll also learn to use "bye-bye" and wave along with it.

Many times you can teach a baby patty-cake. Later in this period, before reaching 12 months, Baby usually says "mama."

You'll want to give Baby encouragement in his efforts. Because babyish first words are so appealing, you'll be tempted to repeat them back to your youngster. Don't do it! Many mothers and fathers make this mistake. It definitely doesn't help your baby learn to talk. He thinks he is imitating the way you talk. If you reverse yourself and adopt his way of saying things, you'll really mix him up.

Don't try to make him change the way he pronounces words. Just be sure you say the words he uses clearly and correctly each time you use them.

Your baby may stop adding words to his vocabulary for a while after his first two or three are understood. There may be a definite lag, too, while he's learning to walk. But he'll make up for lost ground after he's become an accomplished walker. In the meantime, help him add to his unspoken vocabulary by talking to him in short, simple words. Sing nursery songs, and recite rhymes. Don't talk too fast, though, and keep sentences short.

Of course, he'll have other models besides you. He'll copy the speech of anyone who's around him a lot. Keep this in mind when hiring a baby sitter. Relatives and friends are more difficult to control, but ask them not to talk baby talk to the baby, and to try to avoid slang if its use concerns you.

BABY'S IN THE BIG TUB Your baby is really getting big, for now he can take his bath in the big tub. He'll love this, and how he'll splash! Place a towel or mat in the bottom of the tub so he won't slip. Don't let the water get too hot! Let him play awhile with the water toys, then give him a regular bath. Remember, though, that he's still a baby, and *never leave him alone in the tub*. Too many things might happen.

As long as you can keep him on it, the bath table is convenient for dressing and undressing the baby. When he gets too lively, however, you'll have to put this handy object away and graduate to a bigger table, your bed, or a pad on the floor.

DON'T BREAK HIS SLEEP ROUTINE As he gets older, he'll sleep less during the day. He may cut his naps to one a day. For this long afternoon nap, put the baby in his own room with the door closed and leave him there for the full period. If he cries hard, find out what the trouble is, but leave him there for his full nap time.

Don't begin now, or ever, the practice of staying with him until he goes to sleep. See that he's comfortable, then leave his room, and close the door behind you.

Babies' sleep needs vary, which makes it difficult to state a specific number of hours they should sleep at night. By this time, your baby will have established his particular schedule and this should be religiously adhered to for years to come.

HE STARTS TO WALK Once Baby tries to pull himself up

Just two more steps and I'll be in Daddy's arms.

and stand, let him practice at his own speed. Some babies may not even try until they're over a year, while occasionally one will stand at seven months. Just be sure to give him plenty of opportunities to use his newly found power whenever he chooses to.

If your baby stands until he's tired and starts to cry, let him down easily. Chances are he just hasn't figured out for himself how to sit down yet.

After he gains confidence in his standing ability, he'll begin to take a few tentative steps, still holding on to the furniture or playpen rail. Don't urge him at this point. Let him take his time, and somewhere between the twelfth and fifteenth months, he'll probably take out on his own.

Brothers or sisters, especially in the two-year age group, often seem to take delight in pushing a baby that is learning to walk. He may get discouraged if he's continually pushed down and won't even try to walk. If you notice this pushing going on, divert the older child's attention and give the baby a good chance to try his new-found wings.

PRAISE HAS ITS PLACE Your child probably shouldn't be praised extravagantly for every small act of the day. Either it will make him a terrible egotist, or praise will lose its meaning. Too, you want him to conform to good habits as a matter of course. But when he does perform creditably, don't hesitate to tell him so.

Praise, in the beginning at least, is what everyone works for. When a certain course brings the approval of others, efforts are made to continue in that direction. Your praise of Baby when he succeeds helps him know that he did what you wanted, and encourages him to do it that way the next time. Just don't carry praise to the place where it's ridiculous and meaningless.

Boasting about your little one's accomplishments to your friends is likely to get tiresome to them after a while. As proud as you are of the baby's feats, keep your comments in line with their importance.

What if your baby fails or disappoints you? The less attention called to this fact the better, for small youngsters love drama and are apt to repeat the undesirable conduct just to hear you sound off.

14

Your baby
from twelve to
eighteen months

DEVELOPMENT Between the ages of 12 and 15 months, your baby may: . . . walk alone or with a little help. . . . lower himself from a standing to sitting position. . . . repeat his actions if laughed at. . . . blow bubbles. . . . hold a cup to drink from. . . . say a few words. . . . stop when spoken to. Between the ages of 15 and 18 months, he may: . . . show a little cooperation in helping you dress him. . . . build a tower of two or more blocks and fit a peg into its proper hole in a board. . . . walk alone. . . . use a spoon in a messy sort of way. . . . have a five- to ten-word vocabulary. Your youngster has probably tripled his birth weight during his first year and gained about 9 inches in height. There are large differences in the rates at which children grow, however, and your baby may vary considerably from these averages.

His first birthday should find him with good habits of eating, sleeping, and playing.

Continue to have your physician give him regular examinations. Plan your visits for at least every three months.

WHAT TO EXPECT Your youngster is entering upon a year of great mental and emotional development. In contrast, his physical growth will slow down, and his appetite will slacken. His food preferences may change. He is moving out of the baby stage, and during the next 12 months, he'll learn to walk well by himself, begin to talk, may begin to have control of his bowels (although usually not until he's at least 2 years old), and his bladder control *may* develop sufficiently so that daytime training will be successful a good part of the time. He may be going through a period of shyness with strangers, but this will soon pass.

A CHANGE IN EATING HABITS By this time, your child should be deriving most of his nutritional needs from table foods. And if he derives a great satisfaction from a naptime

Mother says I drink milk because its good for me, but I really drink it to get a moustache!

or bedtime bottle, continue to let him have it, as a single bottle a day doesn't prolong infantile behavior.

Somewhere, around his first birthday, there'll probably be a marked change in his eating habits. Suddenly he's got a smaller appetite. There are two logical reasons for his about-face.

First, he's reached the age where the rapidity of his growth is easing off. During his first year, he gained approximately 16 pounds. This is as much as he will probably gain during the next four years. It's obvious that he'll no longer need as much food or be as hungry as he used to be, because his appetite will parallel his growth rate. Also, he's utilizing his food better, so he no longer requires as many calories per pound.

There will probably be one meal a day when he eats very little. This will go on for some months, and then he'll eat even less, until you feel he's eating what could be considered a normal amount of food at only one meal. As he approaches 18 months, it's not at all unusual for him to go several days without eating what *you* consider a normal amount of food. When he finally does eat a meal, he acts as though he's been starved to death and even takes two or three helpings.

It's only natural for his appetite to vary, so let *him* decide how much food he wants. Fussing about it will make him rebel and will lead to feeding problems.

FOOD LIKES MAY VARY About this time, in addition to having a smaller appetite than formerly, your baby's food likes may become unpredictable. A food that's a favorite one week may be rejected the following week. And he may go all out for a certain food for days at a time, never seeming to get enough of it and not wanting much else. Then when his craving for that particular food has been satisfied, he'll lose interest in it for a while.

He may go from one such food binge to another. And in the meantime, you're worrying, because all the books say he should be eating a balanced diet and you're sure he's not.

Dr. Clara M. Davis took children so young they could just finger-feed themselves and set several dishes of wholesome foods before them. After a few tentative tastes, the babies frequently selected one food, ate the entire serving, and signified they wanted more of it—ignoring the other foods on their tray. At every meal, they were permitted to eat as much as they wanted of any one food.

But over her period of observation, Doctor Davis found that the children's preferences included all the elements needed. And, what's more, they gained and developed as well as children eating so-called "balanced" meals.

It's your job to put a variety of wholesome foods (no sweets) before your child at each meal. If a certain meat, fruit, or vegetable that he craves at the time is included in the meal, that's probably all he'll eat, but, as his food likes change, he'll gradually take a little of another food, until he completely switches to another favorite.

If he loses weight or fails to gain over a reasonable period of time, it's a case for your doctor. Nagging or threatening in order to get him to eat a little bit or the same amount of everything won't help. You'll create feeding problems that will last for years.

THE MAJOR FOOD GROUPS A balanced diet of the four major food groups—proteins, fats, carbohydrates, vitamins and minerals—is important for your child's health and a strong body.

Protein foods (lean meat, skim milk, eggs, cottage cheese, cheese) are body builders. Their primary purpose is to build new body cells and tissues, or rebuild and repair worn-out or injured tissue. Nature converts any moderate excess protein intake to carbohydrates. There is, however, no way the body can make up for too little protein.

Fats (cream, whole milk, fatty meats, nuts—as in peanut butter, butter, cooking oils, and shortening) store up energy in young bodies. This stored-up energy is drawn upon during periods of illness or extreme hunger. An excess of fats in the diet leads to overweight.

Carbohydrates (breads, sugar, cake, crackers, cereals, vegetables, milk—a small percent) are energy foods. They are to the body as gasoline is to an engine. If eaten in excess, carbohydrates are converted to fat and stored.

Vitamins and minerals were discussed in detail in Chapter 8.

HE CAN EAT ALL THESE So far, the range of foods has been rather limited, and confined mostly to foods that the majority of children naturally seem to like.

But now the range of food you can offer widens out. Here's the list of foods you can give your youngster after he's 1 year old. It will probably be some time, though, before he develops a taste for strong-flavored foods such as broccoli, Brussels sprouts, asparagus, and cauliflower.

Suitable foods for a 1-year- to 18-month-old child:

Dairy products and eggs

Milk
Cream
Butter
Buttermilk

Eggs
Cottage cheese
Cream cheese

Vegetables—chopped or mashed

Carrots
String beans
Green peas
Tomatoes
Asparagus
Cauliflower
Stewed celery
Cabbage
Turnips
Spinach

Lima beans
Squash
Beets
Parsnips
Brussels sprouts
Broccoli
Swiss chard
Lettuce
Onions
Sweet potatoes

Meats—ground, chopped, or diced

Hamburger
Chicken
Turkey
Lamb chop
Roast pork
Crisp bacon
Beef broth
Roast beef
Roast lamb
Meat loaf (if
  lightly seasoned)

Liver (chicken, calf, beef, or
  pig)
Fish—white, nonoily, all
  bones removed
Any of the meats and soups
  commercially prepared for
  babies
Soft luncheon meats
Skinned hot dogs

All meats should be lean and well-cooked.

Fruits

Orange juice
Grapefruit juice
Orange (sliced)
Ripe apple (peeled, chunks)
Applesauce
Baked apple
Ripe banana

Stewed peaches
Stewed pears
Stewed apricots
Stewed plums
Stewed prunes
Cooked raisins (seedless)
Baked banana

Stewed fruits should be mashed, the skins chopped into particles, all stones removed.

Cereals

All cooked, canned, or specially prepared infants' varieties.

Miscellaneous

White potatoes
Macaroni
Spaghetti
Whole-wheat bread
Whole-wheat muffins
Corn bread
Crackers
Graham crackers
Zwieback
Arrowroot cookies
Plain cookies

Sponge cake
Jelly
Custard
Rennet custard
Rennet custard dessert
Unflavored gelatin
Cornstarch pudding
Tapioca pudding
Rice pudding
Prune whip

It looks as though he's practically grown up, doesn't it? This list doesn't mean that you must start now, this minute, giving your youngster all the foods mentioned. But sometime during the next 6 to 12 months, give him a chance to taste and to like each one.

HOW TO COOK VEGETABLES FOR SMALL CHILDREN

Vegetables are often the least-liked foods. The following cooking hints have proved helpful to mothers of small children.

Little ones don't like strong tastes, and they do like crispness and color. They require only about half as much sugar or salt as adults, and should not have spices or strong seasonings. To have your youngster like the new vegetable you're cooking, use half as much salt as for your own taste and just enough water to keep the vegetable from burning. Cook it fast, and just long enough to be tender and yet to retain some crispness. Make sure your saucepan is tightly covered.

Many youngsters like certain vegetables raw better than cooked. After your child gets to be about 2 years old, you can cater liberally to this fancy. At present, however, there's danger of his choking on food chunks.

HE SHOULDN'T EAT THESE The 12- to 18-month-old child should not have the following foods:

Cocoa
Tea
Coffee
Hot fresh breads and rolls
Griddle cakes
Ready-to-serve cereals
Sweet cakes
Fried foods
Gravies
Sausage
Salt fish
Corned beef
Dried beef
Eggplant
Green corn
Cucumbers
Radishes
Condiments
Spices
Nuts
Popcorn
Pastries
Chocolate pudding
Angel cake
Ice cream
Sherbet
Candy
Berries or melon
Figs
Dates
Rhubarb
Fresh fruits, except those mentioned previously

OFFERING NEW FOODS In introducing a new food or one he doesn't like very well, give him just a taste. Then allow him to eat as much as he likes of the rest of the meal, including several of his favorite dishes. Experiments conducted by nursery schools over a period of time show that if a child has a chance to get used to a food, he'll like it. But he has a better chance to like it if he takes a little at a time.

Now, when food habits are still being formed, it's helpful to present the new or disliked food (usually it's a vegetable) at the first of the meal when the child is most hungry. Put a fair serving on his plate—about 1 tablespoon—of each of the foods for the meal. Give him a small glass or cup of milk—about 4 ounces—and let him eat and drink as he likes. Don't worry about the amounts or variety he takes.

He may have seconds of any of the food if he wishes. When Baby has satisfied his hunger, give him dessert in proportion to the amount of other food he has eaten.

A word of caution about the amount of milk you permit him to drink—too many children are allowed to drink far too much milk. They derive an overabundance of calories from the milk and then fail to eat an adequate amount of solid food. A quart a day is too much for a child this age. A pint is sufficient.

If the family meal is going to be so late that your youngster will be extremely hungry and irritable, feed him first, but if your schedule allows it, let him eat with the family. Very likely he'll spill some of his food and may even need a little guidance now and then. Encourage honest effort, but when he starts to play with the food or tires of feeding himself, take the spoon and food away or finish feeding him yourself.

Big sisters can be a real help to a fellow, especially if they know all about fire trucks.

INDEPENDENCE DEVELOPS Sometime during this next year, your baby will discover that he has a mind of his own, and he will want to exercise it. He'll resist your efforts to get him to do things. He'll become more and more energetic, and in his urge to explore, will be "into everything."

He'll want to touch and handle everything he sees. Sometimes, for his own welfare, you'll have to hold him back. Your common sense must be your guide, however, since this is his way of familiarizing himself with the world about him.

THE INEVITABLE TEMPER TANTRUM The happiest and most wisely handled child in the world may have temper tantrums some time during this period of new-found independence. They usually start around the one-year mark. Occasionally you will find an even-tempered youngster who never has them.

By the time the child is 18 months to 2 years old, he's quite an expert. Between 2½ and 3 years of age, the parent can usually begin to reason with the child. Once most children realize that this kind of behavior is not the way to get what is wanted, there will be fewer tantrums.

Basically, temper tantrums are a result of frustration. The youngster either wants to do something or wants something, and in his efforts to do or obtain this, he is somehow frustrated. Simple things like pulling a toy and getting it caught on a chair, or wanting a cooky and not getting it, or wanting Mother to hold him when she is unable to, may bring on a tantrum.

What happens then? He lies on the floor, screams, pounds his head, kicks—anything to express this frustration. This behavior is common and expected in this age group. As the child gets older, his developing maturity will enable him to handle equally frustrating situations without resorting to such dramatic, drastic, and irritating measures.

If your young one has a tantrum, ignore it. If you expect to have any reasonable control over this problem, you must retain your composure. Losing your temper when he loses his won't help at all.

Remember, you're an adult, and you're dealing with a child. Shaking and spanking him or screaming and yelling at him when he's having a tantrum brings you right down to his level,

Cracks in sidewalks are just one of the hazards that can befall excited, young explorers.

and you'll soon learn you'll never win an argument with a child by behaving like one yourself.

He definitely shouldn't be allowed to get his own way by means of a temper tantrum. If he's simply trying you out, he'll quit when he finds that the tantrum gets him nowhere. Once you give in to him, he'll use this method again and again to get his own way.

It sometimes helps to take him to his room and leave him there until the tantrum is over. Walking away from him may also calm him down. Usually a child will stop screaming when he finds you're not there to watch him.

Children also have tantrums when they're tired, overstimulated, or ordered about too much. Have you yielded to temptation and broken his bed- and naptime or served his meal late? Are you directing every detail of his day? If you can answer "no" to these questions with a clear conscience, just smile up your sleeve when your child pulls out this old trick, and make sure it wins him nothing.

Have you, however, subjected him to too much excitement or stimulation? Are you treating him like an infant with no

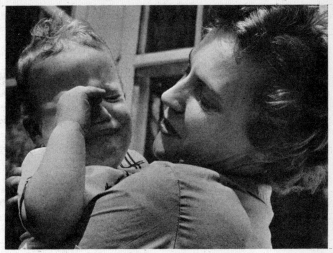

That's when it's nice to have Mother near—
to soothe the pain and repair the damage.

mind or will of his own? If so, take the tantrums as a signal and change your ways.

WHAT KIND OF DISCIPLINE? This period can be very exasperating, and you may be tempted to bear down on him. You may feel that his balkiness shows lack of respect for you, and that both his busyness and seeming destructiveness are deliberate naughtiness. However, the drive for independent thought and action is so important that it's cause for rejoicing rather than dismay.

It's a sign that your youngster is growing up normally from an emotional standpoint. If you make every situation as pleasant as you can, and interfere with your child's actions only when absolutely necessary, he may never develop behavior habits which annoy you.

Good discipline begins with a consistent attitude on the part of both parents. You and your husband should present a united front. If something is wrong and cannot be done today, it's wrong and can't be done tomorrow. If you let him do something one day, you can't expect him to understand why you try to stop him from doing it again.

But if he is sure of your love and faith in him, he'll be able to take limitations when it's necessary to protect or help him.

At this age, punishment has little place in this scheme of discipline. Provide your young one with places to play, indoors and outdoors, where he can "let go" without colliding with adult requirements. If you're continually saying "no, don't do this," and "don't touch that," your commands will lose their significance and he'll ignore them.

At the times when he does run counter to grown-up ways, find out what's causing him to act as he does. Be patient and understanding of his need for independence.

You may feel that occasional punishment is necessary when he's older, knows what's wrong, and does it anyway, but punishment should never become a substitute for positive parental guidance.

Threatening the older child should definitely be avoided. If you feel that a penalty must be imposed for certain behavior, it's only right to give your youngster fair warning. Then if he goes right ahead and disobeys, you carry out the threat which you made. Nothing destroys a parent's authority faster than to make threats that are never carried out!

REGULAR DAILY ROUTINE Keep to the daily routine that you've established. The child who seems naughty is very often tired, hungry, or overstimulated.

After he is past the first year, it may not seem so important that Baby have his meals and go to bed at regular times. You may feel that a few slip-ups won't matter. But don't let yourself be tempted.

The baby is happily adjusted to a regular routine now, which is good for him as well as for you. A good routine tends to make the day go smoother. The necessary chores can be done without the tension that goes with haste and the irritability that shows when a baby is hungry or overly tired.

If every morning you dress him after breakfast and brush his hair and teeth, the brushing becomes as natural to him as breathing. If you're haphazard about these matters, or about mealtimes and bedtime, they often become a contest of wills that ends in some form of punishment before he gives in.

The unspoiled, unabused child is anxious to do what you

want him to do, as soon as he understands what this is. The whole attitude of the young child is of wonder at the world, of a desire to be one with it. He imitates you. If you do a thing twice a certain way, he wants to continue to do it that way. Your greatest allies in training are his desires to do what you want and his imitativeness, provided you yourself use them in the right way.

Parents who keep in close touch with a child can teach him the right way to do each new thing before he has a chance to fall into a wrong way. Sometimes this is easy. Sometimes it's more difficult, but it's always easier than overcoming a bad habit.

Continue an orderly routine throughout the first two years, and you'll be rewarded by an excellent set of habits and a co-operative attitude.

HE NEEDS TO KNOW YOU'RE THERE Along with this desire to express himself as an independent person, there'll be noticeable dependence on you at times. He'll run back from things he's doing to make sure you're right where he left you. He may start to cry when you go out of his sight.

This may seem babyish and to belie his drive for independence. Instead, it means that he's checking up on his security. He wants to be free, but he also wants to be sure that you're standing by. After he has reassured himself on this point, he goes back to his new-found independence.

This doesn't mean that you can't ever leave him alone for short periods in his playpen or fenced play yard. Or that you can't go out occasionally and leave him in the care of someone else. But when he calls you in the midst of his play, or comes running to you, or whimpers at signs that you are going out, give him the reassurance he needs.

GIVE HIM ROOM FOR PLAY Play will occupy an increasingly large place in your child's life, and by now, he'll feel his playpen too confining. It's ideal if you can fence in a whole back yard where he can roam to his heart's content. A sand pile equipped with a pail and shovel, a toy truck or wagon, and a few other safe play toys will keep him well occupied during his outdoor play periods.

Both indoors and out, push-and-pull toys fulfill the need

Every good cook knows always to sprinkle the sand before making pies and cakes. Little brother can only sit watching as he dreams of building grand sand castles surrounded by moats.

of your youngster's growing muscles. At this age, he'll enjoy putting things together, such as placing one empty box in another, or pans that fit inside other pans. And he'll also like to fit pegs of various shapes into their proper holes on a board.

For indoor play, your child needs a room, not too far away from your activities, where he can play with his toys for certain periods of the day. This room should contain a toy cupboard, or shelves, low enough so he can reach his playthings, a small, sturdy table and chair, and any other furnishings you like.

Whether indoors or out, your baby will want to examine everything he sees, explore every nook and cranny. At this age, curiosity is proof of the alertness and growing independence. To make him stay crying in a pen or small enclosure when he wants to get out is to hold back this period of development, and shake his confidence in himself—and in you.

Try to anticipate your baby's desire to roam. If he's still spending some time in his playpen, lift him out before he tires of it, so he won't get the idea that he's getting his way by crying. In good weather you can do small chores outside while your small explorer ranges over his own backyard. And when you go for a walk, let him take his little side trips to examine the many things that catch his interest. Be patient with him.

Again, remember to clear out all things in the house and yard that he might break, or on which he might get hurt. These precautions aren't giving in too much to him, because to learn, he needs to handle, investigate everything he can.

TOY LIST GROWS This is the period for the development of the large arm, leg, and body muscles as opposed to the smaller muscles of hands and fingers (that comes later) and the senses. A number of toys will help to do this:

Small stout wagon—large enough to haul things in but light enough to be pulled. Develops large muscles.

Chairs—small, sturdy, comfortable, with fitted seat and back for correct posture. Develops large muscles.

Trains—small, without wheels, and which have a large fastening between cars. Develops large muscles.

Cloth picture books—containing simple, large pictures of familiar objects. Develops senses.

Glass tables are nice because when you can
see your feet, you know you're out of paper.

Balls—develop large muscles as child runs after them.

Large blocks—no sharp corners. Develop large muscles.

Unbreakable or cloth doll—develops both large muscles
and senses.

Chair swing—develops large muscles.

Pull toys—stout strings. Develop large muscles.

Clothespins—develop senses.

Pans, spoons, and cups—develop both large muscles and senses.

Select those toys which will allow a child to express his own creativity and imagination. A child this age will enjoy large, colorful toys with movable parts he can manipulate.

PLAYMATES ADD TO HIS FUN A child plays spontaneously. You don't have to teach him how to play or provide him with special toys. The urge comes from within.

A child learns, develops, and builds intelligence through play. From all we know, play reflects their basically limited understanding of the world and is therefore a kind of constant testing of the world.

An infant can play only by himself, but as he begins to explore the world while creeping and walking, he will enjoy the companionship of a youngster somewhere near his own age.

These two children will not play co-operatively as yet. First, they will develop parallel play. They will show an interest in each other by pushing or grabbing, but each will play with his own toys for short periods of time. There will be few squabbles because each is too absorbed in his own play to worry about what his companion may be doing, but both will enjoy the idea of having the other around.

If there are no small children in the neighborhood with whom your youngster can play, have friends bring theirs over often.

SHOES WHEN HE WALKS Up to now, the only shoes Baby's needed have been soft-soled, worn mainly for protection from rough floors or ground. Going barefoot has been, and continues to be, good for him. As long as the floor is clean, free from splinters, and the ground is free from broken glass and rubbish, he can go barefoot. He'll strengthen his foot muscles by exercising them.

Once your toddler starts walking alone outdoors, he needs firm, but flexible soled shoes. A salesman skilled in fitting children's shoes should help select the proper fit. The shoes should be:

1. Broad enough to allow his toes to be in their natural position. When he puts his weight on his foot, the sides of the shoe should be full but not bulging.

2. At least one-half inch longer than the tip of the toes to the edge of the soles. This is about one thumb's width.

3. High enough at the instep and toes.

4. Snug-fitting in the heel.

5. No higher in the heel than the thickness of the sole.

Scrape the sole before letting your baby wear a new pair of shoes, so they won't slip when he walks. If the floor is too highly waxed and slippery, and he takes a tumble, he may be reluctant to practice walking.

As soon as his toes come within one-fourth inch of the end of the shoe, you'll have to buy new ones—even though the old ones are still in good condition. Shoes which no longer fit properly can cause lasting damage to your baby's feet. From 8 to 15 months, he'll probably need a new pair every month to 6 weeks. From 15 months to 2 years, he'll need a new pair every 2 or 3 months.

Don't pass on outgrown shoes to the other children. After shoes are worn for a while, they take on the shape of an individual's foot. Each child wears shoes differently. Someone else's may cause a permanent deformity.

If there's any fault in the way the baby stands or walks, special shoes and corrective exercises may be required. Seek professional advice and treatment from your doctor.

NAP AND BEDTIME RESISTANCE Shortly after his first birthday, your child may rebel against taking his nap or going to bed. This is one point on which you must remain firm. There may be times when he screams during his entire nap period, or for an hour after being put to bed in the evening.

If he's been perfectly well up until bedtime, it's unlikely he's ill. Once you give in to him and let him up, you've got a problem. If you remain firm and ignore his protests, his rebellion should last no more than a few evenings. Look in on him from time to time if the crying period is prolonged.

AWAKENING AT NIGHT Following a day during which there is a lot of excitement or tension, your child may awaken during the night and scream or cry out. If he does this, check on him to make sure he hasn't fallen out of bed, caught an arm or leg between the crib bars, or become ill. If he's all right, hold him for a minute, reassure him that Mother and

Daddy are close by, and tell him to go back to sleep.

His dreams may awaken him more than once the first night this happens. It's up to you to be firm and convince him that he must go back to sleep, but don't start walking the floor, rocking him, or taking him to bed with you. Daddy's firmness may be more convincing than Mother's when he tells him to go back to sleep and that nothing will hurt him.

TOILET TRAINING Like any other accomplishment, toilet training requires that the youngster be old enough to learn the specific procedure and developed sufficiently physically to carry out the procedure. Although mothers of a generation ago felt that a baby was ready to toilet train at 6 months, we know now that a child is neither intellectually developed enough to actually learn the procedure nor does he have sufficient control of his bowels and bladder until somewhere between 18 months and two years of age.

For these reasons, we have delayed detailed discussion of training until the next chapter.

ENOUGH TEETH TO BRUSH? Between 12 and 18 months, your child will probably cut six more teeth. Begin brushing them now. Get a tiny, soft brush. Begin by letting him see you brush your own teeth. Be very gentle about tooth-brushing and don't force the issue.

A drink of water after a meal will remove food particles from his gums and teeth, but isn't as effective as brushing.

15

Your baby from eighteen months to two years

DEVELOPMENT From 18 months to 2 years of age, your baby will probably: . . be walking and climbing on chairs and stairs, always on the go! . . . scribble on paper spontaneously and vigorously (the wall, too, if you're not careful), and begin to imitate your strokes with crayon. . . . use the words he has learned in short sentences, and point to his nose, eyes, hair, ears whenever asked to identify them. . . . build a high tower with a number of blocks. . . . fill a cup with cubes as he's playing. . . . use fairly good control when eating with a spoon. . . . turn pages of books to look at pictures. . . . throw a ball into a box. . . . *never be still a minute!*

WHEN HE FEEDS HIMSELF He's a big boy now, and should be doing a pretty good, if messy, job of feeding himself. By now you know just about how much he's going to eat, so it's best to put that amount on his plate. Much more than he can handle will tempt him to play with his food.

If he should start to play, take the spoon from him and offer him a few bites to see if he is through eating. If he is, remove the food that's left on his plate.

HOW NOT TO HAVE AN EATING PROBLEM A good many youngsters, with good eating habits, become problems at this time simply because their parents don't understand that their children no longer require so much food.

Not understanding this, parents are prone to be worried when their child's interest in food lessens. They start urging, pleading, even threatening the youngster to eat more than he really wants.

At this age when left to himself, your child will probably pick at his food for a few meals, then eat everything in sight for a few meals. Over a year's time, the resulting food intake is the same as if he had eaten three good meals every day.

When parents try to bribe, coax, and tease down a set amount of food every day, the child never has a chance to get hungry. Often he gets so that he hates the thought of food.

Let your attitude from now on be "don't force him to eat." If he hasn't eaten well, ignore it. Keep mealtime a pleasant, happy experience to which your child looks forward. Never let it become an issue.

The American Academy of Pediatrics says, "Parents should understand that it is their duty to decide what and when the child should eat, but that it is the child's prerogative to decide how much of it he will eat."

DESSERTS, BETWEEN-MEAL SNACKS This is as good a time as any for your child to learn that desserts, with the exception of fruit, are nonessential. Certainly desserts add food value because their caloric content is high, but with obesity a primary medical concern, it's best if your youngster learns to regard them as an occasional treat, not as a part of every meal.

During their child's infant years, most parents are conscientious about following the diet given them by the doctor. But when Baby turns into a runabout with teeth and the ability to eat most foods on the family menu, he's exposed to a deluge of candy, ice cream, soft drinks, cookies, and the like.

There's something about bread and butter and little boys. The two together always seem to bring out the best in one another!

The one idea most people have of the way to be good to a child is to feed him something, and in most cases, it's something sweet or rich. Thus children learn quickly to want the sweet, pleasant-tasting foods, and to reject those not so exciting. The carbohydrate or energy-producing foods taste better than the body-building and body-protecting ones; so many children grow up starved in protein, minerals, and vitamins, because they are unnecessarily surfeited with sweets.

Don't make this mistake with your youngster. Request friends, relatives, and neighbors not to feed your child between meals. They mean well, but you're the boss in these matters. If your child is actually hungry between meals, offer him good protein foods such as milk, cheese, or luncheon meat.

WEIGHT ISN'T ALL Little has been said about growth since the end of the first year. If your child is given the care suggested, he'll be well nourished. There'll be no need to keep a constant eye on the scales. If you give him the proper food, rest, and outdoor life, his growth will take care of itself.

After his first birthday, the gain is much slower. His weight on an average is 21–24 pounds at 1 year and 24–27 at 2. His height on an average is 30 inches when he's 1 year old, 34 inches when he's 2.

Much more important than weight and height are the brightness of his eyes, the strength of his muscles, and solidness of his flesh, and his animation and happiness. If these are all good, your child is all right, whether he's above or below the average of tables.

Children born of tall, thin stock are likely to weigh less than the average. Short, stocky children will probably weigh more.

THE INEVITABLE "NO" STAGE One of the most common characteristics of behavior you can expect to develop now is technically known as "negativism." All it means is that your child will "no" every suggestion you make. He won't eat his dinner, take his nap, go to his playpen, or pick up his toys. He may even back up his remarks with a temper tantrum, and if it gets results, he'll keep right on.

Some people feel this characteristic should be called positivism, because he's pretty positive on what he wants, which is just the opposite of what you want him to do.

Just ignore his "no" or temper tantrum. This is just another phase of development that may soon pass. Don't give him a chance to say yes or no. When it's time for his nap, announce "we're going to take a nap." Then take him by the hand and lead him to the bed. If it's time to eat, don't ask him if he wants to eat—he's sure to say "no!" Instead, put him in his chair and give him his meal.

Often you can divert his attention by making a game out of what you want him to do. If he says he "won't" go to bed, don't agree. Just say, "Let's see who can get up the stairs first." Children are tremendously suggestible. They respond easily and quickly to play ideas, particularly when you appear to be poised and unperturbed.

Make your commands just as few as possible. Your child can become independent only if he's allowed to take the responsibility for his own affairs. Unless it's a matter of his health and welfare, as food and sleep are, allow him as much freedom as possible.

Always let common sense be your judge. Insist upon obedience when it's absolutely necessary for your child's welfare, and let him make the decisions in other matters.

AGGRESSIVENESS IS NORMAL As your child nears his second birthday, you'll notice that he's becoming more aggressive. After he's been playing for a while, he may push, hit, or

With patience and a deaf ear,
Mother, you'll live to see your
little one outgrow this stage.

bite his little playmate.

Children this age can't be expected to know how to play
with each other properly—that's something they have to learn
by trial and error. They'll probably maul and manhandle each
other a lot before they discover that a human body can't be
treated the same way as a shovel. If the children are approximately the same age and fairly evenly matched, they won't
harm each other and will learn by experience what they may
and may not do.

Many mothers become overly alarmed by this kind of behavior. As soon as they see their child hit another youngster,
they rush right in and punish him for hitting. Soon he begins
to figure that it's all right to slug his playmate, because
Mommy protects him from getting it right back.

Once most youngsters are walloped back a few times, they
become reluctant to start anything. A poke in the nose from
their playmates is more effective than a parental spanking.

As a parent, you certainly have an obligation to supervise
the youngsters and intervene before serious damage is done.
To place a small child at the mercy of a considerably older or
bigger and rougher one is hardly fair. Be guided by your own
common sense in this matter of playmates and play regulation.

WHAT ABOUT TIMIDITY? Occasionally a two-year-old lets
himself get pushed around. Rather than hit back, he just sits
and takes it, or runs whining to his mother. Given a little more
experience and playtime with other children, he'll eventually
learn to stand up for his rights and fight back. When he does
come running to you, resist the temptation to shower him with
sympathy or to fight his battles for him. Matter-of-factly suggest he go and get his shovel or ball back. (Remember, a cer-

tain amount of aggressiveness is normal, desirable.)

Parents who forbid a child to fight back are encouraging timidity. If you take away a youngster's defense mechanism, what can he do but run away. Should your child seem extremely aggressive, talk to your doctor.

HOW TO TEACH OBEDIENCE Some conscientious parents are confused as to how much they should expect in the way of obedience. Do modern methods mean that a child shouldn't have to obey?

Not at all. To get along peacefully in the world, obedience to proper authority is a lesson everyone must learn at some time or other. You, as parents, are the first authority your child comes in contact with.

If he learns to accept reasonable desires on your part, he'll more easily adjust in later life to the authority of the school he attends. As he grows older, he'll understand more readily why there must be rules and laws governing society as a whole.

Any time you want him to do something, always make the request in a pleasant and courteous manner which contributes to his sense of security and accomplishment.

Allow your child as much freedom of choice and action as is possible at this stage of development. He'll soon see why it is useless to rebel when a task is absolutely necessary, and he'll know that the sooner he gets his job done, the sooner he can use his strength and ingenuity to do other things he wants to.

Around the twenty-first month, you can occasionally ask

He will enjoy going outside to play as long as you assure him that you will be nearby.

When the weather is nice, give him the freedom to play outside in an enclosed yard.

him to do a simple task. With your gestures, show him that you want him to "pick up the paper." Make the request pleasantly and courteously, and repeat until he gets the idea.

When you do give commands, *see that they're carried out*. As much as possible, help your child feel that such requests add to his well-being and comfort.

A pitfall into which it's easy to fall is that of so-called "reasoning." At this age, children learn quickly that they can get control of the situation by arguing and resisting. They've a whole bagful of tricks! You should have a reason for your command, of course, and it's all right to explain it—once. That, however, should end all discussion.

If your command is worth giving, it's worth obeying without considerable debate. If you start refuting your youngster's objections and go into lengthy explanations, first thing you know you'll have an argument over every simple operation. Don't ever be afraid to tell your child, quietly and courteously, to do the things he must do. Then see that he does them with a minimum of delay.

KEEP GOOD HABITS GOING Your job really gets interesting now! You'll be tempted to relax the routine somewhat—to allow your youngster to frequently have candy, cake, and soft drinks, or to run free in the neighborhood. Don't! It's much easier to keep good habits than to break bad ones, once they're begun.

Keep him in his play space at regular hours of the day, with plenty of toys. A breakfast nook or sunroom is a good spot, but any place will do as long as he can see you and know that you're nearby. Eighteen months is too young for him to be shut off in an upstairs playroom or confined behind a closed door.

Chat with him when you can, but let him understand that you have your work to do, and he has his. Thus you'll be able to work with your mind more at ease, while son or daughter is taking another step along the path of self-reliance. When the weather is nice, let him play outdoors in an enclosed yard.

It's equally important to have regular periods each day when he's free to roam about the house, under somebody's watchful eye. Set certain times for his exploring to eliminate his expecting you to drop your work every few minutes to entertain him.

RESISTANCE TO NAPS, BEDTIME Resistance to sleep may be stronger than ever now. And you must be just as firm as you were when your youngster first started objecting to taking his nap or settling down for the night. If he screams and yells, let him. He can't keep it up indefinitely, and as soon as he realizes it's not going to get him out of the nap or bedtime, he'll quiet down. Once you give in to him, you'll have afternoon and nightly problems on your hands.

If he has a nightmare and cries out, make sure he's all right and comfort him, but insist he go back to sleep. It's a mistake to feed him or take him to bed with you.

TIME TO TEACH ORDERLINESS The first step is to be orderly yourself, for a child at this age sees everything and is as imitative as a monkey. If you haven't before, you should by now have a regular place for all your youngster's possessions, and be methodical in putting them back after they're used. Set a good example early.

Clothes: Low hooks and hangers in your child's bedroom and in the family coat closet are easily accessible. At first, he'll merely run and get what's needed, but when your little runabout is about 2 years old, teach him to hang up his clothes. If he sees you doing it, he'll get the idea in no time.

Toys: From his first birthday on, your child has needed his own room or corner with shelves or a cupboard for his toys. Begin at 18 months to put things away as he's through playing with them, and call his attention to what you're doing. He'll soon want to help a little. Show him where to put his toys and make a game of "running the cars into the garage," "putting Dolly to bed," and so forth. If he still needs assistance around the ages of 4 and 5, help him sociably.

LAPSES IN LEARNING Your youngster is now in the full swing of one of his most active periods of growth and learning. At a year, he was a baby. By the time he's reached 2, he'll be running everywhere, talking, feeding himself, making some moves toward dressing himself, helping to look after his belongings, and on the way toward being toilet-trained. In a year's time, he changes from a baby to a child.

With so many things for him to learn, it will be helpful to stop and look at the way youngsters this age manage. There is a time when your child is ready to take on easily and quickly each new habit, skill, or accomplishment. It's the time when his nervous system and muscular development have caught up with each other, and he's bursting to try the new powers laid open to him. When he reaches for the spoon, it's his sign that he's ready to begin feeding himself.

Thus it is with all the skills and activities, which will be opening up gradually to your child in years to come. It's your job to catch the signals when he gives them. As you follow his development, you'll get more and more adept in interpreting them, and in helping develop the skill or ability for which he's ready at that time. Don't urge or rush him into an activity for which he isn't ready. But when he gives the go-ahead signal, be sure to go ahead with him.

However, remember this. After your child has mastered a skill, there will be periods when it seems as though he has forgotten everything he has learned. Parents have been up against this since time immemorial, but haven't known what it meant. They probably thought their youngster was being deliberately naughty because he had already shown that he understood what was wanted of him.

Lapses are just as much a sign of development as are increases in skill. To mothers and fathers, this often looks like intentional disobedience and as a result, countless home battles have been waged.

What else is happening? Normally around 9 months of age, he begins picking up tiny bits of food and eating them with his fingers. Part of his food is then given in small pieces that he can pick up and eat with his fingers. After he's learned to carry the spoon to his mouth, he begins throwing and splattering the food around. (That's something else that has been misunderstood by the adults. He's fascinated by a newly found skill.)

After a youngster gets to be about 3 years old, new experiences and impressions are coming so thick and fast that often he forgets to eat at all for a time, he's so busy telling you about them. But in time, he'll learn to talk and eat at the same time.

Ahead of you is a long, patience-taxing period of letting your child learn to dress himself. You stand by, though it kills

Once your little hurler masters the utensils, mealtime will be more appetizing for everyone.

you, letting him feel out buttons and ties that are problems for small, awkward fingers. And then about the time he gets so that he can do it pretty well, he'll lose all interest and dawdle till you'll be distracted. But that's all part of the growing-up process. Don't worry, this will disappear in time.

Every child has an urge to exercise a newly developing function, and once he has mastered it with a fair degree of efficiency, he grows indifferent. A new type of learning will then attract his attention and use up his energies. If you understand and recognize this fact, many storms and temper tantrums will be avoided. When his developing skills seem to be going backward, look for the rapid unfolding of other aspects of behavior.

The same laws govern learning later on in sports, the arts, and all kinds of things. As each stage of development appears, you as a parent should provide the opportunity for exercising these powers. During the first 18 months, motor development is the most outstanding. Give him a chance to climb and use his arms and legs. As speech develops during the last part of the second year, take time to talk and read to your child.

Expect that once a new thing has been mastered, something else will come along to claim your child's interest. Don't be disappointed if he drops the first skill. Soon he'll develop to the point where he can co-ordinate the new habit with the old, and the old skill or habit is there again, good as ever.

Once you understand the reason back of the training lapses, which are bound to come, it's easy to see why calmness and patience are better parental methods than crossness and punishment.

"TELL ME A STORY" Any time now the story hour may begin. The year-and-a-half-old child won't understand much of a story but loves to look at the pictures. The last 15 minutes before bedtime, when he's all ready to be popped between the covers, can be spent in looking at the pictures and telling what the objects are. The period can be varied with songs, either on the piano or record-player. The story and music hour will provide a precious custom both to you and your child.

TIME FOR A TOOTHBRUSH If you haven't already started to teach your youngster to brush his teeth, now's the time to do it. Children love to mimic their parents and take great delight in brushing their teeth when Mommy or Daddy are brushing. Toothpaste makes it even more fun!

You'll have to help him so that a reasonable job of brushing gets done. And don't be surprised if he gets his toothbrush and scrubs the sink, floor, or wall with it. He may even end up throwing it in the potty. In spite of all this, start him in the habit of brushing after every meal.

GOOD DENTAL HYGIENE A combination of factors contributes to good teeth or lack of tooth decay. Heredity plays a part. If you or your husband have poor teeth, the chances are great your child will also have poor teeth.

Your diet before and during pregnancy is extremely important for the proper formation of your baby's teeth. A wholesome diet during infancy and childhood is also essential if your child is going to have good strong teeth.

Tooth decay is caused by the action of bacteria in the mouth upon the carbohydrate foods that adhere to the teeth surfaces or get stuck in the crevices between the teeth. An acid is produced that eventually destroys the enamel of the tooth and, as a result, a cavity is formed.

Between-meal snacks such as candy, cake, pie, ice cream, chewing gum, and cookies constantly bathe the teeth with sugars and cause decay. These foods do contribute needed calories to the diet, but if you occasionally let your child have sweets, be sure his teeth are promptly and properly brushed.

Brushing after each meal or after food has been eaten is important, but if there are times when it is impossible, have him rinse his mouth with clear water. Although it's not as good as brushing, it will help remove some of the food particles.

The introduction of a proper amount of fluoride into the community drinking water also helps prevent tooth decay. If your community doesn't have this public-health measure, ask your dentist about painting fluoride on your child's teeth. Fluoride drops and tablets are also available in a prescription from either your doctor or dentist.

TOILET TRAINING There are no hard and fast rules governing toilet training. You may set your baby on the potty as soon as you wish or postpone this step for as long as you desire. There are no adverse effects from either method. Let your own good judgment and preference be your guide when toilet training.

Toilet training requires that a youngster be old enough to learn the specific procedure and sufficiently developed physically to carry out the procedure.

Some mothers boast that their child was trained to have his bowel movement in the potty by the time he was 1 year old. Actually, this means that the baby had a fairly regular bowel movement, and the *mother* was trained to catch it in the potty.

Bowel training usually precedes urine training. If your child's movement usually comes right after breakfast, start placing him on his toilet chair when he's about 18 months old. Don't keep him there long. Suggest that he tell you the next day when he's ready. When you're changing soiled diapers, tell Baby how grown-up it is to be clean and encourage him to come and tell you beforehand the next time he wants to use the potty.

His own small potty chair is probably more reassuring to him than a seat that fits on the toilet. He's close to the floor and won't be afraid he'll fall off, and he can sit down on it without your help.

SIGNS OF READINESS FOR URINE TRAINING Sometime during the next six months, there will probably be several signs that indicate that your child is ready for urine training. He may come to you *after* he has wet pants and ask to have his diaper changed. His timing may be a little off, but it shows

While little girls are fascinated by flowers and nature, fathers find fascination in their little girls.

he is associating a word with the act. It also shows that he is beginning to realize he should have voided in the toilet, and probably indicates that he is beginning to prefer his pants dry. He may hold himself or tug at his diaper when he has to urinate.

And, during the next three months, he may begin staying dry for as long as two hours at a time. When he has reached this stage in the development of his bladder, take him to the bathroom at two-hour intervals, before and after his nap and meals. Don't worry if he isn't able to stay dry as long as two hours. Many babies, especially boys, may have to urinate much oftener, even at 2 years of age.

Even after remaining dry for two or three hours, he still

may lack the muscular control to hold his urine even a second longer, once his bladder is full. It takes time for him to develop this control. And, he must learn how to let you know when he has to go. Bladder training, like bowel training, is a product of both physical and mental development. It can't be expected all at once.

And don't compare your baby's progress in this respect with that of other babies. It may be a long time before he tells you when he has to go to the toilet, and longer still before he's absolutely perfect. It's the mother who demands immediate and perfect results who finds this phase of learning a source of worry.

Psychologists believe that punishments, shaming, or other unpleasant associations with toilet training have an unwholesome effect upon your child. He'll learn just as quickly if he's praised as if he's punished and harangued. Studies also show that training goes more smoothly at two years than earlier. Years from now it will make little difference how long it took, but a great deal whether or not it was taught with love and patience.

KEEP TRAINING CASUAL The training procedure is simple. Put him on the potty when he gets up in the morning, before and after nap and meals, and after he's been dry a couple of hours. He'll soon get the idea that the potty is the proper place to urinate.

Go easy on the *ecstatic* praise. This is a very matter-of-fact function. If you make too much fuss over this accomplishment, your child will begin to wonder why it's so important and will place too much emphasis on it. If he has an accident or doesn't perform the way you want him to, and you lose your patience, he'll begin to realize that he can use this natural function as a tool.

Under no circumstances should you strap your child to the potty or force him to stay on it. When he says he's through, whether or not he's done anything, respect his wishes and let him get off the potty.

Nothing you can do can force him to urinate or defecate, so don't try. If he should have an accident almost immediately, show no signs of concern. Clean him up without comment or with a quiet suggestion that next time he use the potty.

Whether digging clams or building sand castles, the proper equipment is an absolute necessity.

TRAINING PANTS When he begins to stay dry for two-hour periods, substitute training pants for diapers. This change is often very effective. Some authorities think it is because the baby has been accustomed to wetting his diapers, whereas the training pants represent a step forward in his growth.

THERE'LL BE ACCIDENTS Accidents will occur even after he's reasonably well trained. Stress or excitement may cause an accident. In cold weather, your child may wet more than in warm, because there's less evaporation through skin pores. Take these things into consideration and make allowances.

Your response to those accidents is important. Anger, displeasure, spanking, and threatening are completely out of place. Simply mention that it's too bad, and suggest he head for the bathroom sooner next time.

My horse is faster than your horse because

IF TOILET TRAINING BREAKS DOWN Once your child is well-trained, he *may* fall back into his baby habits because of new experiences, changes in times of bowel movements, change in sleeping habits, illness.

This behavior may embarrass you, and your impulse may be to bear down on punishments or keep him on the toilet for longer periods of time. As a result, many youngsters develop an aversion to the toilet itself and the whole idea of training.

They may go to fantastic lengths to keep from eliminating when on the toilet, only to do so immediately when allowed to get off. He may even hold a stool for days. That is because the situation has been turned into a battle of wills, and Baby is asserting his independence by refusing to go to the toilet.

Sometimes this behavior is not defiance on his part, but inability to release the muscles of the bowel when he should. He's learning how to control his rectal muscles, but he doesn't know when to let go. Sitting on the seat intensifies the contraction. When he gets up, the muscle contraction is relaxed.

he gets go-power from eating my breakfast cereal.

It may help if you grunt so he'll imitate you and relax his muscles. Whether it's independence or a muscle contraction, don't scold or shame him for this withholding behavior.

Keep calm and unperturbed if your child suddenly becomes balky or unconcerned about when and where he urinates and has his bowel movements. It's only a passing phase, unless you let it turn into a problem.

If he actively resists sitting on the toilet, drop the matter. Don't make him try to conform to the times you select, but observe his own natural timing instead. Rather than have toilet training become an issue, forget about it altogether for a few weeks. Clean panties and a diploma from the school of toilet training aren't as important as a happy, well-adjusted child.

"BOOSTER" SHOTS The first booster series of the D.P.T. immunizations should be given at or have been given by the time your child reaches 18 months. Your doctor will tell you what schedule he prefers and will give shots accordingly.

This is what
boys are made of!

Boys are little men comprised of complex qualities
like love, learning, laughter, and most of all, life!

Boys find excitement in the simplest things; balloons, leaves, snowballs and soaring kites. Boys are as changeable and refreshing as the seasons themselves.

Boys are brave. They pick up worms, hold fish, catch bugs and mice, and try to make pets of them. A boy's room can be like a small private zoo.

Boys are mechanical. They delight in tearing something apart to see what makes it work. In the process of re-assembling the thing, there are always a few spare parts.

Boys believe that it is better to give than to receive. They'll round up the whole neighborhood to ride their favorite horse, Daddy. Then, they offer cookies and milk to everyone.

Your child from two to six years

The age period from two to six
years is one of the most entertaining
and intriguing periods of life.
Your child is no longer a baby.
He is an individual anxiously
seeking experience and adventure.
He will be going everywhere
and getting into everything.
Enjoy him now for today will soon
be tomorrow's memories.

16

Your child from two to three years

If you've followed the suggestions in Section 2, the following
will be a pretty accurate picture of your youngster at 2 years.
Physically he's: . . . about 34 inches in height. . . . 24 to
32 pounds in weight. If a tall, large-boned child, he'll weigh
more—less if short or of slender body build. . . . the proud
possessor of from 16 to 20 teeth. . . . rosy, sturdy, running
and playing tirelessly. Mentally, he: . . . is happy and cheerful. . . . says many words and may make a few sentences.
. . . understands much that's said to him, and sees and is
interested in everything in the world about him.

And he also: . . . should be feeding himself. . . . goes to
bed cheerfully most of the time. May raise an occasional pro-
test. . . . plays happily by himself, indoors and out. . . .
may be bowel-trained; may have daytime bladder control, and
as he approaches 3, may stay dry all night. . . . accepts the
daily routine of bathing, dressing, brushing hair and teeth.
. . . knows where objects belong and can help to put them
there. . . . obeys simple directions.

The foundations for all the fundamental habits—those
things which a child should perform instinctively, without
thought and without conflict—have been laid. Thus his energies are released for activities which will foster his native abilities and capacities.

From now on, your child's mind will develop at a pace that
will delight you. Don't force him, but give him the materials

that will aid its development at the right time.

KEEP HIS FOODS EASY TO MANAGE In preparing foods for your child from 2 to 6 years old, continue to make them as easy to handle as possible, and as appetizing as you can. A child of 2 with sufficient teeth may eat raw vegetables and like them this way.

Wash carrots, lettuce, celery, turnips, cabbage, rutabagas, and cauliflower. Remove any tough spots or woody leaves or fibers, and cut into attractive sticks or break into leaves and flowers. Soak them in cold water until very crisp, then serve as one vegetable at mealtime.

Preschoolers gobble up tiny sandwiches of whole-wheat bread, buttered (cut a regular-size piece of bread into quarters), and filled with bits of raw vegetable or fruit. Any you have on hand may be used this way—apple, carrot, tomato, lettuce, cabbage, and celery.

Prepare the vegetables or fruits as above, and cut into thin slices or easily managed bites. Such sandwiches should be passed only after your child has eaten a fair amount of his meal, for the preschooler will fill up on bread at the expense of other foods if you let him have his way.

Make cream soups thick enough so they won't slip from the spoon. Cut or chop such foods as tomatoes and spinach to make them easy to manage.

Cereals and starchy desserts such as cornstarch, tapioca, and rice puddings shouldn't be made too thick. Children like these dishes best when they're made with about one-half the amount of cereal or starch called for in adult recipes.

In seasonings, use pepper and spices lightly, if at all. Use one-half the amount of salt you would for adults and limit the amount of sugar added.

Make meat, liver, and fish loaves very moist with plenty of milk and several eggs.

To get the iron he requires, offer a child an egg a day, plus meat at each of the other two meals. Vegetables and fruits should also be offered at the other two meals. At this age, he may not be interested in a variety of foods each meal or day, and may eat less of a food than you think he should, but remember, it's up to you to place a balanced diet before him, and then it's up to him to decide just how much of it he'll eat.

The average child will drink around a pint of milk a day. It's not necessary that all this be drunk as a beverage; part of the quantity may be used in cooking.

Vitamins A, D, and C should be continued as your doctor directs.

It's difficult for most children this age to go from their noon meal to the evening meal without a little something to eat at midafternoon. If your youngster does want a snack, make it a desirable food. Dairy products—milk, cheese, cottage cheese —make excellent snacks. A meat patty or slice of luncheon meat increases their protein intake. Fruit is a favorite. Skip ice cream, cake, or other sweets as these can spoil appetites for supper.

Most two-year-olds can generally eat the food prepared for the entire family. Few mothers have the time to prepare a special meal for a child, in addition to fixing dinner for the rest of the family. Of course, if the evening meal is going to be late, then you'll want to plan an earlier meal for your hungry youngster. This will eliminate the possibility of unpleasant irritability.

At this age, a child especially enjoys eating with the rest of the family. His manners won't be perfect, and he'll still be a bit messy, but he'll welcome being an active part of the family circle. When he's through, let him get down. Otherwise, he's likely to play with his food, upset his milk, or drop silverware, while you're finishing dinner. Never force him to stay at the table until he's eaten the amount and variety of food which *you* think he should have. He'll probably eat fine at the next meal.

KEEP HIM ON SCHEDULE The routine remains the same as to mealtimes, nap, and bedtime. Observe these as faithfully as you did when your child was an infant (even though he may occasionally object), and he'll continue to be happy, healthy, and for the most part, well-behaved.

It's a common weakness for parents to relax the routine as the infant becomes the toddler. And right there countless behavior difficulties get a start. Many of them can be avoided if you continue to see that your youngster eats the right things at the right time, and goes to bed at his bedtime. If you have held to regular times for these daily events so far, it will be easy to continue. Both you and your child will have learned the habit of regularity.

His day may begin at 6, 7, or 8 A.M., and end at 6, 7, or 8 P.M., according to your convenience and his sleep requirements. By all means arrange it so that Dad can have as much time as possible with his youngster. But whatever your child's routine is, stick to it as closely as possible.

PROVIDE PLAYMATES From 2 years on, your child needs contact with other youngsters if he doesn't already have it. This is as essential to wholesome development as are food and sleep, and you must provide it in some way. If there are no children in the neighborhood, arrange frequent visits with friends who have children the same age. The ideal social contact for your youngster is in a good nursery school, if there is one in your community.

Social development is a learning process and, like any other, unfolds gradually. Your 2-year-old is still largely nonsocial. Most of the time he'll play by himself, and won't concern himself with the children around him unless they interfere

Well, if we play like I'm a boy, will you
let me play soldiers and Indians with you?

with him in some way. Yet he needs the chance to become accustomed to children his own age.

Fairly soon, you'll find him stopping to watch the others, and he'll do this more and more frequently. Next, he includes one or more other youngsters in his play. His first advances are apt to be physical—pushing, pulling, or hitting. He uses playmates as he does the rest of his environment, and with no more ill will. He must learn from sad experience—for his victim will hit back—not to trespass upon the rights of others.

Presently he's playing with another child in co-operative enterprise. Gradually the group enlarges, and by the time he's 3, your little fellow will probably be a happy member of a neighborhood "gang" of small children and be having the time of his life.

It's an advantage for him to play with both older and younger children. In this manner, he'll learn to both lead and to follow.

In your child's relations with other children, interfere just as little as possible once you have provided suitable playmates. Let him attack his problem of social learning in his own way, pick his own chums, and form his own groups.

SELF-RELIANCE THE KEYNOTE One of the principal goals of this period is to develop your child's self-reliance. He has already learned to feed himself. In the same way, he'll want to perform from time to time the other operations of his daily routine. He'll try to lace his shoes, put on his stockings, although there'll be no doubt that he'll do a better job of taking them off.

At first, these efforts are futile and of short duration. Wait patiently. The attempt will grow more effective, and soon, with a little help, your child can really manage. Each accomplishment of this sort is a step forward in his development. You can't make better use of your time than to stand by while his awkward, little fingers work out the problem.

"PUSHING" IS A MISTAKE Many parents are eager to "push" their children, to teach them to do things much earlier than they are actually capable of doing them. These parents are constantly struggling to get their child to accomplish things faster than their neighbor's child.

For some reason, it's important that their little one be eating solids first, drinking from a cup first, walking first, and on through a whole list of accomplishments.

Walking, talking, eating without help, and learning other physical tasks are accomplished at an optimum age, although with a bit of effort and work on your part, your youngster might do these things a few months earlier.

But why bother? The playmate who learns at his own speed or at the normal rate of development is just as capable by the time he reaches kindergarten as the child who's been pushed by overambitious parents.

Each stage in growing up has its special delights. As parents, relax and enjoy your children. Let babies be babies, and toddlers be toddlers. You'll all be much happier.

HE LEARNS TO DRESS HIMSELF Learning to dress himself is a long process. It must be taken gradually, or your runabout will tire of it. Undressing himself is much easier and should come first. It may become something of a nuisance, because this is the age when children like to undress themselves when you'd rather they stay dressed.

It's not uncommon for a 2-year-old to take his shoes and socks off, or take his pants off and run around the house with nothing on. Or, he'll want to take off one set of clothes and try to put on another outfit. Patience!

He's ready to begin dressing himself when he starts to identify the parts of his clothing and to know where they go. At first, though, he's able to do little more than get his clothes out of a drawer or closet and put them away; not always correctly but he's trying.

Your role in this first stage is to provide clothing he can manage and to stimulate his interest in dressing himself. Keep his attention on the job in hand, prevent distractions and play, and direct him in the simplest parts of the routine. Let him think he's doing a great deal himself, even though you do practically everything. If kept busy, he'll feel he has accomplished a big and important job.

When he develops an interest in dressing himself, instruct and assist only when necessary. This period requires patience, for you are able to get him in and out of his clothes faster than he can. Only with actual practice can he advance in skill and the desire to handle the matter himself. He'll probably insist "me do it" anyway!

As he becomes fairly adept in dressing himself, he loses interest. By this time, he does it with comparative ease. Your job now is to keep him on the job and maintain order, without giving him more than casual attention.

If you follow these directions, your child will be able to dress himself fairly well by the time he's 4, except for difficult fastenings. He can't be expected to manage things like back buttons before he nears 5.

HE'LL ENJOY WASHING HIMSELF—AT FIRST It's easier to teach small children to wash than to dress themselves, for they love to play in water. Transfer his delight from mere dabbling in water to getting his face and hands clean. Supervision of the "washing-up hour" will be necessary until he's about 4.

Set up washing arrangements he can use without help. Pro-

A pair of Daddy's sneakers, some sand, and a channel. Add some water. And, we've got a moat.

vide a box or steps in the bathroom on which he can climb up to the lavatory. Place a mirror where he can see himself as he cleans up, and have low hooks, or rods which he can reach for his washcloth and towel. When he's a little older, keep his comb, brush, and toothbrush on a low shelf. Right now, he's too young to resist scrubbing the floor with his toothbrush or combing the dog with his comb.

Your emphasis will be upon his finishing the job speedily and efficiently. Let him have water now and then to play in and emphasize that washing-up times are business.

Your standard of cleanliness must not be too high at first— polish him off at bathtime. So far as his own efforts are concerned independence is more important than removing all high-water marks.

ALLOW TIME FOR DAWDLING A big problem for you will be how to handle your youngster when he begins to dawdle.

It's most exasperating when he slows up on things he has learned to do so well himself, such as dressing and feeding. Now that he has mastered the task, he's no longer interested in it, and has his mind on other things.

You can help him by allowing plenty of time for him to carry out the job. Keep his attention on what he's doing by gently placing his shoe in front of his foot. He'll resent your help at this stage, and may hurry through more quickly in order to do it by himself. If he doesn't and time is important you may have to go ahead and force him to get going or dress him yourself.

PICKING UP NAUGHTY WORDS Between 2½ and 3, your child may begin to pick up "dirty" words, swear words, and expressions from the other children. To him they are very funny; to you they are just plain embarrassing. Youngsters at this age are just now learning that they, as adults, can be worldly and just a little bad. If you show your child he's shocked you, chances are he'll be delighted with what he's done.

Don't threaten him, or he'll build up his vocabulary of such words even more. At first, just ignore his speech while diverting his attention to something else. If he persists in using them, tell him in a matter-of-fact way that you don't like to hear them, other people don't like to hear them, and that you don't want him to use them any more.

DISLIKES INTERFERENCE When your youngster is between 2½ and 3, he usually can get along satisfactory with one parent, but flies into a rage when the other tries to interfere. At this age, when he's learning to do things for himself, he's sensitive about being bossed. Instead of doing what he's told, he'll try to do the bossing.

Don't take your child's abuse seriously, and avoid interfering in situations where the other parent is assisting him. He'll soon come to you for anything he wants, and show that he still loves you very much.

HE'LL EVEN BOSS YOU Balkiness and contrariness reach

You'll find him exasperatingly slow, but look how proud he is when he finally completes the task.

new heights and take on new forms during this stage. Besides contradicting you, he'll probably even contradict himself. He can't seem to make up his mind, and once he does, he'll very likely want to change it again. He'll insist on doing things just as he has always done without any interference from you.

It's your job to be very understanding during this difficult, contrary stage. Inside him, he's trying to fight two battles at once—deciding things for himself and resisting pressure from you.

Some children not only boss but also try to hit and bite their parents. Handle this situation firmly and gently and let him know that you won't stand for hitting and biting. It's important for you to keep your self-control. Hitting or biting back brings you down to his age level and this will not solve the problem.

PLAY IS PART OF LEARNING One of the most important ways in which your child is educated is through his play. If adequately directed, it leads to the formation of habits of concentration, discrimination in choice of activities, and eventually to the development of individual interests and abilities in your child.

You help his development in many ways when you furnish an adequate place for him to play, indoors and out, and a good choice of toys and play materials. His outdoor play yard should be fenced in until he is 3, if you can possibly arrange it, for he can't be expected to stay within bounds much before that age, and will constantly be running or wandering away if he has the chance. He should always have access to a house door so he can come inside whenever he wants. If you can't have a fence, set certain boundaries and have someone there to see that he stays within them.

Have his play yard where you can see what's going on by glancing out of the kitchen or dining-room windows. You can keep a check on things without interrupting your work. In planning his play yard, leave plenty of space for running and vigorous play, and include something your youngster can climb on. Children at this age are little monkeys. You'll be picking yours down off the top of the piano—every ladder he sees will be an invitation and a challenge to see how high he can climb.

This desire for activity should be encouraged, not discouraged. Your youngster should not climb on your furniture, so provide things of his own that won't break or tip over. Very small children like to climb a plank supported by low boxes or on low ladders, and swing by their hands from the low bars of climbing equipment. Firmly piled logs over which your tot can scramble will entertain him endlessly.

A good general rule is to furnish the best equipment you can, then stay out of the picture except to keep him from actual harm. Allow him to choose his activities and to drop them when he gets tired or bored. In this way, he has a chance to pursue and develop his own individual interests.

Don't hesitate, however, to use your own good judgment in this the same as in other matters. There may be situations where a little help or a suggestion from you would enable your youngster to get more value from what he's doing. If that's the case, give it, but don't dominate his play. If he does well, commend him, but don't overdo praise.

Your 2-year-old goes quickly from one object to another without plan. Let him alone, and by the time he's 4, he'll be making intelligent selections of play materials, spending much time on one activity, and going from one play sequence logically into another.

SHOULD PICK UP HIS TOYS Tidying up after play is part of your youngster's education, too. He should help at 2, even though he puts away only one toy. Gradually he can take care of more and more. If your 3-year-old picks up his toys at the end of a play period and puts each back in its proper place, you can be assured that he's doing well enough for a child this age.

Young children get very intent in their play—the beginning of the habit of concentration. This is a desirable trait which should not be broken. Allow your child 5 or 10 minutes in which to conclude whatever he's doing.

Taking things apart is as much a part of play to the 2-year-old as putting them together. Tearing down is as much fun as building. Give your youngster plenty of toys that he can take apart, and teach him to respect the others. Keep them in his own play areas, and let your small experimenter carry on such researches as occur to him. (Within limits, of course, of his own personal safety and that of his playmates.)

PLAY EQUIPMENT AND MATERIAL FOR CHILD TWO TO THREE YEARS OLD These develop and teach control of the large muscles:

Chair swing
Board swing
Rocking chair
Board to walk on
Tricycle
Slide
Large wagon
Sled

Broom
Snow shovel
Garden tools
Large floor blocks
Balls of all sizes
Heavy train
Heavy truck
Heavy automobile

Develop large muscles and senses:

Sandbox
Pans

Shovel and similar
toys

These will help develop muscles and teach co-operative play:

Balls of all sizes

Materials that encourage self-expression and skill:

Block nest
Hammer and nails of
different sizes
Large dominoes
Crayons and paper
Building blocks in brick
shapes

Blunt scissors and cutting
paper
Blackboard and chalk
Easel and water colors
Beads to string
Color cubes
Modeling clay

These stimulate imitative play and develop imagination:

Picture books
Telephone
Dolls and animals
Outdoor tools
Household utensils
Small table and chairs

Doll furniture
Laundry equipment
Unbreakable or cloth doll to
dress
Toy dishes

DISCIPLINING THE RUNABOUT If you've established a good, daily routine, discipline won't be much of a problem. Because your child doesn't get overly hungry or tired, he's better natured and less likely to have temper tantrums. When discipline is necessary, be firm. Anger and abruptness don't belong here.

It's extremely important that parents see eye to eye on matters of discipline and what the children can and cannot do. Nothing is more frustrating to a child than to have one parent give permission to do something and the other parent forbid it. At this age, a child will turn from the disciplining parent to the other parent for sympathy or approval of what he has done. It's, therefore, essential that the mother be able to turn to the father for reinforcement.

Being very inexperienced, your youngster is bound to err at times. Situations are sure to arise in which you'll have to divert him from unacceptable ways of doing things. And the brighter and livelier he is (the way you want him), the bigger handful he's going to be. Keep in mind that what you're after is not to get even for any annoyance he may cause, but to help him learn ways of doing things that are acceptable to society.

Various ways are acceptable in teaching your child how he should act in a certain situation. Always keep the same constructive attitude. Attempt to make him understand that you require him to do a certain thing because it is the right and proper thing to do—not just because you feel he should do it.

Whenever disciplining a child, approach him with the attitude that you expect him to do what you tell him. If he fails, the best thing is to mete out the consequences according to the greatness of the act and how well he understood what he did. Any consequence should be logical, arising naturally out of the child's own conduct. Administer only a well-thought-out consequence—if it fails to accomplish what you're after, it has lost all merit. If you handle your child in a friendly way, he'll want to do the right thing.

Suppose he refuses to follow your directions? Removal from the family or play group has proved ample punishment in countless cases. If he usually gets along well with you, he'll feel just as unhappy as you do after he's done something wrong. Jumping on a child who is already sorry, sometimes reverses his feelings and makes him argue.

DEVELOP YOUR CHILD'S INTEREST IN MUSIC AND BOOKS Giving your baby the best possible start from the standpoint of health and habits has been your main preoccupation for the first year or two of his life.

But now comes the time for which you've been waiting, perhaps impatiently. You can introduce him to the world of books, music, and art, and a thousand other things which give pleasure and meaning to life.

Of course, your 2-year-old won't be able to appreciate Shakespeare and Rembrandt right off the bat, any more than he can play football. But he can and will enjoy stories, music, and pictures which are appropriate to his particular stage of growth.

If you love these things yourself, the story or music hour will probably prove to be the happiest time of the day for both of you, since there's no pleasure more keen than sharing things with those we love.

Moreover, it's one of the most pleasant times of companionship. Your little fellow is bathed and clean and all ready for bed. In slippers and bathrobe, he snuggles against you while the two of you pore over books or listen to the music.

A 2-year-old's attention span is very short. It's time to stop reading or listening to the music as soon as he becomes restless and loses interest. He'll be 2½ or 3 before he shows any prolonged interests in reading or listening to music. By then, he'll also be a real procastinator and will do everything he can to stall his inevitable bedtime. To avoid this, set a definite amount of time for reading and listening, and stick to it as closely as possible.

Don't hurry him along too fast in the realm of books and music. Always remember that he has his own way of learning and his own time for doing it.

Perhaps when you were young, *Alice in Wonderland* was a high spot in your life, and you couldn't wait until your child grew old enough to live it as you did. However, if you introduce it into your child's life now when he may not be ready for it, he may refuse to have anything to do with it.

A better way is to provide a plentiful supply of enjoyable books and stories for each stage of development and let your youngster choose the ones which attract him at that time. How preschoolers react to books at different ages and how to interest them in books was told most interestingly by Louise Bechtel in *The Horn Book Magazine*. Through the courtesy of The Horn Book, Inc., the following excerpts are reprinted:

FIRST EXPERIENCE WITH BOOKS "In my little bookroom at home, the majority of children 'before 5,' if left alone, simply slam over the pages of one book after another. They shout or sing if some single picture catches the eye. They look up away from the books for something active to happen in the room. Suppose I gather them on the sofa and read, showing them the picture slowly: then the brighter ones respond, but half still squirm and shout in irrepressible spirits about nothing at all. But if I have found a very good story and tell it, stopping frequently with a question or a chance for imitation, the audience is absorbed. That is the story they want again next time. Meanwhile, of course, an unusual child may have crept off alone with a book she loves, to apply her more mature powers of eye and mind, murmuring her own tale to herself as she fingers the lines of the pictures lovingly.

If I'm good, Daddy promised to read me
all about the horse and the little gray goat.

Even your one-finger perform-
ance will be enchanting music
to your child's ears.

"Only the home can have the greatest pleasure of discovering books. Mothers *could* have the same fun the school has,
with experiments in storytelling. But parents are still apt to
push small children too fast in language process and picture
appreciation.

"The first 'book' is a recognition book of simple objects.
Babies of 2 love to pull apart the big color advertisements in
a magazine. Years ago they were given the Steichens' *First
and Second Picture Books,* which still are popular. The objects
portrayed should be those really familiar to a baby, for this
book is merely a tool for talking. At this age of 2, most words
are sound, not meaning; most nonsense verse and songs are
not understood in the adult sense, yet can be a very soothing
influence, or a source of laughter.

"Then come the very first stories, at 2 and 3 years old.
No one who has not worked daily with children will believe
how simple they should be. To say that 200 words is long
enough puts it too easily. The point is, much more, the utter
simplicity of word and content. In these first experiments in
attention, as opposed to songs and nonsense verse, there
should be a delicate balance of reality—something that could
happen to you—and of nonsense and action.

"At 3 and 4 years old, attention has grown in power, and
we meet more sharply the problem of style. The body which
has been developing an exciting lot of varied responses, the
mind which has heard songs and poetry, quickly feel the wet
blanket of dull prose. Then there is the matter of the 'come-

back,' the question or pause for answer or imitation that lets the child actively enter the story.

"We know how the really good story has to be told over and over—how it is changed with the book upside down. It ought to be very good!

"Then, toward 5, horizons have widened; one can sit more quietly; one can listen longer. We have gathered a few criteria for style for these years; rhythm, repetition, brevity, sensory range, 'comeback.' As to content, we all agree on those elements of 'just like me' of humor, the love of bump and fall and grimace that mark this primitive age, and we are apt to differ only on the fantastic.

"Only Mother's experiments unlock attention and imaginative response. But she must realize that these early steps are important—that it does count enormously to tell stories, each year a bit longer; to read poems, each year with more variety; to have the child treasure lovely books. With a little investigation, she will soon see how one writer speaks of 'here and now' very dully, and another so well that it is the beginning of literature.

"Mother or teacher, she will be amused at discovering the stories a child likes, those he does not, and why. As the child's sensitiveness and appreciation grow, she will know that the audience for good books has a new recruit."

MUSIC APPRECIATION BEGINS Quite as gradual will be the growth of your youngster's response to music. There are many classical and semiclassical pieces, tuneful and rhythmical ones, which delight quite small children. There's descriptive music, such as "Hunt in the Black Forest" and "In a Clock Store." Countless nursery songs are readily available. Children especially like records such as "Bozo at the Circus" and "Yogi Bear and Boo-Boo." Older children will enjoy recordings such as "Winnie The Pooh and Christopher Robin."

A record-player and a selection of records he can enjoy is an invaluable aid in developing your child's love for music. He can soon be taught to run the machine himself, and can put on the records he wants to hear. Prepare yourself to hear him play his current favorite dozens of times in a row, for that's the way he likes to do it. Even though the constant repetition of a tune may seem almost unbearable to you at times, that's the way he'll learn to carry a tune and get pleasure from music.

Many children's records are play stories that are educational. They also keep a child busy when his mother is too busy to read to her youngster, but they should never completely take the place of reading.

He'll be especially pleased if you sing and play to him yourself. If you can do no more than pick out a melody with one finger, here's an audience that will prefer your playing to Serkin's.

Most children can't carry a tune much before the third or fourth year. But at any time you may find your youngster joining in when you sing a simple song, or when he hears one on the record-player. At first he may repeat only parts of song in a monotone, and at his own rate. Let him improve at his own speed. The ability to carry a tune and to keep time develops slowly in most youngsters, and then it's largely the result of interest, imitation, and practice.

Your youngster will also learn to like doing things to rhythmic music. For this purpose, the tune should be easily recognized, the best accentuated, and the selections short. Let him interpret this music in his own way—running, jumping, trotting, or galloping like a horse, "flying," "swimming," or "skating."

Simple instruments help keep up the interest in rhythm—drum, tom-tom, cymbals, triangle, bells, and tambourine. One or several may be acquired to help your youngster express what the music makes him feel. He'll like trying different instruments.

Whether he has any musical ability or not, and whether or not he does anything with music in later years, he can get infinite pleasure from it if it has been presented to him as a pleasurable experience in childhood.

TODDLERS AND TELEVISION Television can be an excellent teaching medium for the preschooler. It's your job to select the programs which your child is to view. There are several programs designed especially for preschool viewers which are both educational and entertaining. However, you should check to make sure that even the "children's programs" are suitable for young minds. Letting your child watch anything and everything is definitely a mistake.

BEHAVIOR AT THE DOCTOR'S OFFICE Up until at least
3½, but especially between the ages of 18 months and 2½
years, children are usually a problem in the doctor's office.
They're still fearful of strange situations and strangers, and
the doctor falls into the category of stranger as far as the
child is concerned. They're also strong enough at this age to
be difficult to handle, and their voices are loud enough to be
heard all over the office.

A doctor used to dealing with children isn't disturbed by
this behavior because he expects it; most all children behave
this way. It's embarrassing to you, but this acting up is not
sufficient reason to refuse to take the child to the doctor's
office.

Avoid getting upset if the doctor handles your child quite
firmly. The examination is necessary, and the doctor, not your
youngster, is definitely in charge. Most doctors proceed with
the kindly, but firm attitude, "You're going to be examined

"And then guess what we did, Mommy?" When your child starts
playing the "guess what" game, you may find your patience
wearing thin, but take time to play along. Later, you'll be glad.

whether you like it or not, young man!"

By the time he's 3½, you'll be able to reason with him and explain that the doctor is going to examine him because he wants to help him, not harm him.

IMAGINARY PLAYMATES As he approaches his third birthday, your youngster may add a new member to the family—an imaginary Susie or Billy who's very real to him. You may have to set an extra place at the table, or bring a small suitcase on vacation for this new friend. Active conversations are also a part of this friendship. This new-found friend may also be an animal, a dog or lovable lion, for instance, or he may be called Mr. Somebody-or-another. A child's inventiveness is amazing!

It requires a certain amount of intelligence on the part of a child to create an imaginary situation, so you needn't be overly concerned about this new development.

However, if your youngster seems to be spending *all* his time in a dream world, provide him with extra loving companionship. See to it that he has little playmates his own age with whom he can keep busy.

BEDTIME RESISTANCE Now that your youngster is more than able to climb out of his crib, you might just as well lower the crib rail. Otherwise, he may fall when he climbs over the rail.

He'll also come up with every possible excuse to put off the inevitable moment when he must go to sleep. When he's ready for bed, round up his doll, his blanket, or whatever other things he's used to taking to bed with him, or he'll use them as an excuse to get out of bed. Even then, you'll probably get the old song-and-dance about needing a drink of water and having to go to the potty.

Give him his drink, and by all means take him to the potty, because if you don't, you're going to have to change his bed. Then make it perfectly clear that that's it, and he's to stay in bed and go to sleep. You'll probably have to repeat yourself, but a little firmness usually works with most children.

Occasionally, a child just refuses to stay in bed, and every night there's a battle-royal. Although it sounds cruel, the best solution for this lies in tying, in 6 to 8 places, a tennis or badminton net over the top of his crib. This is a very effective method of keeping a child in his bed.

Many parents resort to using a harness, but it's no trick at all for a child to get caught hanging halfway over the crib rail. A net can be used in complete safety as a last resort. Certainly it's much kinder than locking the bedroom door and making the child feel he's been deserted.

The first three or four nights there'll be objections to the net, but once they're used to it, they often insist on it. Leave the bedroom door open, so your youngster doesn't feel totally imprisoned.

FEARS AT NIGHT Children often have frightening dreams at this age. They'll get out of bed at night and wander into your bedroom: they're now old enough to tell you they're frightened.

If your little one does this, pick him up, comfort him and reassure him, and carry him back to his bed. If he seems unusually frightened, sit beside his bed for a while. Don't let him climb into your bed with you. As we have mentioned before, this too easily turns into a habit that's hard to break.

SUCH FLAT FEET! Your two-year-old has flat feet all right! This is because there is a little fat pad in the base of a child's arch which supports the child's bones until the bones become hard enough to support the child's weight. This fat pad disappears during the two to three year period of a child's life.

Don't ever let a salesman sell you corrective shoes. Your child may have flat feet, but if he does, let your physician make the diagnosis and prescribe the proper corrective shoes. He'll tell you where you can buy them.

Only in severe cases is it possible for your doctor to tell before that fat pad disappears that the arch will not have enough support on its own and will need additional support.

Should you buy high shoes or low shoes? Many people feel that the high shoe adds some support to the child's ankle, but this is questionable. One great advantage of the high shoe is that youngsters can't just pull them off. They must untie them first. Otherwise, it doesn't make much difference which you buy.

No doubt about it
he's every inch a boy

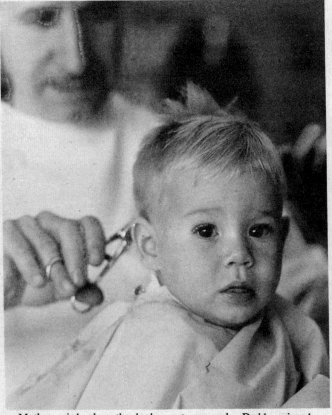

Mother cried when the barber cut my curls. Daddy grinned and called me *his* boy. And I sat straight and still in the big chair wondering how come it doesn't hurt when your hair gets cut.

Bread and honey is my secret weapon. It helps me to climb tall trees and hit grand-slam homeruns.

I'm really not afraid. I just haven't ever petted a fish before, especially one this big.

Setting up a campsite is really hard work. Everyone has to pitch in and do his share of the work.

It takes a while to get the hang of skiing. First you have to learn to walk on long, narrow boards.

17

Your child from three to five years

DEVELOPMENT Around the age of 3 your child may:
. . . measure 36 to 40 inches in height. . . . weigh 28 to 38
pounds—more if tall or large-boned, less if short or of slender
build. If dressing routines have been followed, he can: . . .
unbutton and button side and front buttons, if buttons and
buttonholes are big enough. . . . little girls can put on panties
and dresses, with a little help (usually backwards). . . . little
boys can manage T-shirts and pants. . . . put on and pull up
leggings and snowsuits with a bit of help or advice. . . . un-
lace and take off his shoes. . . . put on his shoes if someone
holds the tongues down, and if the shoes are marked to distinguish right from left. . . . later on in this age span, he'll
be able to put on and take off galoshes, if they're large enough
to slip easily over his shoes. Tightly fitting galoshes will be
too hard for him for a long time.

PHYSICAL AND MENTAL GROWTH Your youngster may
not gain more than 3 or 4 pounds a year during the next year
or two, but mental development leaps forward.

He'll begin to use numbers, but not in consecutive order.
One day he'll count 1, 4, 7, 10, and the next 2, 3, 8, 6. As he
approaches 5 years, he should be able to count to 10 in
consecutive order.

Your youngster will also learn nursery rhymes. If you read
to them frequently, they'll know immediately if you make an

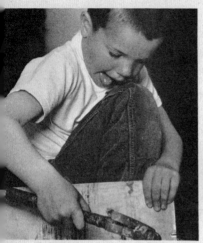

A hammer, some nails, and a few boards provide some boys with hours of creative play.

Others will find this boring and prefer a more complicated toy such as an erector set.

error or skip a page in a favorite story. Many times, they'll tell you the whole story once you get them started.

Since your child is able to reason, he can understand what you tell him, and he can learn to stay within the safe bounds you set for him. It's a good thing, too, for by 3, it's difficult to keep him in his play yard.

His active little body, plus an equally active mind, will carry him into many things that may look to you like mischief, but to him they are really exciting and quite necessary explorations of his world.

During the next year or two—maybe it has already happened—your lively little chap may get into your perfume and cosmetics, cut his own or some other child's hair, ransack your bureau drawers and cupboards, and decorate your wallpaper after his own artistic fancy. The healthier, stronger, and smarter he is, the more ways he'll find to upset the household routine.

He'll be the world's champion "why-er," for his whole environment to him is one big question mark to which he tries to find the answer. He'll run so fast and so hard in his quest that he'll always be falling and bumping himself. But that won't slow him down.

He'll go through various phases of behavior which may annoy you unless you understand that it's all a sign of growth. In a few months-he'll forget a trick you don't like, but may replace it with another one which is just as distasteful to you.

At the same time, he'll have settled down in his habits. He'll be able, at last, to look after his own toilet needs. He can wash himself after a fashion, but you can expect him to overlook a few areas. He can get in and out of his clothes, except for those which have more difficult fastenings.

You realize suddenly that he isn't a baby any more. Three, in fact, is an age of transition from infancy to childhood. One authority calls it the "adolescence of the preschool period." Like the adolescent period of the teens, it often keeps parents guessing, simply because they don't know what is normal behavior for the period, and they don't know how to treat it.

GIVE HIM LEEWAY It will be your job to supervise his daily routine until your child is through high school. But aside from necessary matters, allow your little fellow as much leeway as you can in his explorations. Your aim should not be to suppress his eager interest, but to supply plenty of legitimate material to which he can apply himself.

Develop his self-reliance and independence by having him do everything for himself that he possibly can at each stage of growth.

BEHAVIOR PROBLEMS FROM 3 TO 5 At this age your youngster will exhibit one annoying phase of behavior after another, no matter how wisely you handle him. It's a little difficult sometimes for a bewildered parent, going through this for the first time, to know what behavior is normal curiosity and what has more serious implications. We'll point out normal behavior patterns so that they can be recognized as such when you're directly faced with them.

A broad rule may be set up. If you have a healthy, happy youngster, you can be pretty sure that he is basically all right. If his undesirable behavior is accompanied by a generally unhappy, rebellious, or unsocial attitude, then it's wise to look

280 · THREE TO FIVE YEARS

further into the matter. Try to understand why he co-operates under some conditions and rebels under others. Then remove the cause of the trouble, if possible, or help him understand it.

Many otherwise well-behaved children become peevish or have temper tantrums late in the afternoon after a hard day of play. Or they become unmanageable when a meal is long delayed. *The real problem in such cases is not how to treat peevishness or temper tantrums, but to see that the child doesn't get overtired, and that his meals aren't overly late.*

Don't forget that quite often physical condition is the cause of naughty behavior. When you're confronted with a problem that refuses to yield to gentle but firm methods, take your child to his doctor for a thorough physical examination. Even if your child is perfect physically, medical advice will be a great help in tackling a behavior problem that has baffled you for some time.

You must not feel that you've failed or are disgraced as a parent if your youngster displays any or all of the following traits during the next year or so. It would be rare, almost abnormal, for a 3- to 5-year-old to exhibit none of them.

Any of the more common problems of the preschool period may discourage you, but you can take heart in the consoling fact that now you can begin to reason with your child.

After he's misbehaved or calmed down after a temper tantrum, and you've calmed down over his misbehavior, sit down with him and tell him that this is not the way to behave. You don't like it, and Daddy doesn't like it, and he's not to do it anymore. He'll soon understand why screaming and yelling will get him absolutely nowhere.

However, "reasoning" doesn't imply that you must give him a reason for every single direction you give. When he's older, a simple explanation is sufficient, but don't assume he wants an explanation for everything you tell him he must do.

MANNERISMS AND TICS *Thumb-sucking.* Most children have stopped sucking their thumb by this time, but some continue. If your youngster is happy, well-adjusted, and isn't nagged, he'll usually drop it of his own accord as soon as his developing social consciousness shows him that it brings derision from playmates.

Just before giving up the practice, however, some thumb-suckers go at it harder than ever. It's best to ignore the habit, as calling your youngster's attention to it may prolong the thumb-sucking and turn the habit itself into a psychological problem.

Thumb-sucking that continues past the age of 5 may be a symptom of a psychological disturbance and deserves special consideration (see Chapter 18 of this section). But at the age of 3, thumb-sucking is best handled by simply ignoring it.

"Bumping" and "rocking." (We briefly discussed this in Chapter 8.) By now, most youngsters have outgrown this, but if yours is still at it or starts it, equip his crib with rubber bumpers, available at surgical supply houses, to protect the wall and crib, and ignore it. The habit will pass.

Try to divert his energy to another activity that you know is equally satisfying to him, and easier on your nerves. You might add some new cuddly stuffed animals to his crib menagerie to occupy his attention.

Three-year-olds can even understand a request to stop, whereas it's asking too much of the 2-year-old.

Nail biting, ear pulling, nose picking, and face twitching. Life is so exciting for the 3-year-old that he often develops lttle nervous habits. This indicates a certain amount of emotional tension which is usually due to pressure from the parents, at other times it can be attributed to rivalry with an older or younger sibling or even with a little playmate.

As a parent, you must remove undue emotional pressure within the home. You may be guilty of yelling at him, expecting more from him than he is capable of during this age period, playing favorites (sometimes a child feels that he's not as favored as one of the other children, although it is often just his imagination). It's also important that he not be physically overtaxed.

Having made these things as right as you possibly can, forget about the mannerism. Nagging and constant suggestion or reference to them will only make them worse.

Stammering and stuttering. Somewhere around the age of 3, many children begin to stutter. There is no particular need to worry.

Between 2 and 6, your boy or girl will make enormous strides as a conversationalist. It's during this period, however, that he may get pronouns mixed up ("me" for "I"), may be unable to say certain letters or combinations (he may say "free" for "three," "widdle" for "little"), may stutter some, and may repeat words and sentences over and over.

None of these things should cause you any concern. It's better not to try to correct your youngster's speech except by speaking correctly yourself or by making an occasional suggestion in regard to grammar or the correct usage of a word. No reference should ever be made to repetition or stuttering, or you may fix the habit in his mind and it will persist and become a problem. If a defect such as stuttering continues after 6, there is probably some emotional tension causing it, and the help of a specialist in speech correction should be sought.

Let him talk. Between 3 and 5, your budding talker will probably become a chatterbox. He's discovered the pleasure of communication through words, has become sociable, wants to attract attention and tell you things.

If his chatter starts to wear you out, direct his interest to something else—a game or some physical activity. *Don't* scold or squelch him for talking too much.

At this age, you should see that he has other children and grown-ups outside the family to talk to. In this way, he'll learn to talk to others before he starts to school.

Some children are *not* talking by this age which always concerns their parents. If the child can hear, there's usually no need for this concern. He'll talk when he's ready.

TOILET ACCIDENTS Involuntary urination is common throughout the whole preschool period, and should be treated casually. Any small child, when excited or interested in play, may have an accident. This is particularly true when he's playing outdoors.

Don't shame or punish your little fellow if this happens. At this age, most children are chagrined enough when they have an accident. Added comments are unnecessary.

Take him to the toilet, change him with the suggestion that he start for the bathroom a little sooner the next time, and make the intervals between toilet trips shorter.

However, if your child of 3 or older has been trained for a long time, and then has extended lapses of control, there are two probable causes. The child may have a urinary tract infection, which happens frequently, especially in girls. The doctor will do a urinalysis to determine if your youngster does have an infection.

He may be emotionally upset. After eliminating the possible physical cause, take a look at the family situation to see if there is excessive emotional pressure.

BED-WETTING Bed-wetting is a *common* problem that often continues well into the 3- to 5-year period. Many children who have been sleeping through the night and awakening with a dry bed for a long time may take to wetting the bed after a new baby has been added to the household. This is especially true of first-born children. A perfectly trained youngster who finds himself in a strange place may wet the bed. And some continue to do this after they're old enough for camp and boarding school. A youngster may wet the bed as a bid for adult attention or to "get even" for having been punished for something.

Also remember that urinary tract infections or urinary diseases may cause relapses or be the cause of a chronic problem. Your doctor can check on this possibility.

If he's remained dry through the night for some time, treat the toilet lapse casually. If there is no organic cause, try to find out what emotional cause is behind this behavior. In your own mind, determine what your child hoped to accomplish by his actions. Then you can more easily correct this condition.

You may get him up in the night a few times if he's easily awakened or doesn't cry or stay awake for a long period afterward. If he's big enough, however, it's best to let him get up by himself. Speak to him to encourage him when you hear him getting up. Have a low-watt night light in the bathroom. Place a gate at the top of the stairs if your bedrooms are on the second floor.

What about the chronic bed-wetter? This child usually sleeps so soundly that the impression of a full bladder never fully registers. Parents of sound sleepers say it's impossible to awaken these youngsters. In some families, there appears to be a long history of chronic bed-wetters. Father or mother or sisters and brothers, aunts and uncles have also been bed-wetters. Whether or not this is a problem of capacity, inadequate signal from Mother Nature when they have to urinate, or lack of good control over the urinary tract, has not been determined.

What is the solution to this problem which has confounded physicians for generations? There's probably no better answer today than there was fifty years ago, but there are several things you can try.

It's probably helpful to cut down on the amount of fluids your youngster takes at suppertime and at bedtime or cut out any fluids at bedtime. See to it that he goes to the bathroom before he goes to bed. If it is possible for you to awaken him without unduly disturbing him, take him to the bathroom when you go to bed and later in the night if it is possible to do so.

But if your child fights or cries at being awakened, or is unable to get up by himself, don't force him to do so. This will only make an issue of the bed-wetting, and it may continue for a much longer time.

Bribing, threatening, and punishing only make the situation worse. In most cases, the chronic bed-wetter doesn't want to wet the bed and would do anything to stop it. When parents put pressure on the child, the excitement or attention increases his urinary output, decreases his bladder capacity, and intensifies the problem.

Mechanical devices which awaken the child when he starts to urinate are a poor idea during this age period. Even when the child is older, you should talk to your doctor about the wisdom of purchasing such a device.

It's a little easier to try to solve the problem during the summer months rather than during the winter months, because more fluid is lost to perspiration during hot weather, and the total quantity of urine is cut down.

Protect the mattress with a waterproof sheet and pad that will soak up the urine so the youngster doesn't stay soaking wet. You can put waterproof pants on him so he won't be "floating" by morning. Be sure the waterproof pants aren't airtight, or a painful and irritating rash may develop that will add to the problem.

One last word of advice: it's always wise to discuss the problem, especially if it appears to be chronic, with the child's doctor.

MISCHIEVOUSNESS With the 2-year-old, tearing things down is quite as much a part of play as building them up. At 3, your child will be an even more accomplished wrecker than he was at 2, but for the most part there's no malice in his destructiveness, just mischief.

The lively little fellow who threw Grandmother's book over the garden wall, and hid Grandfather's favorite magazine behind the bookcase was merely carrying out what had seemed like good ideas at the time. There will be plenty of this when there's a 3-year-old in the house. Adults have to learn to be good retrievers.

But if all his play seems to be the destructive kind, you should investigate the situation. Maybe your youngster hasn't enough opportunity for activity, and gets bored. Perhaps his toys are so flimsy they invite being torn to pieces. Perhaps his destructiveness is a sign of rebellion and unhappiness.

If your study shows that the fault is with poorly made toys, buy better ones. If the difficulty lies in your child's environment, try to correct it. Then lead him on to constructive play, and help him succeed at it.

Children should have their own sturdy books to look at when they wish. Their good books, and adult books, magazines, and newspapers, should be handled only under supervision. If your youngster seems unreasonably destructive and constantly goes from one thing to another, tearing everything apart, talk it over with the doctor at the next physical checkup.

IMAGINATION Rapidly developing imagination will probably lead your 3-year-old into telling tall tales. The imaginary situations which he creates aren't lies, and should be entered into as a game which both of you enjoy.

During this period, he'll develop imaginary bears which are very disconcerting to you. It's not unusual for him to have a bear or tiger under his bed or in the closet or a masked bandit at the window. It may even be necessary for you to turn on the light, get a broom, and chase out the bear! But point out that there really isn't any bear there.

A night light in his room will help counter these fears. Help your child to learn to distinguish between the real and the imaginary things, but expect these imaginary fears to be very real to him for some time to come.

What can be more discouraging to a make-
believe family than to have wagon trouble?

You may also expect your child to make the discovery one
of these days that he can escape consequences by saying he
didn't do something which he really did do. If he has older
brothers or sisters, he'll say they did it. Even the dog or cat
may be accused with a pointing finger. This is perfectly
normal behavior at this age.

Harsh punishments increase a child's tendency to "lie out"
of things. Our scheme of discipline, of course, doesn't call
for harsh punishments. Nevertheless, your child has to be
taught truthfulness the same as he must be taught other things.

Take care that your own attitude in questioning him doesn't
frighten him into a denial. Don't ask him if he did something
you're pretty sure he did, or you'll make it too easy for a
small offender to resort to falsehood. Say quietly, "Johnny,
where did you put the hose nozzle when you took it off?"
rather than "Johnny, did you take the hose nozzle?" Johnny's
whole reaction will be to tell you where he put it—if he
remembers. Then you can have him get it, and explain, as
he puts it back on, why he must not remove the nozzle again.

If he does something he knows he shouldn't do, however, don't withhold deserved consequences as a reward for truth telling. You want your child to tell the truth, not to escape punishment, but because telling the truth is the only way in which people can have confidence and trust in one another.

Explain to him that if we tell the truth always, people will believe what we say, and that's a much more satisfactory state of affairs than to be doubted.

Your youngster should learn to take the consequences of his unsocial acts. If the matter is approached impersonally, and your attitude is one of trying to get at the facts rather than of prejudging your youngster, you'll help him to admit his wrong and, at the same time, be prepared to take his punishment when it's coming to him.

CONTRARINESS During the 3- to 4-year period, a child is usually quite willing to help his mother do the dishes or set the table, even though he really doesn't have the ability to do the job.

But as the youngster approaches 4, an age when he can begin doing a few helpful tasks, his attitude changes. He "can't," "doesn't know how," or simply doesn't "want to." When a youngster still hasn't performed an assigned task after a reasonable time, take him by the hand and say, "Come on, Son. We're going to do this." Sometimes you'll get him started and he'll finish the job by himself; at other times it will be necessary to stay with him until the task is completed.

Also, the 4-year-old often becomes a whiner. He whines when he can't get his way or when he is asked to do something. He seems to be happy only when one of his parents or a playmate is playing with him, when activity is organized for him. Here is where preschool attendance might be considered. In some communities, groups of mothers take turns providing organized activity.

PLAYING WITH OTHERS The 3-year-old is now willing to play with other children and plays simple games well. He's also more willing to share his games and possessions. The hitting, biting, and pushing that was so prevalent during the 18-month to 2½-year period has stopped.

The bid for leadership is a problem that may show up.

Most youngsters aren't ready to be leaders in group play until they're 4 or 5 years old, because they don't as yet have the qualities which induce other youngsters to follow them.

An ambitious child may want to lead before he has the ability. He may then try to win his place by showing off, or by interfering with and bullying the other children. With proper discipline and discussion with the youngster, his behavior will improve. Take the utmost advantage of his ability to reason.

SLEEPING Both naps and bedtimes may continue to present problems. Remember that sleep requirements vary from one child to another.

In the period between 2 and 5 years, most children go through three stages in regard to their afternoon nap. Until 2½, your child will probably fall asleep almost immediately if all conditions are made right for him, and he may continue to do so until he's around 3.

Any time after 2½, however, he may periodically decide that he's not going to take a nap. He has so many things to think about that he can't take time out for anything as dull as sleeping.

Insist that he stay in his bed after you've put him there, but leave it to him whether or not he sleeps. After a period of staying awake during nap time, many youngsters go back to sleeping again until they get to be 4½ or 5. Then they'll sleep some days and stay awake on others. Some children will no longer sleep during their afternoon nap period once they reach 3 or 3½. It's proper to let your youngster take a picture book or toy to bed with him, so he can amuse himself quietly if he doesn't sleep.

Bedtime. Once he reaches 3, and sometimes earlier, he's learned how to get out of his crib if he's still sleeping in one. As we suggested in a previous chapter, round up his blanket, doll, or whatever, give the final glass of water, make sure he goes to the bathroom, and then insist that he go to bed and stay there. He may come up with another excuse you never thought of, climb out of bed, and wander into the living room. Don't compromise. Put him right back to bed. By the time he's 3½ to 4, he'll know you mean business and when put to bed, will stay there.

Children in the 3 to 5 age group continue to have bad dreams and to come into their parents' bedroom for reassurance. Comfort your young one but take him back to his own bed. Don't let him get in the habit of staying in bed with you.

If you've been traveling, are in strange surroundings, or have just moved—anything that changes the normal routine—sleep disturbances will increase for a short time.

EATING It's quite natural for your youngster's appetite to slacken as his growth rate slows down. At 3, moreover, the excitement of developing mental impressions often makes children forget their hunger. You must also allow for the inevitable period of boredom, or regressions, after your youngster has learned to feed himself well.

Aside from these factors which may enter into the most nearly perfect eating situation, there are six ways in which your child may now become a mealtime problem:

1. Too much interest in what's going on around him. He shouldn't eat where he's surrounded by toys and playthings.

2. Too much food. You've seen already how discouraging that can be to a little fellow with a limited stomach capacity.

3. Dislike for foods offered.

4. Trying to get adult attention.

5. Too tired.

6. Too much insistence on your part that he eat.

Treat your child's problem according to its cause. If his appetite has dropped off, cut his helpings in two. He can always have another if he wants it, but don't try to urge more food upon him than he needs.

If he's bored with feeding himself, let him help set the table and serve himself. Serve his milk in a small pitcher, and let him pour it into a small cup or glass. A drinking straw may stimulate his interest. When through, let him remove his dishes and help himself to dessert, according to the amount of the other food he's eaten at the meal.

If he gets too wound up eating with the family, have him eat ahead of the adults.

If there's more food on his plate than he can manage, you may "divide" it. That is, take the plate away, remove part of the food, and let him finish the rest.

If he dislikes a number of foods, try to find substitutes that

When rush hour sidewalk traffic gets hectic,
a wise motorist pulls over and refuels.

will appeal to him. Then let him eat as much as he likes of favorite wholesome foods, without urging that he eat more.

Ignore his bids for attention.

If he's tired, have him come in from his strenuous play and lie down for a while before dinner and supper, or at least engage in some quiet occupation.

Don't show any concern whether your child eats or not, and particularly don't let eating become an issue between you. Mealtimes should be treated as pleasant interludes in the day when everyone eats as a matter of course—not because he is forced to eat.

Understand that there will be times when your youngster has very little appetite, times when he will want to eat several helpings of one food and none of any others, and times when he will not really care whether he eats anything at all.

Don't worry about these fluctuations. If he doesn't feel compelled to eat, he will make up at another meal for the small amount taken previously. He'll balance his diet by switching to another food when he has had his fill of a favorite. If he wants to skip a meal, he may be hungry at the following one. Always remember that there are times when you and other grown-ups, too, aren't as hungry as usual.

To a 4-year-old child everything is a beautiful,
fascinating mystery just waiting to be solved.

THAT ETERNAL "WHY" When he gets to be 3 years old,
your child will expect you to be a walking encyclopedia. By
all means answer questions that are asked with a sincere
desire for information. But your youngster is apt to find this
new game so amusing that he'll ask a million senseless questions every day.

If he already knows or can easily figure out the answer to
his question, have him answer it himself. Otherwise he may
have you do all his thinking for him.

"Why" often becomes almost automatic. When you have
replied to one question, he'll ask "why" again.

There's no need to answer this kind of "why." You'll only
wear out your patience if you try. Very often the "why" is
just a way of putting off necessary functions like dressing,
undressing, going indoors, and so forth.

It's best to phrase your remarks so that there's no chance
for your youngster to ask "why." For instance, when it's
mealtime, just say, "Let's go in now and eat lunch," and take
his hand to go indoors. Most of the time he'll come right
along without a word.

THE BEGINNING OF SEX INSTRUCTION A child's sex

education actually begins when the baby finds the various parts of his body. First he finds his hands, then his feet, and somewhere between 5 and 6 months, he discovers his genitalia. It's perfectly normal for a baby to be curious about himself.

Your reaction to this curiosity is important. If you're horrified, you'd better pause and review your own attitudes toward sexual matters. Otherwise, from an emotional standpoint, you'll never be able to teach your child anything about sex.

Between 2 and 3, it's quite natural for your child to be curious about the opposite sex of the family members. If you find it necessary to lock the bathroom door each time you go in, insist that your child never see you in the nude, your child is bound to wonder what secretive activity is going on in the bathroom or what's so different about Mommy and Daddy.

If they learn there are differences and secrecy is absent, what curiosity they have at this age will soon be satisfied. Insistence on *absolute* privacy will keep your child from learning that basically, with male and female variations, all people look alike.

This doesn't mean you should go to the opposite extreme and deliberately walk about undressed or leave the bathroom door wide open. If your child should walk in on you unexpectedly, don't act shocked or scold him. Finish dressing or calmly ask him to wait outside until you're dressed. This avoids making a big issue of it, and lays the groundwork for respect of reasonable privacy of others when he's older.

Any time after your child is 2½, 3 is the usual age, you may expect the question, "Where do babies come from?" Nearly all children ask it in just this form. Answer simply and matter-of-factly, "They grow inside their mothers." This will, in most cases, suffice for some time. Then they will ask some other question, usually one which elicits the information that the baby was once a tiny egg, which grew until the baby was ready to live in the world with its mommy and daddy.

These first questions are often as simple as can be, and can be answered without difficulty from your own knowledge. Answer each time as much as is asked, unless an opportunity is given to expound some point you think desirable. See "When your child asks about life," for more detailed answers.

During the 4- to 6-year period, it's natural for your child to show a renewed curiosity about the opposite sex, not so much within your family, but more toward neighbor children.

Some parents feel that if there are brothers and sisters, this curiosity won't be present, but this is seldom the case although there may be a little less curiosity.

It's not uncommon for neighborhoods to be upset because a little boy and girl were found examining each other. Don't look upon this as some degraded or perverted manifestation, but as a purely natural curiosity. Handle it tactfully and without alarm.

Small children in the same family may have their baths together, and it's not necessary to separate the sexes for dressing.

If yours is an only child, when a small playmate of the opposite sex comes to visit, treat the two in the same way you would a brother and sister. A perfectly legitimate curiosity will thus be satisfied in a natural and matter-of-fact way, and will then pass.

Don't be alarmed if you discover your youngster handling his genitals. The physical conditions necessary to pleasure sensations are given even in small children. Do not consider such activities as sexual yet. Excessive masturbation is usually a sign of tension or worry. Diversion may sometimes eliminate the problem, but it's more important to find out what's causing the tension and to remove it. A direct attack on the masturbation itself never succeeds, because the masturbating becomes the problem rather than the symptom.

If you find your child involved in sex play, it's perfectly all right to let him know in a friendly, matter-of-fact tone that you'd rather he didn't do it anymore. You can also tell him that he should always keep his pants on when he's playing outside.

PLAY EQUIPMENT TO ADD AT 4 YEARS It's not necessary for children to have a lot of playthings, but whatever you buy for them should be well-constructed. If their toys aren't serviceable, they're not usable. A hammer you can't *pound* with is useless, as is a sewing kit you can't use for sewing.

For outdoors: Swing; rings; bars; trapeze; sled; wagon; jumping rope; ice skates; roller skates; boxing gloves; football; seesaw.

For indoor play: Toy tool chest; tools; real cooking utensils; sewing material; construction sets; games; electric train; stamp books; doll for which a girl can sew.

Gee! This works better than Bobby's water gun.

Sugar, spice
oh so nice!

Sure hope they taste better than they look!

Rain beats the park's water fountain any day!

Why does it always have to rain on Saturday?

Riding a horse is easy if you hold on tight.

See Kitty, now I look
just as pretty as Mommy.

I wish I had a birthday
at least once a week.

I just don't know how babies can get so dirty!

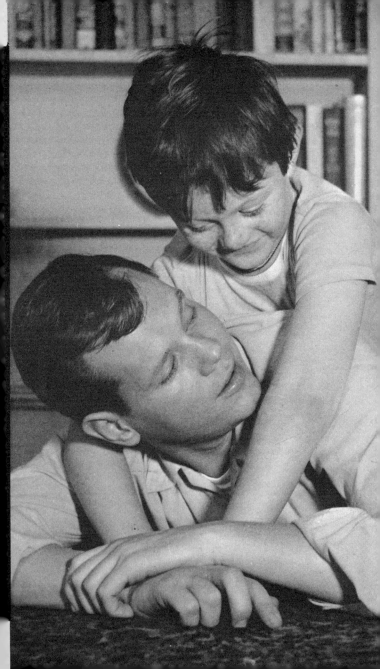

18

Your child from five to six years

DEVELOPMENT At 5 years, your child will probably: . . . weigh 36 to 50 pounds. . . . measure 41 to 46 inches in height.
He should be able to: . . . button and unbutton all buttons, except the most difficult. . . . put on and take off all his clothing. . . . handle his toilet needs without assistance. . . . wash his face and hands without help. . . . count to ten. . . . know his primary colors. . . . know a dime is more valuable than, for instance, a penny.

HIS EATING HABITS During this 5-year period, you'll notice a distinct change in your child's eating habits. This is because he's going to double his rate of weight gain. His intake of food must, therefore, increase. After he's completed this growth spurt, his appetite will level off and his day-in, day-out consumption of food will be about the same as far as the amount he eats.

The 5-year-old will continue his food jags, however. One month he'll prefer one type of meat or vegetable, then suddenly decide he likes something else. He may also increase his milk intake. Remember, although milk is an important and good food, it is not a complete food. If he drinks more than a reasonable amount a day (16–24 ounces) he's sacrificing the nutrients found in solid foods.

Once the 5-year-old starts school, he'll develop more inti-

Daddy doesn't really mind being a captive
audience for his daughter's performances.

mate relationships with his playmates. This certainly doe
affect his eating habits. When playmates come to his hom
during mealtimes and wait while he finishes, it's difficult fo
him to show any interest in his food. He'll want to return t
his friends.

Once a child this age finishes his meal, let him excuse him
self and leave the table. He's still young enough to get restles
and cause a commotion if he finishes before the rest of th
family is through eating.

READINESS FOR SCHOOL Is your youngster matur
enough to start kindergarten? If there is a question in you
mind, discuss his maturity with your family doctor or pedia
trician. It might help to talk to the kindergarten teacher tha
the youngster will have the following year. Frequently, sh

can advise you as to whether she feels he has the emotional maturity to cope with kindergarten. It may be better to enroll him in a nursery school first, rather than have him held back in kindergarten when his classmates go on to first grade.

If there is still some question in your mind, you'll save the family a lot of heartache by consulting beforehand with a qualified clinical psychologist. You certainly don't want to push the youngster into a situation he is mentally incapable of handling.

KINDERGARTEN Your youngster will be leaving home this fall for one-half day, every day, five days a week. This will be a new experience for both you and your child, and if your child is to make a satisfactory adjustment in school, it must be a happy one.

There are four categories relating to the child which are of primary importance if the school experience is to be a successful and pleasant one—independence, good health habits, and hygiene, security, and parental interest.

Independence. Begin developing independence by familiarizing your child with the route to school. Before school starts, walk the route with him several times until he is sure he knows

Who says grass has to be green and sky, blue?

"I thought sure I heard him go 'Whoo-Whoo'."

the way. Even though there will probably be classmates and older children for him to walk with, there will undoubtedly come a time, before he is completely sure of himself, when he'll have to walk it alone. It's easy to imagine the panicky feeling he'll have if he's unsure of the way.

Teach him a *safe* way to and from school. If there are no sidewalks along the route, teach him to walk facing the traffic. Encourage him to adhere to the safety rules and to respect and follow the directions of the school safety patrol.

He should know how to put on and remove his wraps and how to do all the tying and fastening he possibly can. Select clothing that is easily fastened, especially if he has a little trouble along this line. He'll feel more independent if he can put on his coat, hat, mittens, and overshoes without the teacher's help. Besides, she has enough to do without buttoning and unbuttoning, putting galoshes and rubbers on 30 to 40 children.

Health habits. There are many hygienic and health habits which are taken for granted when a child starts school. But, is he able to disclose the need for elimination quietly and matter-of-factly, so that he can ask the teacher without hesitation or embarrassment for permission to go to the toilet? Does he know how to care for himself hygienically at the toilet and wash his hands afterwards? Can he use a handkerchief for blowing his nose properly? Does he know how to cover his mouth and nose and to turn his head when he coughs or sneezes? These are things he should know.

If your child is a thumb sucker, it often creates additional psychological problems, especially if you put pressure on him to stop before he starts school. If too much pressure is put on the child, he may switch to another emotional outlet.

It would be helpful to let the child's teacher know your feelings on the matter. Many teachers feel they know the cure for this and, in attempting to carry it out, cause more problems than existed before.

Most children are healthy, exuberant characters who seem to have an overabundance of pep and energy. If they're going to start kindergarten in the afternoon, they need to unwind after a morning of hard play. Call your youngster in from play early. Let him soak in the bathtub or color in his coloring book for a while. Many television stations have programs at this time of the day that are educational and entertaining. Whatever the activity, it should give him a chance to relax before going off to school.

Your youngster will have his hands full once school starts. He'll have enough little problems without being hampered by physical problems. If your youngster has visual, or hearing difficulties or other surgically correctable defects that might handicap him, they should be detected and, if possible, corrected before he starts school.

He'll probably need a smallpox revaccination and boosters for diphtheria, tetanus, and whooping cough. Make your appointment sufficiently early so that any defect that might be detected can be corrected.

Security. A sense of security is essential for a happy school experience. At 5, a child's main interest deals with his home and those involved with it. He needs to know that they are safe and secure while he is away and will be there when he returns. He also needs to know that he will return to them safely.

Knowing his address, phone number, and being unafraid to tell them to an older person will make him more secure. He should also know whom to call in case you can't be reached in an emergency. You should never be gone from home when he returns from school without having told him you would be. Make arrangements to have someone there when he gets home. An empty house is frightening to a youngster.

A 5-year-old is also concerned about his belongings. It disturbs him when he loses an article of clothing or a possession. Marking his clothing, wraps, mittens, or boots, with his name enhances his feeling of independence and security by making identification of his belongings easier for him and also it makes things easier for his teacher.

Parental interest. This interest in his school work is very important. Your child will have notes, papers, books to be examined, praised, and digested. Everything he brings home is vitally important to him.

But there is always a lot of confusion at home at 3:30 each school afternoon. Little ones are getting up from their naps, the baby is awake, the school children are coming home—bubbling with excitement over something that happened or is going to happen or that they've achieved. Someone may even

Last thing I told Mommy was I wouldn't get
dirty. But, I accidently tripped over that log.

be unhappy over a major or minor catastrophe.

So, it's usually impossible for you to go over notes and
papers at that hour. Perhaps the best way to handle them is to
take what he brings home and put it in a special place. Then,

after dinner, before bedtime—some quiet time—sit down with him and go over everything he has brought home.

Never fail to praise any bit of work brought home, no matter how bad it is or how hard it is to decipher. There is some praiseworthy good in it, and encouragement is the best incentive a child can have.

Visit school often. This gives him a chance to show you the work he does and how he does it in school. Encourage him to talk about daily activities. Parents can build a splendid feeling toward school by pleasant discussion of subjects whenever possible.

Starting school certainly cuts a child from his mother's apron strings, and most children thrive on this new independence. If you provide your youngster with the security he needs and show the parental interest he deserves, he'll have a happy kindergarten year.

NAPS AND BEDTIME By the time most children are 5 years old, they've stopped taking naps, although they should be observing a rest period during the early afternoon. Thirty minutes to an hour of quiet activity makes a big difference in behavior toward end of the day.

If your child is still taking a nap, discontinue it several weeks before he enters school, especially if he's going to be in an afternoon kindergarten session. The child who is used to an afternoon nap and has to stop it abruptly when he starts school will have considerable difficulty making an adjustment.

Children should have a regular time to go to bed. Difficulty arises when bedtime is 7 o'clock one night, 9 o'clock the next. Make every effort to get your child into bed by the same time each night. The exact hour, of course, will depend upon the amount of sleep your child seems to need.

It's not unusual for a child this age to lie awake for an hour or so after going to bed. Now that he's started school, a whole new world has opened up and, like an adult, he starts to mull the day's events over in his mind before he goes to sleep. Too many parents become disturbed and think that perhaps school is emotionally too difficult for their child, or that he is worried about something. But if you ask him what he's thinking about, he'll tell you, usually willingly, and it won't be at all worrisome.

Unless there is a considerable amount of emotional pressure on children of this age, they have very few night disturbances.

BABY DAYS ARE OVER Just as 3 years is a transition age between infancy and childhood, 5 years is gradually marking an end to the baby period.

Not on his fifth birthday, necessarily, but during his fifth to sixth year, your child is expected to say good-bye to baby ways and to take on a more mature role. But parents sometimes go to extremes.

One parent type permits the baby traits to continue and even encourages them. They don't let the child accept the responsibility that he's capable of accepting.

The other type tries to make a little man out of the 5-year-old and expects him to do things far beyond his age capabilities. Now more than ever, parents should reach a happy medium concerning how they react to their child's developing maturity.

The parent that would continue to make the 5-year-old a baby must accept the idea that he's no longer a baby but a school child. And the parent who would have his youngster mature too rapidly must remember he's still just a kindergartener.

While your child was under 5, lapses into infantile traits were not taken too seriously. You gave annoying habits a chance to correct themselves with some occasional gentle and indirect help from you. However, if thumb sucking, bed-wetting, and stammering show themselves into the fifth to sixth year, you should now give them more attention.

The first step is always to take your youngster to his doctor for a thorough checkup to make sure you're not overlooking physical reasons that may account for the problem. Psychology can't help bed-wetting, for instance, if the youngster has a renal malformation or infection which makes control impossible to achieve.

If the doctor rules out physical causes, then you must look to the emotional environment. The child who suddenly starts sucking his thumb again, or who continues to suck his thumb much past 5, except for a little sleepy-time indulgence, is not adjusted in some way and quite often unhappy.

It may be undue emotional pressure at home or school, or

This trick is kind of fast and tricky but you can probably catch on if you watch me very closely.

an inability to get along with playmates that causes his unhappiness. Whatever it is, help him as much as you can.

Take care, moreover, not to shame or worry the youngster about it. He's none too secure as it is, or he wouldn't be sucking his thumb. Don't add to his unhappiness and feeling of insecurity. Approach the matter reasonably and understandingly. Remind him with a look or an upraised eyebrow to stop when you see him doing it, and you'll help far more than by making him the butt of attention.

If your youngster continues stammering into the fifth year, discuss it with your doctor. Slurring is quite common and will correct itself if pressure is taken off the child.

BEHAVIOR PROBLEMS *Name-calling.* Although this isn't a new problem, there seems to be a renewed vigor and an increase in vocabulary that makes it a bit more disturbing. Now that your child has a wider range of friends, he'll pick up more derogatory names, and will bring them home where he'll apply them to you. Not all of them are printable, and many times the child doesn't realize their significance.

You must realize that this is normal behavior. Your response to the use of these names is extremely important. If you fly off the handle and make a big issue of it, your youngster has accomplished his purpose in applying these words to you.

This doesn't mean that you should completely ignore the matter. After he's calmed down over the situation which made him feel it necessary to use the words, talk to him about it. Tell him that these words just aren't used, especially not when talking to his mother and father. Once he realizes that they won't invoke anger, or accomplish what he expected them to, he'll stop using them.

Showing off. He'll continue to take every possible opportunity to be the center of attention. This is especially irritating when you have guests and your child tries to monopolize them or climb all over them.

A little family discussion before company arrives may help. Don't be disturbed if you have to repeat yourself. Before the sixth year has ended, most children are reasonably well-behaved in company situations.

Procrastinating. This problem is especially maddening to parents. It's exasperating behavior but typical at the age period. You tell your child to do something and expect him to do it. You come back in half an hour and he hasn't moved an inch. If you're like most parents, you'll then try to shout him into doing it. This doesn't work, either. He suddenly loses his hearing.

When you want a child this age to do something, especially when you're in a hurry and don't have time to wait it out with him, get him started on it and make sure he finishes. At this age, he needs considerable leadership. But don't overdo it! If he misses the school bus some day or is late for an event that's important to him, he'll soon learn what the consequences of dawdling are.

ASSUMING FAMILY RESPONSIBILITY Five is certainly not too young for a child to have a little chore to do. He must learn that each member of the family must do his share if family life is to run smoothly.

He can be responsible for hanging up his clothes and putting dirty clothes in the hamper. Little girls are capable of setting, or at least helping to set the table. The 5-year-old boy can carry garbage out to the garbage container or cans and bottles out to the trash barrel. He's still too young, however, to take waste paper to an incinerator.

ALLOWANCES This is a good age to begin giving an allowance, however small. You want your child to learn the value of money, and an allowance is an excellent teaching aid. If you give your child an allowance, it's your job to supervise it to see that it is used wisely.

There are three goals which you should try to achieve in teaching the value of money. First, you want your child to learn how to save. Second, you want him to learn how to spend wisely. Teach him that if he wants a particular article, he must use his allowance to buy it. This doesn't apply to items which you as a parent should provide for him. But if he spends his money on a little game today, then wants something else tomorrow, he'll learn to plan a little more wisely.

Third, you want your child to learn how to give. He's old enough now to put a coin in the collection plate or the box for a worthy cause. This is a step in learning to share part of his "wealth" with others.

The amount of the allowance which you decide to give to your youngster is entirely up to you. Certainly, 50 cents, or even 25 cents a week is too much for a 5-year-old. As he gets older, you'll probably increase it.

Although some psychologists feel an allowance shouldn't be considered a payment for chores, it *is* in some ways a reward for being a helpful, responsible family member. They also differ over the question of withholding an allowance because of poor behavior.

General Information

When your child asks about life

When your children ask you where they came from and other questions about human reproduction, they're entitled to honest answers. How you help them at this point is a measure of your success as a parent. Know your facts and state them clearly. Give the essentials; don't overload with details.

If your answers don't quite clear things up for your child, he'll ask more questions. When he does, keep on answering.

He'll probably ask about pregnancy, birth, fertilization, and mating, usually in that order. Most questions arise from something observed in everyday life. Some may seem to come out of a clear sky.

Your answers should be friendly, not evasive, vague, jocular or frivolous. Be serious, but not sentimental. Never conclude with "That's why we love you so." And *never* say, "That's why you should love Mother and Daddy."

You can expect the first question about birth and pregnancy before Johnny or Nancy is 6, quite often earlier. Most children know something about human reproduction by the time they enter first grade.

BABIES Q. Where did Mrs. Graham get her new baby?

A. It grew inside of her in a special place mothers have for babies to grow in.

It's best if you can answer this first question without going into much detail. Preschoolers just aren't that interested. They'll probably change the discussion from Mrs. Graham's baby to themselves.

Q. Did I grow like that in you? (Or did I grow in Mother like that, Daddy?)

A. You certainly did!

Don't confuse a small child at this point with names, either fanciful or scientific. No "cradle" or "nest," no "vagina" or "uterus," and no "under Mother's heart," though the affection and welcome indicated in that old-time answer were not misplaced, even if the baby was. When your child is older, tell him correct names—"uterus" for sac in which baby grows, "vagina" for birth passage.

Q. Where was I when you were a little girl? (Or when Mother was a little girl?)

A. The beginning of you was hidden away in Mother waiting for her to grow up and find Daddy, and make a home for you to come into.

Avoid the quick answer, "When Mother was a little girl, there wasn't any you." Your child has a strong feeling for the continuity of life. So don't abruptly deny him any existence before he came into the world. Here's an answer that's less harsh, still truthful.

Q. Is there a baby growing in you now, Mother? (Or in Mother now?)

A. No, not right now, but I'll tell you where there is one this minute. In Aunt Barbara. You've seen how much rounder she is now. That's because her baby takes up a lot of space. The bigger her baby grows, the rounder Aunt Barbara will get.

You can't predict how questions about babies will be asked. Whatever your answer, always establish: *Babies grow in their mothers.*

BIRTH Q. How does the baby get out?

A. Every mother has a little passageway made just to bring the baby out into the world when he's ready to be born. This passageway has a small opening at the lower part of the body, where the legs begin. The baby grows for nine months in a small sac which stretches a little bit at a time to make room for him. (Make a little pantomime by cupping your hands together with wrists and fingers touching.) When he's old enough and strong enough to live out in the world, his head swings around into the passageway, and he's ready to be born into this big world, a little tiny baby.

At this point, with your hands still cupped, demonstrate, moving your finger tips apart and pushing downward with our wrists, how the canal begins to open. Show how the muscles begin to press on the baby, carrying him farther and farther along the canal until he reaches the opening and there, ready and waiting for him, are the doctor's skillful hands. Explain this coming down the passageway into the world is called being born.

Q. Does it hurt the baby (or the mother)?

A. No. When a baby is born it's just about the size of your doll or your puppy. Besides being very tiny, the baby's all folded up. His little arms are folded across; his little legs are drawn up. As for the mother, she may feel tired, but the doctor takes very good care of her and the baby.

FERTILIZATION Q. How does the baby get in the mother in the first place?

A. The baby didn't get in there as a baby. It started from a tiny speck of living matter inside the mother. (If the child is old enough to grasp scientific names, give the correct term "egg cell" or "ovum.") By itself, this little cell can't grow to become a baby. It must be joined with a father cell. These two cells must come together inside the mother before the baby starts to grow.

Another question asked by both girls and boys arises almost as often as questions on reproduction and may come any time from preschool on. It concerns menstruation.

With the very young children, the question is usually prompted by some puzzling object.

Q. What's in the big package? May I open it?

A. If you wish. They're just a lot of sanitary pads that take up moisture. Mothers and big girls wear them to protect their clothing from a discharge that appears now and then. The discharge is part of being able to be a mother and contains some blood and other substances that she doesn't need at the time. So Nature lets them drain away at certain times. The pads are like a bandage.

MATING To answer questions on mating clearly and without embarrassment, you must have laid a foundation of several facts. Before children can understand mating, they must know the difference between boys and girls. Little brothers and sisters should be allowed to dress and undress together so that

they can observe casually that one is made differently from
the other. If your child has no brothers or sisters, work out
some casual way for him to see a baby of the opposite sex.
Don't be surprised if Nancy asks:

"What is that on Dougie?"

If you're prepared, you'll answer:

"That's a penis. Little boys are made differently from girls.
Dougie's penis shows that he's a boy. On your body the part
is called the vulva." If Dougie asks a similar question about a
little girl, you can merely turn the answer around.

This familiarity with bodily parts and differences is essential for an understanding later of your answers to the question
about the actual mating process. Sooner or later, Johnny or
Nancy is going to ask:

"How does the baby get started?"

Here's how you can answer:

"Men and women are made so that when they grow up and
get married they can be fathers and mothers. The father's
penis fits into the inner passageway of the mother, the one the
baby comes down. Then the father, or sperm, cells pass up
into the mother in a white fluid. If one father cell joins with
a mother cell (or ovum), a baby may begin to grow."

There are books, written for elementary school children.
Leave them on the table in the living room as you would any
other book. If the book disappears, don't send out a tracer.
If it remains apparently untouched, don't quiz or fuss. Keep
your relationship with your children free and open, and they
will discuss the book with you if they feel the need.

If they don't ask any questions, perhaps it's because you've
missed their first expressions of interest, or have put them off
or shown displeasure. They probably found their answers else-
where.

It's best not to probe to find out how much a child already
knows. But if your boy or girl is approaching 10 and has never
discussed human beginnings with you, you might throw out a
leading remark or two and see what happens. Even if it produces no response, at least you have shown yourself to be
open to the subject.

Confidence between you and your children must be established before puberty—the period when they start to mature.
You'll find it difficult if you wait until then! By the time

ey're adolescents, they may shrink from your comments and
utions.

There is one question that bothers parents from the very
ginning of their children's sex education . . .

"Should I caution my child not to discuss sex matters with
her children?"

The answer is "No."

Give your instruction in simple terms and to the best of
ur ability. Do this; then trust your child with it. His associ-
es are bound to talk about sex and reproduction. (We adults
the same thing when we get together.)

If children have the matter well in hand, without a feeling
f guilt, they are very good teachers of each other. The child
hose talk and conduct we disapprove of is the one who has
d to get his teaching hit-or-miss. If you inform your own
ild properly, you need not worry about the influence of a
ild whose knowledge is garbled or incomplete.

You need not fear exploration or sex misconduct as a re-
lt of good teaching. Sex education wisely carried out is the
st possible assurance of a balanced, happy play life among
owing children, and the best possible preparation for a
ppy adjustment to the problems they'll face in the future.

Developmental Schedule

Every child's examination should include an assessment of
velopmental progress.

Listed below are selected items, in gross motor, adaptive,
nguage, and personal-social development, divided into differ-
at age periods, from birth through 5 years of age.

The primary purpose of the developmental inventory is to
miliarize parents with normal child development. It is sug-
sted that parents, in turn, keep an accurate record of at
hat age each of the items is first carried out successfully.
ive all information to the doctor.

This is not an intelligence test. Superior achievement does
ot reflect high intelligence any more than does a minor delay
dicate retardation. Your doctor is best qualified to ascertain
e significance of underachievement and whether further test-
g is indicated.

AGE	MOTOR	ADAPTIVE
Birth 1 month	When lifted, head falls backward loosely. When sitting, head falls forward. Lies on back with head held to one side. The arm on the same side is outstretched, the other is flexed and held near the head and chest (tonic neck reflex).	Follows an object or lig
3 to 4 months (12 to 16 weeks)	Tonic neck position disappears. Now lies on back with head held in the midline (symmetrical position). When on abdomen, raises self on forearms, holds head up 45°. At 4 months head and chest off bed, head raised 90°. When pulled to sitting, neck lags only slightly. Head erect when body supported.	Recognizes feeding bo Brings hands together a watches them when he plays. Tries to reach objects but overreaches or underreaches.
5 to 6 months (20 to 24 weeks)	Rolls from stomach to back. Held sitting, no head wobble, head erect. At 24 weeks, sits supported in high chair. Held in standing position, bears weight on legs.	Reaches out and grasp objects. Holds bottle. Grasps feet. Palmar gr of cube.
7 to 8 months (28 to 36 weeks)	Rolls from back to stomach. At 28 weeks, sits leaning on hands. At 32 weeks, sits momentarily without support. At 36 weeks, sits for 10 minutes without support.	Likes to play with pap One-handed approach. Transfers from one har to another. Takes a seco cube while holding anoth
9 to 10 months (40 to 44 weeks)	Sits up well indefinitely. Pulls to standing. Starts holding on to furniture. Standing, lifts foot.	Can pick up small objec with finger and thumb. Pokes at things with ind finger. Begins to release objects. Begins to put objects into or take out a cup or box.
12 months (48 to 52 weeks)	Crawls openly on all fours. Walks with two hands held and later with one hand held. May stand alone for a few minutes.	Picks up small objects v precisely with thumb a index finger. Throws o jects to floor purposely Points out objects he wants.

As your child completes each task, place check mark in ruled colum

LANGUAGE	PERSONAL-SOCIAL
...npassive face. Be-...omes quiet when bell ...rung. Makes quiet ...roaty noise when ...ontent.	Indefinite gaze at surroundings. Listens to sounds. Watches Mother's face when she feeds him or talks to him.
...oos. Vocalizes when ...ooken to or pleased. ...aughs aloud.	Spontaneous smile. Brings hands together and watches them. Pulls clothes over face when he plays. Recognizes feeding bottle.
...aughs, chuckles, ...queals in play.	Puts everything into mouth. Plays with toes and grasps feet. Pats bottle with both hands when being fed. Smiles or talks to image in mirror.
...yllables BA, DA, KA. ...our or more different ...ounds.	Pats image of self in mirror. Feeds self cracker. Holds bottle. Responds to name.
...houts to attract atten-...on. Says "Ma-ma," ..."Da-da."	Puts hands around cup. Plays peekaboo. Shows shyness, fear of strangers, and clings to familiar persons. May not want to be left by Mother.
...wo words with mean-...g besides "Ma-ma" ... "Da-da." Imitates ...nimals.	Waves good-bye and pat-a-cakes. Co-operates with dress. Holds arm or leg out. Gives toys upon request. Drinks from cup without help.

...ecord each testing date with a different color.

AGE	MOTOR	ADAPTIVE
15 months	Walks. Can get to feet alone. Crawls upstairs.	Builds tower of 2 cubes. Holds 2 objects in hand a one time. Scribbles when shown. Shows preference for using one hand.
18 months	Walks well. Carries toy or doll while walking. Seats self in chair. Walks up stairs, one hand held. Creeps backward down stairs.	Makes a tower with 3–4 cubes. Imitates a pencil stroke on paper.
2 years	Goes up and down stairs alone holding on to wall or rail. Pulls a toy by a cord. Throws a ball.	Handedness well developed. Builds tower of 6 t 7 cubes. Imitates a circula scribble. Removes paper candy wrapper.
2½ years	Jumps with two feet together. Can stand on tiptoes if asked. Kicks a ball.	Builds tower of 8 cubes. Holds pencil in hand instead of fist.
3 years	Walks up stairs alternating feet and down stairs two feet per step. Rides tricycle. Stands on one foot for a few seconds.	Copies a circle. Matches 2 or 3 colors. Builds towe of 9 to 10 cubes. Cuts with scissors. Builds a bridge.
4 years	Goes down stairs one foot per step. Skips on one foot. Hops on one foot. Throws a ball with full arm movement.	Copies a cross. Matches four colors correctly. Draws a man with 2 part Counts three objects correctly.
5 years	Skips on alternate feet smoothly. Can stand on one foot 8–10 seconds. Dances to music.	Copies a square and triangle. Draws a man with 6 parts (head, face, trun arms, and legs). Names colors.

As your child completes each task, place check mark in ruled column.

LANGUAGE	PERSONAL-SOCIAL
Speaks. Two to six words and recognizes more. Vocalizes wishes and needs at table. Points to objects when requested.	Feeds self. Uses a spoon but is messy. Imitates Mother in household duties.
Jargon. Many intelligible words. Uses six to twenty words.	Drinks without much spilling. Takes off clothes.
Puts two or three words together. Refers to self by name. Joins in nursery rhymes and songs.	Helps dress self. Less messy when eating. Turns down handle and opens door. Washes and dries hands.
200 word vocabulary. Uses pronouns I, me, you. Knows full name. Says a few nursery rhymes.	Helps put things away. Domestic make-believe play. Toilet trained during the day.
1,000 word vocabulary. Gives full name and sex. Uses plurals and pronouns. Lisping and stuttering common. Knows several nursery rhymes.	Feeds self well. Drinks with help. Puts on socks. Unbuttons clothes. Likes to help Mother (set table, clean). Sometimes shares things.
1,500 word vocabulary. Gives home address and age. Listens to and tells stories. Asks questions—who? why?	Dresses self unassisted. Can button clothes. Washes and dries hands and brushes teeth unassisted. Understands taking turns.
2,000 word vocabulary. Gives age and birthday. Names four colors. Repeats four digits. Asks meaning of words.	Independent and self-sufficient. Dresses and undresses self. Ties shoelaces. Uses knife and fork.

Record each testing date with a different color.

CHAPTER
20

Common diseases and complaints

Parents are justifiably alarmed by the sudden onset of illness in their children and quite surprised by their usual rapid recovery. New parents often find it difficult to judge how ill a child is and if a doctor is necessary.

The height of the temperature doesn't indicate the seriousness of a child's illness. If a youngster has a high temperature, 104° to 105°, but is otherwise happy and playing, you needn't be as concerned as if he has a lower temperature but appears quite ill.

If your youngster does have a temperature, it's better to give him the proper dosage of aspirin and keep him comfortable than to sponge him with ice water or give him a cold water enema. There is no magic height the temperature has to go to before a child convulses. Some children have a low threshold and will convulse at 101°; others won't convulse no matter how high the temperature goes.

Treatment of fever: Aspirin (one grain per year up to five years) given every four hours is reasonably safe. If the youngster is vomiting or having diarrhea, the use of aspirin should be somewhat curtailed. You may sponge the child with lukewarm water, never ice water.

CONVULSIONS A convulsion is terrifying to parents, but a baby rarely, if ever, dies because of one.

Convulsions that occur with fever are quite common, especially with some viral illness, and *usually* aren't of a serious nature. They're usually of short duration and seldom recur. Such illnesses as encephalitis and meningitis can have their onset with a convulsion and would, of course, be of a serious nature. But other symptoms would suggest these illnesses to your doctor and he would order further laboratory tests to determine their presence.

Convulsions that occur without fever should be thoroughly investigated by your physician.

If your child has a convulsion, remain calm. Remove anything that's loose in his mouth (food, gum, candy) which he might choke on. Lay him on his abdomen with his head to the side to prevent obstruction of the airway.

Call your doctor. He may want you to take the child to the hospital or his office where oxygen can be administered and anticonvulsic drugs safely given in doses large enough to abate the convulsion.

THE COMMON COLD A stuffed or runny nose, and a slight cough without fever indicate the common cold—a problem most parents encounter. Babies have difficulty breathing through their mouth, so when their nose is obstructed, they're irritable, have difficulty nursing, and are unable to sleep. If a fever accompanies a small baby's cold, call your doctor.

Treatment of the cold: Using a nasal aspirator or bulb syringe will help clear the mucus from the baby's nose. Compress the bulb and fit the syringe tightly to the baby's nostril. As you release the bulb, the suction pulls the mucus from the baby's nose. Then expel the mucus. Repeat as necessary. Your baby won't like this and will fuss, but it can be done safely even to the tiniest infant.

When the humidity in your home is low in the winter time, raising it seems to eliminate nasal soreness. Either cold or hot steam is a satisfactory means of raising the humidity. Cold vapor is safer than hot steam. The vaporizer you select should run for a period of 8 to 12 hours. Always place it out of reach of the baby's bed and protect the surface beneath it. Keep small children out of the room when you're using a vaporizer. Plain water is satisfactory. Most medications that are added to the water will cause some irritation if they are used for any extended length of time.

If your doctor doesn't suggest a specific cough syrup, honey will help, especially for a small baby. Put a few drops of lemon juice in the older child's dose, but, unless the baby is taking orange juice, leave the citrus out.

If during or immediately following the cold, the baby suddenly becomes extremely irritable and fussy, he probably has developed an ear infection. He may not run a fever, but may refuse his formula, or he may act as if his formula no longer satisfies him and will eat every hour or two. Have your doctor check him to find out what the trouble is.

ALLERGIES The child under two is most likely to become sensitized (allergic). In a family where there is already an allergic member, the incidence will be over 25 per cent.

Symptoms which may indicate your child is developing an allergic disease (asthma, hay fever, eczema) are: a cold that hangs on, continuous, recurring coughing, frequent chest infections—with or without wheezing, or a rash in the folds of his arms and legs.

Steps should be taken to prevent or minimize allergies with the potentially allergic baby. Diet should be kept as simple as possible and new foods should be started one at a time and with care. Eggs, wheat, orange juice, and chocolate should be withheld until the child is a year old. Evaporated milk or prepared formulas, or breast milk, should be used instead of cow's milk for the same period.

Wool blankets, fuzzy toys, and other obvious dust catchers, should be avoided. A sponge rubber or dacron pillow should be used instead of a feather pillow. It would be advisable not to let Baby crawl about on carpeted floors. Household dusting should be done often and with a vacuum cleaner or a well-oiled mop or rag. Some allergists feel pets should not be allowed in the house.

Your regular doctor may be able to determine the nature of a suspected allergy and prescribe medication which gives relief. He will refer you to an allergist if more intense diagnosis and treatment is indicated.

Common Diseases
and Complaints

DISEASE	CAUSE	APPEARS
Allergies (*See Hives, Asthma, Hay Fever*)	Sensitivity to foods, dust, molds, pollen, dog's hair, cat dander, etc. Exact cause sometimes unknown.	After exposure to allergy-causing items. May be year-round if sensitizer is food or household object.
Asthma	Allergy to foreign substance or infection. (House dust, molds, foods, pollens, infections, etc.)	Whenever irritating substance reaches bronchial tubes.
Blocked tear duct	Tear duct from eye to nose becomes blocked. Prevents drainage of tears from eye.	Occurs in approximately 5% of all infants during the first month of life.
Bronchiolitis	Bacteria or virus. The majority are caused by virus.	Disease of infants and young children; frequently seen in the winter and spring months and may occur in epidemics.
Bronchitis	Bacterial infection of bronchial tubes. May be initiated by irritating gases, dust, or other substances.	When mucous membranes of bronchi become inflamed.

SYMPTOMS	DURATION OF ILLNESS	TREATMENT
Red, swollen, watery eyes; sneezing, headaches, spasmodic coughing; hives; rash; gas pains in abdomen; vomiting; diarrhea; eczema; nose rubbing; constant cold; asthmatic child may be fatigued, cross, depressed, restless, jittery.	Until sensitizer is removed. Seasonal if due to pollen.	If not severe, antihistamine drugs prescribed by physician. If severe, have doctor determine cause and remove offending substance. Avoid unnecessary exposure to allergen, possibility of an infection precipitating or causing allergy. Your doctor may prescribe one or more of a variety of drugs, epinephrine, aminophylline, antihistamines, steroids, etc.
Thick mucus is secreted; breathing becomes difficult, labored; wheezing; coughing. Attacks most common at night.	Each attack varies with the severity. About 75% of children outgrow asthma by puberty.	Mild cases: Symptomatic medication. Severe or prolonged cases: Have doctor determine causes and start desensitization program. Repeated attacks may have harmful effect on lungs.
Matter drains from eye. Causes eyelid to become crusted. Tears overflow on cheek.	Some clear spontaneously. Usually of short duration if treated.	Keep the eyelids clean with a cotton ball that is moistened in sterile water. Your doctor may prescribe heat, eye drops, or daily massages of the tear duct. Massage gently with a cotton swab, with a downward stroke 3 or 4 times a day. If the symptoms persist for 3 or 4 months, the duct may need to be probed by an eye specialist.
Rapid and labored breathing with wheezing on expiration. Spaces between and below the ribs pull in during inspiration.	About a week depending on the severity of the illness.	Adequate hydration with fluids. Cool mist vaporizer. Suitable antibiotic if due to bacteria. Some cases require hospitalization.
Low-grade temperature usually accompanies cough. Cough usually loose; may be dry, hacky. Loss of appetite; lethargy; headache.	Seven to 10 days.	Specific antibiotic therapy usually results in prompt relief. Moisture (cool vapor or steam from a vaporizer) gives good relief. Limit child's *(Continued)*

DISEASE	CAUSE	APPEARS
Canker sores	Viral infection	In the mouth when conditions permit virus to become active. damage tissue. Similar illness, known as Herpangina, occurs in epidemic form in spring and early summer.
Carotonemia	Ingestion of foods containing carotene particularly yellow vegetables (carrots). May be present in thyroid deficiency cases.	Quite noticeable in children during their first two years of life. Frequently mistaken for jaundice.
Chicken pox	Highly contagious virus infection. Spread by direct contact with someone who has the disease. The period of contagiousness is the day before the rash appears and during the 5 days the new lesions are appearing. The crusts do not contain live virus.	Eleven to 24 days after exposure. Usually 14 days.

SYMPTOMS	DURATION OF ILLNESS	TREATMENT
		activity. Expectorant cough syrups are helpful. Depressant cough syrups give child chance to rest at night. Hospitalization may be required if respiratory distress develops. If there is repeated infection or exposure to irritating substances, problem may become chronic. Pneumonia may result.
Small painful ulcers involving the cheeks and the gums and in close proximity to where the cheek meets the gum.	Seven days plus 3 more days for sores to completely heal. Secondary bacterial infection may occur.	Mouth must be kept scrupulously clean with mouth washes. Use soda, salt-water mouth wash. Many commercial powders and liquids are available for local application.
The skin, particularly the palms, soles, and nose, have an orange-yellow color. The eyes are not yellow as they may be in jaundice.	Disappears or decreases when the carotene containing foods in the diet are decreased.	No treatment necessary. Benign condition.
Fever may appear 1 day prior to observance of initial skin lesions. Lesion is small, clear blister, about size of match head. Usually start on face and scalp and move downward. Appear in crops. Blisters easily broken, quickly form itchy crusts or scabs on spots.	New lesions appear in crops over 3–5 day period. The crusts may persist for 5–20 days and are not contagious. Removing scabs by scratching or itching may cause scarring.	Keep child in bed if possible. At least limit activity and keep away from other children. Aspirin and antihistamines taken by mouth help relieve itching. Soda, starch, oatmeal baths also help. (A cupful of starch or soda for small tub of water. Oatmeal colloidal material available at drugstore.) Doctor may suggest local application of lotion. After scabs fall off, bathe and shampoo child thoroughly with hexachlorophene soap and shampoo. Guard against scarring. Infection of lesions may occur. Secondary bacterial infections are possible. (Throat, ear, intestinal.)

DISEASE	CAUSE	APPEARS
Chorea (*St. Vitus's dance*)	In many cases thought to be associated with rheumatic fever; cause cannot always be determined; may be emotional.	Between 6 and 15 years; more frequent in girls than in boys.
Colds	Probably several different viruses.	After exposure to person having the infection. Chilling and fatigue seem to play part.
"Colic"	Tension	Between 2 weeks and 4 months of age, frequently occurring in late afternoon and evening.
Conjunctivitis	Infection; allergies; irritation from foreign objects or chemicals.	Inflammation of eyelids, whites of eyes, accompanied by itching, tearing, or discharge of pus if infectious.
Constipation	Multiple: lack of water, lack of bulk. In babies: Poorly prepared formula.	Bowels move with difficulty. All babies strain with bowel movements during the first 2 or 3 months. Breast-fed infants may go several days without bowel movement.

SYMPTOMS	DURATION OF ILLNESS	TREATMENT
Jerky, spasmodic, irregular body movements; worse if attempt is made to suppress them; nervousness develops gradually; child is irritable, fretful, and fatigued.	One to 4 months, or longer.	Bed rest; sedation helpful. Definite diagnosis essential. If associated with rheumatic fever, treatment of rheumatic fever imperative. If associated with rheumatic fever, penicillin or sulfa treatment will combat streptococcic infection, prevent further attacks.
Sneezing; running or stuffy nose; flushed cheeks; dull-looking eyes; little appetite; may have slight fever or cough.	Three to 7 days.	See *Treatment of colds,* page 334. Bronchitis, pneumonia, ear, throat, and sinus infections may develop.
Hard, persistent crying; red face; and hard abdomen.	Attacks may be very infrequent or regular until 4 months of age.	Does no permanent harm. Should not be mistaken for ear infection, urinary tract obstruction.
Sore, red eyes; yellow discharge.	Prompt response to treatment unless associated with viral illnesses or allergies.	Doctor may prescribe antibiotic eye drops or ointment. Keep eyes clean with cotton moistened in water. Warm, moist packs on eyelid alleviate some of burning. Foreign objects should be removed as soon as possible. If due to allergy, doctor will prescribe drops that relieve itching and redness. Proper treatment prevents chronic infection.
Small, hard, dry, pellet-like stools or large bulky stools which are difficult to pass. Blood streaked and painful bowel movement. Thin ribbon-like movements should be reported to doctor.		Increase fruit—especially prunes, other dried fruits—and fruit juices. Babies: Alter sweetening in formula. Older child: increase bulk in diet or give bulk-producing medication. Give enemas, laxatives, and suppositories only under doctor's supervision. Molasses or other crude sugars (available commercially) are good for use with young children. Chronic constipation *(Continued)*

DISEASE	CAUSE	APPEARS
Croup A. Spasmodic	Postnasal discharge locally irritates vocal cords.	Usually children under 5 years of age.
B. Laryngitis	Inflammation of larynx or vocal cords due to either viral or bacterial infection.	Usually children under 5 years of age.
Diabetes	Unknown. Disturbance in carbohydrate metabolism. Inadequate production of insulin or interference with normal insulin activity.	Twenty to 25% of children with diabetes develop it before 5 years of age and 35% between 5–10 years of age.
Diaper rashes	Younger infant: Sensitivity to soap, bleaches, diaper rinses with which diapers have been washed; various foods; oils, powders, lotions used on diaper area. Irritation from urine, stool, wet diapers infrequently changed; rubber or plastic pants. Older baby: Reaction of the skin to ammonia formed by bacteria in the urine.	Usually in early months of baby's life; in hot weather when bacteria work quickly on wet diapers; when diapers aren't sterilized.

SYMPTOMS	DURATION OF ILLNESS	TREATMENT
		may become a problem. *Avoid overanxious parental attitude toward correction of constipation.*
Sudden onset; usually without fever; starts with barking cough; difficulty in breathing; usually occurs at night when child is lying down.	½ to three hours.	Call doctor at once. Usually responds promptly to treatment; create intense steam by draping crib with sheet. Put steaming vaporizer in front of it. Or take youngster into bathroom and turn on hot shower. Keep child away from hot stream of water. Vomiting may relieve spasm. Expectorant cough medicines are helpful. Respiratory obstruction may require hospitalization.
Gradual onset; preceded by hoarseness during day, fever usually present.	Slower to leave.	Slower to respond to treatment. Same type of treatment as for spasmodic; doctor may want to use antibiotic if he feels bacterial infection is cause.
Weight loss despite normal or increased food intake. Fatigability and lethargy. Increased thirst and fluid intake. Increased urination. Generally awakens at night to urinate or wets the bed one or more times each night. Excess glucose in urine and in blood.	Lifelong. Child's life can be near normal with proper medical control.	Education of family and child about diabetes. Proper diet. Insulin.
Small red pimples or patches of rough, shiny, itchy, red skin. Pimples may develop whiteheads or become raw. End of penis may develop rash or ulcerate and bleed (rare). Tissues may swell. Diapers will have an ammonia smell.	Depends on response to treatment.	A. Younger infant: Eliminate bleaches, rinses; wash in mild soap and hot water, rinse thoroughly; remove rubber pants. If severe, expose to air. Cornstarch, zinc oxide, other protective ointments are helpful. B. Older baby: Ammonia rash. Boil diapers, especially those used at night, for 10 minutes; rinse *(Continued)*

DISEASE	CAUSE	APPEARS	
Diarrhea	Improper formula. Faulty feeding habits. Viral or bacterial infections. Food allergy. Antibiotics.	At all ages. May develop suddenly.	
Diphtheria	Bacteria. Source is secretion from nose, throat, skin or other lesions of infected persons or carriers. Direct contact with articles contaminated by infected persons.	Two to 6 days after exposure.	
Discharge from ear (*See ear infection*) and nose (*See Colds, Allergies, Hay Fever*)	May also result from foreign bodies children put in ear or nose.	Several days after foreign body is put into ear or nose.	

SYMPTOMS	DURATION OF ILLNESS	TREATMENT
		well, using commercial diaper rinse in final rinse water. Ointments are helpful. If rash is severe or doesn't respond to treatment, call physician. Don't allow baby to remain in wet or soiled diapers. The use of disposable diapers at least at night may be beneficial.
Frequent, loose watery bowel movements. Stools may become green or contain mucus or blood. Abdominal discomfort. Irritability, restlessness, lethargy, refusal to eat, fever. Skin, tongue, and lips become dry. Skin stays wrinkled when pinched. Reduced urine output.	Depends on cause of diarrhea and response to treatment.	Breast-fed infant: Mother should eliminate laxatives, fruits, or foods which might cause loose stools. Bottle-fed infant: Cut down sugar in formula. Child no longer on formula: Give diluted skim milk in relatively small quantities at frequent intervals. Offer water between milk feedings. Doctor may want to give specific medication. Restore solid foods gradually. Applesauce, bananas, smooth cereals are good to start. Failure to treat may result in dehydration. *Do not give laxatives!* Don't add salt to *milk or water.*
Fever; sore throat; membranes of throat, tonsils, palate, and nose slightly grayish.	Isolated until several nose and throat cultures show bacteria no longer present.	Isolation; diphtheria antitoxin immediately; antibiotic therapy to kill bacteria. Can be avoided by protective immunization. Improper treatment may result in obstruction of larynx; membranous croup; paralysis of palate; peripheral neuritis; heart damage; death.
Child complains of pain, discomfort. Discharge present.	Discharge subsides a day or two after object removed.	Removal of object. Proper treatment should prevent infection of area.

DISEASE	CAUSE	APPEARS	
Discharges from vagina (*See Vaginal discharges*)			
Ear infection	Usually associated with a cold; may accompany viral infections, e.g. measles, chicken pox. Irritation of eustachian tube by milk from improper feeding of baby.	After child has cold for several days; conclusion of most contagious diseases; frequently in young infants.	
Eczema	Food allergies; irritating substances in contact with skin.	When body rebels at repeated exposure to offending substances.	
Enuresia (*See Index, "Bed-wetting"*)			
Erythema Infectiosum (Fifth Disease)	Virus. Mode of transmission unknown.	Appears suddenly without any other symptom. Tendency for it to occur in epidemics and to involve more than one member of a family. Rash appears 6–14 days after exposure.	
Eye infections (*See Blocked tear duct, Conjunctivitis, Pinkeye, Sty*)			

SYMPTOMS	DURATION OF ILLNESS	TREATMENT
Cold may precede infection; infants become irritable; fussy; sleep short intervals; awaken crying, act hungry. (You may feel formula inadequate.) May pull at ears. May be discharge from ear.	Respond well to specific antibiotic therapy.	*Should be treated by physician.* Home remedies relieve only pain until doctor sees child. If ear drum isn't ruptured, warm (to the wrist) mineral or olive oil may be dropped in. Aspirin or cough syrup containing codeine may relieve pain. Heating pad or hot water bottle may help. Inadequate treatment may result in hearing loss, mastoiditis, secondary infection of external ear canal.
Patches of light red or tannish-pink rough, thick, scaly skin on face, in folds of arms, and backs of knees. Scales like dried salt. Scales later become moist deeper red, and itchy. Can become secondarily infected with discharge of pus. Miserable, irritable child.	Clears up between 1 and 2 years or becomes milder. If offending substance can be determined, can be eliminated.	Prevention is most important. In allergic child, great care should be taken in starting all foods. Egg, wheat, orange juice, peanuts, peanut butter, chocolate should be delayed until much later date. Physician should prescribe specific treatment for lesions; undertake intensive program to locate offending substance.
First appears on face as a flushed or "slapped-cheek" appearance. Second stage involves pink blotchy spots on back of arms and hands. Next appears on thighs, buttocks, and trunk.	About 9–11 days. There is a tendency for the rash to recur after exposure to sunlight or changes in temperature. Entire illness may cover a 3-week period.	No specific treatment. No need to keep child home from school, particularly since the rash has a tendency to recur over a period of weeks.

DISEASE	CAUSE	APPEARS
Fever blister	Virus	When child has a fever or when there is specific irritation of lips from nasal discharge.
German Measles (Rubella, 3-day measles)	Rubella virus is spread through infected droplets from the respiratory tract. Virus may be present a week before to 2 weeks after rash appears. Period of greatest contagion is a few days before the rash. Mothers who develop measles during the first 3 months of pregnancy may give birth to a severely deformed baby.	14–21 days after exposure.
Growing pains	The cause is often obscure. Excessive activity and fatigability. Postural defects (flat feet). Emotional disturbances. Allergy. Atmospheric changes.	Any age but more frequent in 6- to 10-year-old children. Affects lower extremities more than the upper. Occurs in intelligent and often high-strung children. General health usually good. Occurs at night.
Hay fever	Allergy to pollens. Allergic rhinitis, condition like hay fever caused by sensitivity to dust, animal hair, or dandruff, molds, etc.	Early spring and summer if due to tree, grass pollens. Mid-August if ragweed pollen. Year-round if due to dust, animal hair.
Hernia A. Inguinal	Failure of pouch to close when testicles descend into scrotum. Also occurs in girls— involves analogous organs.	Any time from shortly after birth until adulthood.
B. Umbilical	Opening in deep muscular layer of abdomen through which small part of intestine is pushed when baby cries.	Shortly after birth.

SYMPTOMS	DURATION OF ILLNESS	TREATMENT
Small, sore, tender areas on lips with slight swelling; blisters form later. Ooze and form scabs.	Usually 5 to 7 days.	No specific treatment. Ointments to keep lips soft may be helpful. Protect lips against offending substance. Usually no complications.
Mild fever, headache, nasal discharge, and enlarged glands behind ears, head, and neck. Small red spots appear on the face and spread rapidly to neck, trunk, arms, and legs. There may be some rash inside the mouth.	Usually 3 to 4 days.	Isolation to avoid exposure. Gamma globulin is given to pregnant women who are susceptible and have been exposed. The value of this is questionable. *German measles can be prevented by vaccination.*
Muscle pains. It does not affect joints. No pain on movement. Child is vague about the site of pain. No temperature changes or swelling is present.	Disappears as child grows older.	Hot or cold compresses or alcohol rubs. *Reassurance.*
Stuffed-up, itchy, running nose; red, watery, itchy eyes. If allergic rhinitis, only nasal symptoms present.	Depends upon effectiveness of treatment; elimination of offending substance.	Remove offending substance. Antihistamine-type drugs usually offer good relief. If severe, allergic investigation and desensitization program may be indicated.
Baby may be fussy when hernia is evident (area of groin).	Until surgically repaired.	Consult physician. Surgical repair usually indicated. If not treated, strangulation of intestine may occur.
Slight bulging may be noticed at navel. Larger when baby cries or strains. Does not cause baby to fuss.	Usually disappears by 1 year of age.	No specific treatment indicated. Surgery seldom necessary unless defect is extremely large. Taping with adhesive tape not necessary.

DISEASE	CAUSE	APPEARS
Hives	Sensitivity to serum injections; plants, foods, and drugs; exposure to heat or cold; emotional stress.	Within few seconds to several days after exposure.
Impetigo	Staphylococcus organism	After personal contact with infected person. More frequent in summertime.
Lockjaw (*See Tetanus*)		
Mastoiditis	Serious inflammation of mastoid system of skull from ear infection.	As complication of ear infection.
Measles (Rubeola)	Viral infection transmitted from person to person.	Ten days after exposure.

SYMPTOMS	DURATION OF ILLNESS	TREATMENT
Swelling of eyelids, lips, hands, feet, frequently accompany hives. Raised welts, pale in center, may itch unbearably.	Each attack can vary from a few hours to several weeks. Can be once in a lifetime or repeatedly.	If due to allergy, every effort should be made to prevent taking or eating substance again. If cause is unknown, try to determine. If it's a food, put child on elimination diet. Antihistamines by mouth often give relief. Bathe child in starch, soda, or oatmeal colloidal bath. Calamine lotion may help. Keep child from scratching. If hives are severe or prolonged, consult physician.
Starts as a small runny blister, often on the face. Sometimes develops into infected sore. Generally has light tan or honey-colored crust.	Usually heal in 7–10 days. Recurrences may occur. Untreated lesions will spread to most areas of body.	Physician will probably prescribe ointment. In specific cases, injections or oral dosage of antibiotics may be indicated. Good hygiene essential to prevent spread to others in family. Lesions should be scrubbed with hexachlorophene soap. Caution older child against picking at lesions. Each family member should have own towel. Scrub bathtub carefully after bathing child.
Tenderness and swelling of mastoid bone (directly behind the ear); vomiting; diarrhea; fever.	Short term if good response to antibiotics. Serious complications may follow if treatment is delayed.	Consult physician. Most children respond to intensive antibiotic therapy. Surgical treatment may be necessary.
1st symptom: Fever; harsh, deep cough; runny nose. Next day: Red, watery eyes. 3rd–4th day: Koplick's spots (fine white spots, sometimes surrounded by reddish ring inside cheek). 4th to 5th day: (*Continued*)	Nine days; 4 days of prodramal symptoms; usually 5 days of rash. A single attack confers lifelong immunity.	Quiet and bed rest. Avoid bright light if it is uncomfortable. Aspirin for fever. Encourage liquids. Cool mist of steam and cough medicine for the cough. *Vaccination with live attenuated virus gives lifelong immunity.*

DISEASE	CAUSE	APPEARS
Mumps	Virus transmitted by direct contact with person who has disease. Contagious a few days before the swelling and until the swelling has subsided.	Fourteen to 28 days or average of 18 days following exposure.
Nephritis	Most often follows an infection with group A beta hemolytic streptococcus. Other infectious agents, bacteria, and virus may be involved. Hypersensitivity reaction to the infection.	One to two weeks after an infection of the upper respiratory tract with streptococcus.
Nephrosis	Unknown. Hypersensitivity disease involving the kidneys. May also follow bee sting, exposure to metals, drugs, and systemic diseases.	Most common in children between 2–5 years of age.
Pinkeye (*See Conjunctivitis*)		
Pneumonia	Serious inflammation of lung from bacteria or virus.	May have abrupt onset in child, or occur after cold, measles, whooping cough.

SYMPTOMS	DURATION OF ILLNESS	TREATMENT
Fine rash starts on face, becomes blotchy, spreads down to cover body. Fever may remain for 2–3 days after rash breaks out; becomes extremely high with possible slight delirium.		
1st symptom: Usually complaint of earache before swelling noticed; fever. 2nd symptom: Swelling immediately beneath ear at angle of jaw; spreads out onto face, behind jaw, frequently under chin, one or both sides involved.	Swelling disappears 7 to 10 days. Immunity following an attack is lifelong.	Aspirin. Cold or warm compresses for relief of discomfort. Bed rest is not necessary except for those who are more acutely ill. Involvement of the testes does not occur in children before puberty. Encephalitis and hearing loss may occur. *Mumps can be prevented by vaccination.*
Fever, blood in the urine, reduced urine output, swelling of eyes and feet, elevated blood pressure, headache, vomiting, convulsions, signs of heart failure.	In majority of cases, recovery in one to three weeks.	Eradication of streptococcus with penicillin. Bed rest. Control of high blood pressure with anti-hypertension drugs.
Swelling of face, abdomen, lower extremities, reduced urine output, excess protein in urine, low protein and high cholesterol in blood.	Chronic disease lasting years in some cases.	Corticosteroid drugs.
May start without warning; high temperatures not uncommon; usually associated with harsh, deep cough; rapid, grunting-like breathing; pain in chest or abdomen not unusual; vomiting may occur.	If due to bacteria; usually good response to antibiotics with rather rapid improvement. If due to virus: active illness may last 7–10 days; equal period for full recuperation.	Call physician as soon as disease is suspected. Specific treatment: Antibiotic therapy. If child has trouble breathing, hospitalization and administration of oxygen may be necessary. Cough preparations (expectorant and depressant) may help. Rest is essential. Feed child bland, easily digested foods. *Follow physician's advice.*

DISEASE	CAUSE	APPEARS
Polio (Poliomyelitis)	Three groups of polio virus: Types 1, 2, and 3. Transmitted in nose and throat secretions of polio patients or carriers. May be spread indirectly by flies.	Epidemic form in summer and autumn. All age groups involved. Commonly 1 to 5 years. Seven to 21 days following exposure.
Prickly heat	Too much heat and overdressing.	Usually in hot weather when babies are overdressed.
Rheumatic fever	Specific cause unknown. Follows streptococcus infection.	May occur in all economic groups, not just poor and undernourished. Seldom seen in children under 4 or 5 years old. First symptoms follow strep infection in about 10 days.
Ringworm	Contagious fungus infection.	Usually on feet and scalp.

SYMPTOMS	DURATION OF ILLNESS	TREATMENT
Fever, severe headache, stiff neck and back, pains in arms and legs. Bulbar type associated with difficulty in swallowing, nasal twang to voice, respiratory difficulty, paralysis of cranial nerves. Weakness may develop anytime from onset or not be noticed for some time after recovery from acute illness. Areas of body stricken are legs, arms, trunk, respiratory, and swallowing muscles.	Fever lasts 5–7 days. May be difficult to evaluate full extent of involvement for a number of weeks or months.	*Prevention is most important.* Families should be immunized with Sabin oral vaccine. Treatment during acute stage, bed rest, control of pain, assist respiration if necessary, warm packs. Later physiotherapy. Braces or orthopedic surgery in some cases.
Small clusters of pink, raised rash; first appear on neck and shoulders. Tan-looking rash may appear later.	Until weather cools or baby is reasonably clothed.	Sunshine helps prevent and clear rash. Caution! *Don't burn.* Cool sponge baths several times a day; specific heat rash powders or cornstarch helpful for small baby. Treat promptly to avoid secondary bacterial infection.
Fever; fleeting pains in joints which are frequently red, swollen, hot; fatigue, irritability; loss of appetite; skin rashes; nosebleed.	Depends on severity; may require many months of bed rest or limited activity.	Because of severe consequences of inadequate treatment (further heart damage), it's essential that a complete diagnosis be made to definitely establish presence of disease. Specific treatment: Bed rest; penicillin or aspirin and cortisone. Activity may be resumed when temperature, pulse, and laboratory tests return to normal. Daily penicillin or sulfa must be given to prevent subsequent attacks.
Circular lesions, outer part slightly raised; intense itching and smarting; lesions may ooze, become secondarily infected.	Mild cases clear promptly; many respond poorly to medication, however, and may last period of years.	Consult physician for proper treatment. Prevention: Dry feet carefully after bathing; avoid stepping in special foot baths at public swimming pools and *(Continued)*

DISEASE	CAUSE	APPEARS
Roseola infantum	Viral infection.	Chiefly in infants or children under 3.
Rubella (*See German measles*)		
Rubeola (*See Measles*)		
Rupture (*See Hernia*)		
Scabies	Itch mite buries itself in skin to lay eggs.	After personal contact with person having disease or with bedding.
Scarlet fever	Streptococcus organism.	Two to 5 days after exposure to infected person. All ages are susceptible.

SYMPTOMS	DURATION OF ILLNESS	TREATMENT
		bathing areas. Proper treatment will prevent spread of lesions; infection of others; secondary bacterial infections and possible permanent areas of baldness.
Onset is abrupt; usually high fever; restlessness; fretfulness; irritability; poor appetite. Do not appear seriously ill; may be playful. On 4th day, fever drops to normal. Blotchy red rash appears on head and trunk. Lasts for 3 days. Fever convulsions may occur.	Usually 6 to 7 days from onset of fever.	Bed rest; liquids; light diet; aspirin. Don't confuse with measles!
Burrows in skin caused by mite crawling under surface. Areas become inflamed, itch intensely, become infected, may be filled with pus. Itching more severe at night and may disturb sleep. Infection usually on underside of wrists, armpits, around waist, between fingers. May spread over body.	Depends upon treatment. Not more than two weeks if child doesn't scratch.	Application of prescribed medication applied to thoroughly washed, clean skin. Leave ointment on overnight. Put boiled, laundered clothes on each morning. Sterilize all clothing and bedding each day. Secondary infections may develop from scratching. Skin may react to ointments and require special treatment.
Sore throat; fever; lethargy; loss of appetite; possible vomiting. Fine pinpoint rash appears within 24 to 48 hours. Most noticeable under arms, abdomen, thighs; face usually flushed, pale around mouth; tongue has strawberry-like appearance.	Prompt recovery with proper treatment.	Penicillin should continue to be given for full 10-day period. If child is allergic to penicillin, other antibiotics will be prescribed for 10-day period. Infected person should be isolated. People who have history of rheumatic fever and are exposed should receive preventive shot of penicillin. Rheumatic *(Continued)*

DISEASE	CAUSE	APPEARS
Smallpox	Highly contagious viral infection.	Average incubation period is 12 days. (Ranges from 10–16 days.)
St. Vitus's dance (*See Chorea*)		
Sty	Infected gland of eyelid due to staphylococcus infection.	When gland becomes infected.
Tetanus (*Lockjaw*)	Tetanus bacteria in soil and fecal discharges of man and animals.	Need not look like severe wound. Particularly following puncture or dirty wounds, compound fractures, or burns. Usually 5 to 14 days after a wound. May be 3 to 5 weeks.
Thrush	Yeast or fungus infection in mouth. Principal cause—from vaginal infection of mother.	In poorly nourished child; child on antibiotic therapy; if mother has vaginal infection.

SYMPTOMS	DURATION OF ILLNESS	TREATMENT
		fever, nephritis, throat and abscess infections may follow.
Abrupt onset with severe headache, backache. Rash appears 3 to 4 days after onset, consisting of separate papules, then blisters and later pustules, and finally crusts. Affected lesions in some stage of development are more common on the face, forearms, hands, legs, and feet than on the trunk.	Crusts loosen and fall off in 4 to 6 weeks. Contagious until all crusts are shed.	By adequate vaccination, this disease can be prevented. Vaccination should be given every five years. Yearly in areas where smallpox exists. If exposed, vaccinate immediately.
Red, tender, swollen eyelid; usually comes to a head, breaks, and requires no further treatment.	Three to 5 days. Repeat infections common.	Apply hot moist, or warm moist packs to help relieve soreness. Physician may prescribe antibiotic ointment. If chronic, he may take other measures to try to avoid recurrence.
Stiffness of muscles in neck and jaw; inability to open jaw; difficulty in swallowing and speaking follow rapidly; severe, repeated convulsions; some fever.	Two to 4 weeks.	*Prevention is essential.* Child should be immunized when infant. A booster should be given after any wound of significance. Tetanus antitoxin given at time of injury to non-immunized child gives relatively poor protection against the illness. Patient must be hospitalized. Death rate extremely high.
Small white sores in mouth like spots of milk. If severe, mouth may be quite sore; child may refuse to nurse vigorously.	Depends on response to treatment. May become reinfected.	Apply one percent gentian violet to mouth 2 or 3 times a day for no more than 3 days at any one time. Your physician may prescribe an oral anti-fungicide. Complications involving esophagus, stomach, or pneumonia may occur.

DISEASE	CAUSE	APPEARS
Tics (*habit spasms*)	Spasmodic, irregular movements of separate muscle groups repeated over and over. May be copied from another person.	Usually in later childhood or pre-school age.
Tonsillitis	Bacterial and viral.	Depending on cause: Bacterial—2–5 days; viral—5–10 days incubation period.
Tuberculosis	Infection by tubercle bacillus. Most often caused by intimate contact with adult having tuberculosis or raw milk from infected cattle.	In lung and lymph glands at root of lung. Except in small children, first infection usually heals and becomes surrounded with lime deposit. Infection may spread through blood or lymph vessels to brain, joints, kidneys. If person who has had first infection is later re-exposed, or if there is lightening up of first infection, reinfection tuberculosis develops. First infection in some individuals is progressive and continues into reinfection.
Typhoid	Direct contamination of milk, other foods or water with typhoid bacillus from typhoid carriers or from active cases of typhoid. May be spread by flies.	1 to 2 weeks after exposed.

SYMPTOMS	DURATION OF ILLNESS	TREATMENT
Blinking of eyes; sniffing; throat clearing; dry coughing; grimacing; shoulder-shrugging. Begins as voluntary movements, later habitual.	Until underlying tension and nervousness is relieved.	Differentiate from chorea or St. Vitus's dance. Adjustment of home or school environment to relieve pressure. Help child attain self-confidence and gratification from accomplishment. Scolding, punishment increase difficulty.
Bacterial; sudden onset; relatively high fever; later in illness sore throat; difficult swallowing; bad odor to breath; mushy-sounding voice. Viral; not as sudden in onset; fever or headache may accompany it. Both may cause swollen glands in neck.	Five to 7 days.	Consult physician. Hot salt-water gargles and sprays may give relief. Apply hot or cold compresses to neck. Occasional complications: Rheumatic fever; nephritis. Antibiotics may be indicated.
First infection may occur without child's being ill. May be some fever, irritability, loss of appetite. Early symptoms of reinfection are fatigue, slight rise in temperature, pain in chest from pleurisy. When patient loses weight, coughs, has night sweats, disease is usually well-advanced.	In mild cases, clinical cures are common in 6 months. In severe cases, prolonged therapy is required.	Diagnosis by skin test, X ray, recovery of tubercle bacillus by gastric washings. Treatment must be directed by doctor. Keep children away from infected persons. Those with tuberculosis should be isolated.
Fever, abdominal pain, diarrhea, rash, respiratory symptoms, gastrointestinal bleeding, prostration, delirium.	Until controlled by specific antibiotic therapy.	Specific antibiotic. Patient isolated. Active immunization of household exposures.

DISEASE	CAUSE	APPEARS
Urination frequent	Infection or abnormality of urinary tract. Increased fluid intake. Diabetes. May be normal in some children, especially those up to two years of age.	Sudden appearance of frequency in a previously healthy child should make one suspicious of a urinary tract infection or abnormality.
Vaginal discharge	Vaginal infection or foreign body in the vagina.	At all ages.
Vomiting	A variety of causes. Faulty feeding, infection, intestinal obstruction, appendicitis, metabolic disorders like diabetes, drugs, allergy, psychogenic-factors, nervous system disorders, and many others.	At all ages.
Whooping cough	Bacterial infection spread by droplet infection on contact with secretions from nose and throat of an infected case.	5 to 21 days after exposure. The average is 10 days.
Worms	Intestinal parasites or their eggs, carried into body by hands, food, or picked from soil through feet when barefooted (hook worm).	

SYMPTOMS	DURATION OF ILLNESS	TREATMENT
Dependent upon cause. Urination several times within an hour. Burning. Fever and chills. Abdominal or back discomfort.	Depends on specific cause and its correction.	Consult physician. Investigate cause. Infection present, treat with proper drug. Correct urinary tract abnormality when it exists.
The vulva may appear inflamed. Itching and discharge. Discharge may be mild. It may be light yellow, thick yellow, and sometimes, bloody.	Depends on the cause.	Consult your physician. Condition may clear up with hygienic measures, sitz baths, or irrigation with warm saline. In certain cases, the use of antibiotics may be prescribed. Removal of foreign body when present in vagina.
Depends on the cause. Loss of appetite, nausea, vomiting, fever, abdominal discomfort, headache are some of the symptoms.	Depends on the cause and its correction.	Consult your physician particularly if abdominal pain is present. In epidemic vomiting, withhold everything for 1 to 2 hours. Then give small sips of water, carbonated beverages, tea, or juices, ice chips, or a popsickle. Doctor may prescribe medication to control vomiting.
Begins with a mild cough and gradually increases in severity. Cough is more frequent at night. Not until the end of the second week do the coughing paroxysms and inspiratory whoop appear. When coughing, the child chokes, gets red in the face and may turn blue, frequently vomits. Cough ends in an inspiratory whoop. The cough becomes less severe in the 5th and 6th weeks.	Four to 6 weeks.	*Prevention through vaccination is most important.* Hospitalization and close supervision of young infants with whooping cough. They are treated with antibiotics and pertussis immune globulin. Exposed susceptibles who have been immunized previously are given a booster dose of pertussis vaccine. Immune globulin can be given to those not vaccinated previously.
Itching around rectum; moderate indigestion; disturbed sleep; worms in stool.	Depends on type of worm.	Physician will prescribe treatment. Varies with different types of parasite.

DISEASE	CAUSE	APPEARS
A. Pinworms	Ingestion of eggs. Eggs carried to mouth after touching infected objects. Anus to finger to mouth infection common.	Three to 6 weeks after ingestion of eggs. May infect the entire household.
B. Roundworms	Ingestion of eggs from soil or food.	Eggs hatch into larvae in the intestinal tract. The larvae migrate from the intestinal tract to other parts of the body in 2–3 weeks.

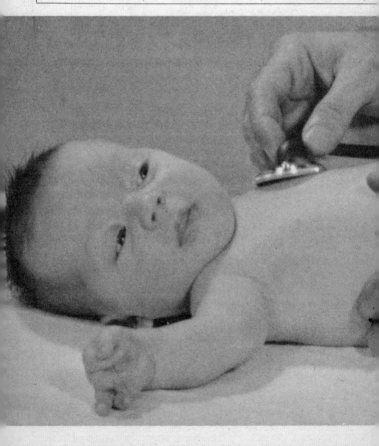

SYMPTOMS	DURATION OF ILLNESS	TREATMENT
Perianal itching. Vaginal itching in girls. Disturbed sleep. Abdominal discomfort and irritability.	Treatment with drugs is more than 90 percent effective. Recurrences are frequent.	Personal and household hygienic measures. Piperazine drugs and Pyrvinium pamoate highly effective.
Abdominal discomfort, irritability, cough during lung stage.		Piperazine

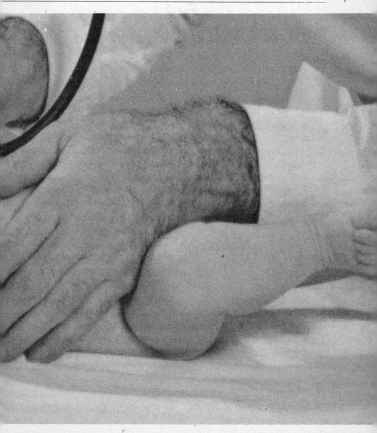

First aid

Here's what to do in case of minor injuries, and while waiting for the doctor in serious emergencies

Today more children die from accidents than from the seven most serious diseases. Far too often, these tragedies could have been avoided if simple precautions had been taken. Uncomplicated measures like locking medicine chests, placing matches out of a child's reach, and seeing that guards are placed around fires, could have prevented at least 90 percent of all accidents involving children.

The leading causes of accidental deaths in children from ages 1 through 4 are: Automobiles, fires, drowning, poison, and falls.

In spite of all that is being done in education, engineering, and legislation, automobiles are today's number one child killer. The very young child must be protected from the auto —both inside and out. Safety belts and harnesses have been developed to protect the passenger. However, to be beneficial these safety devices must be used.

When traveling with children, protect them by strapping them in the back seat and locking the doors. If the trip is going to be a long one, plan ahead: Devise a set of car behavior rules for your children, collect material for car games, and have supplies handy in case of sudden motion sickness.

The second largest cause of accidental deaths in children results from fire and burns. In the United States, there are an estimated two million serious burn injuries to children each year.

The major causes of fire and burn accidents are: Improper storage or use of flammable materials; defective wiring and dangling cords; smoking by adults; improper use of cooking utensils; and flammable clothing.

Most fires occur in the home and are preventable. And, children are frequently the helpless victims of fire because they are unable to escape a burning building by themselves. Protect your family from this by devising a fire escape plan and making sure that each family member knows what to do and where to go in case of fire.

Another major contributing factor to burn injuries and deaths is the flammability of fabrics commonly used in clothing. As yet, there is no really good "flammability" test for fabrics, so remember that wool and fiber glass are the safest fibers while cotton and some of the synthetics are the most hazardous.

Drowning has become the third largest cause of fatal accidents involving children. As more and more private pools are built, drowning could become an even larger accident factor.

Enroll your child early in Red Cross or YMCA swimming programs. Never allow a young child to swim alone. Also, as it only takes a small amount of water for a person to drown, never leave a child in or near water without supervision. This includes the tub.

The fourth highest cause of accidental deaths in children results from poisoning.

The only proper form of storage for all medicines and household cleaning supplies is under lock and key. Never rely on the old out-of-sight, out-of-reach methods. Never put poisonous substances in bottles that at one time held food or soft drinks. Leave all drugs in their original containers and make sure all labels provide rapid identification. Discard all prescription drugs after the illness has passed—by flushing them down the toilet.

Falls are the greatest non-fatal cause of accidents and have the fifth highest death rate among children's accidents. Falls, bumps, and bruises are all a part of growing up. It would be impossible for a parent to provide this kind of thorough protection. However, parents should protect their children from major falls from beds, bathinettes, stairs, and open windows.

Because most accidents happen up to the age of 2, the parent must anticipate hazards and eliminate them. Discipline is of the utmost importance, and during this time it should be concerned primarily with your child's safety. It should be reasonable; your command must be stern, but loving. Punishment must be related in your child's mind to the particular misdemeanor.

A doctor can immunize your child against many diseases and guide you in the prevention of many more, but only you as a parent can protect your child against accidents.

Pay particular attention to these danger areas:

Kitchen—hot stove, gas, boiling liquids, coffee percolator, electric appliances, knives, detergents, grease solvents, ammonia, furniture polish.

Bathroom—hot tub of water—or to a small baby, a tub of water, electrical appliances near tub, slippery surfaces, razors, medicines, cosmetics, disinfectants.

Basement and garage—paint, paint remover, turpentine, power tools, sharp tools, electrical outlets, gasoline, poison, poison items in refuse cans, empty aerosol cans, insecticides, broken glass, rusty nails, car.

Stairs—inadequate lighting, defective tread or carpet, no handrail.

Yard—pools, unsafe play equipment, sprayed vegetation, garden tools, daredevil play, broken glass.

Driveway—cars.

Automobiles—children should always ride in the back seat. Safety belts are recommended and should be fastened. Car seats for younger children should be firmly anchored. Doors should be locked.

As a parent, preventing accidents is only part of your job. You must also be able to handle any accident which might occur. To do this efficiently and effectively, you must be prepared. Make a complete list of emergency phone numbers and keep it by your phone. Include the numbers of your doctor, hospital, police department, fire department, and area poison control center. Also for emergency medical treatment, collect or purchase first-aid kits for your home and automobile.

As time is very important in any emergency situation, have a working knowledge of first-aid measures which you can apply until the proper medical help arrives. Study the following pages on first aid and either keep this or some other first-aid manual recommended by your doctor, handy for quick referrals.

Abscess. If a tender, inflamed, throbbing infected area develops on a finger tip, around a toenail, or at the site of a cut, apply a warm, wet compress to the area constantly. Place a thick sterile bandage (or a clean towel or sanitary napkin) over the area, wetting it with a solution made from a cup of warm water and a tablespoon of Epsom or table salts. The compress will soften the skin, allowing it to break and release the gathering pus. If the child has a fever, a noticeable swelling around the area, or red streaks appear up the limb or arm involved, consult your physician.

Artificial respiration. If a child stops breathing for any reason, start artificial respiration *at once*! Continue until the child starts to breathe again or until a doctor arrives. If the community has a rescue squad, it should be called immediately. Smothering, electric shock, drowning, or gas inhalation are common causes of breathing cessation.

The most efficient and practical way to save a life is to blow your breath into the child's lungs by either mouth-to-mouth or mouth-to-nose resuscitation. For infants or small children, your mouth should be placed over both the nose and mouth of the child. Remember, never give artificial resuscitation to someone who is breathing!

Clean visible foreign matter from mouth with fingers; place child on back; tilt head back with the chin up; use fingers of both hands to lift lower jaw from beneath and behind so it juts out to prevent the tongue from falling back blocking the air passage. Place your mouth over the child's nose and mouth to make a "leakproof" seal. Breathe into child with shallow puffs of air, about 20 per minute. If air exchange seems to be blocked, and you cannot breathe easily into child, check "jutting-out" position of jaw to be sure the tongue has not fallen back and that the airway is open.

If air passages are still blocked, suspend child by ankles—or—hold child head-down over one of your arms and give several sharp pats between shoulder blades to help dislodge

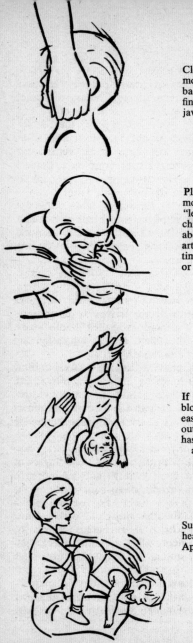

Clean visible foreign matter from mouth with finger; place child on back with head tilted back; use fingers of both hand to lift lower jaw from beneath and behind so it juts out.

Place your mouth over both mouth and nose of child to make "leakproof" seal. Breathe into child with shallow puffs of air, about 20 per minute. Continue artificial respiration until the victim begins to breathe for himself or until a physician arrives. Recovery should be rapid.

If air exchange seems to be blocked, and you cannot breathe easily into child, check "jutting-out" position to be sure tongue has not fallen back. If air passages are still blocked, act at once!

Suspend child by ankles or hold head-down over one of your arms. Apply sharp pats between shoulder blades.

obstructing matter in the air passage.

An airway tube (resuscitation tube) is desirable first-aid equipment. Drugstores sell inexpensive tubes made of plastic. One end is inserted over the victim's tongue, the other end projects and serves as a mouthpiece through which the rescuer breathes into the victim. The tubes come in child and adult sizes and are first-aid equipment no home with children should be without. You may also wish to carry one in your car. Follow the directions for use of the tube *very carefully* or you may do more harm than good. If the tube is not instantly available, give direct mouth-to-mouth respiration immediately. Both are equally effective means of artificial respiration.

Recovery should occur quickly except in electric shock, and drug or carbon monoxide poisoning which may necessitate long periods of artificial resuscitation.

Discontinue resuscitation when the child begins to breathe.

Bites, animal. Wash the wound thoroughly with soap and water to remove saliva, holding the wounded area under running water if possible to rinse thoroughly. Dry with clean gauze and rinse with hydrogen peroxide. Notify your physician at once. Tetanus booster should be given. Every possible effort should be made to capture and infence the biting animal so that it can be observed for rabies. The animal should not be killed unless absolutely necessary, and if it must be destroyed, the head should not be damaged. It must be examined to determine the possible presence of rabies. Notify the health department or police who will handle the investigation of the live animal or arrange for laboratory examinations of the head. If the animal can't be located, anti-rabies shots will have to be considered. A word of caution to parents: All family animals should be immunized against rabies.

Bites, bees, wasps, hornets. Make a paste of baking soda, moistened with cold water. This can be held in place by a bandage, but should be kept moist. Diluted household ammonia applied to the bite and surrounding skin may give relief. Calamine lotion with 1 percent phenol is beneficial for the itching. Cold compresses reduce swelling and pain. If available, cortisone-type ointments provide more relief. Oral antihistamines may also help relieve swelling, itching, and discomfort.

Some children are extremely sensitive to these bites and may have a severe reaction. If this has happened previously, talk to your physician about desensitization or treatment to be followed in case of a repeat bite.

Bites, chiggers, *See bites, mosquito.*

Bites, human. Cleanse thoroughly with soap and water and dry with gauze or cotton. Take the child to the doctor if the skin has been broken. Human bites often become infected and need close attention.

Bites, mosquito and chigger. To relieve discomfort, apply a paste of baking soda and water. An application of calamine lotion with 1 percent phenol will also give relief. Keep scratching to a minimum and keep skin clean with a hexachlorophene soap. If your child has a severe reaction to this kind of bite, talk to your physician. He may prescribe small doses of an antihistamine which will prevent swelling, itching, and redness.

Bites, snake. If there are no poisonous snakes in your locality, you needn't proceed with the idea that the bite is from a poisonous snake. If you live in an area where there are poisonous snakes, the type of bite wound will establish for your doctor whether or not the snake was poisonous. Venomous snakes leave two puncture wounds from the fangs and in less than 15 minutes there will be excruciating pain and swelling (coral snakes, found in the South, are an exception). To be effective, treatment following a bite from a poisonous snake must be carried out almost immediately. A tourniquet is applied above the first joint nearest the bite, not too tight, so as not to block the blood supply. One-eighth-inch incisions are made through each of the fang marks and suction is applied for an hour. Antivenom should be administered soon if the treatment is to be effective.

If the snake has been killed it should be taken along with the child to the physician so that it can be properly identified.

In communities where poisonous snakes are found, antitoxin for snake bites is usually readily available. And certainly

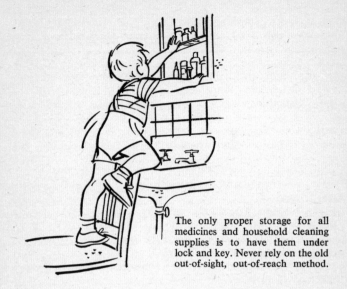

The only proper storage for all medicines and household cleaning supplies is to have them under lock and key. Never rely on the old out-of-sight, out-of-reach method.

the doctor will be familiar with the use and administration of the antivenom.

Bruises. For the first 24 hours, apply iced and cold cloths (immediately) to keep down any slight swelling. After the 24-hour period is up warm compresses will hasten the disappearance of the swelling and removal of discoloration. If skin is broken, it should be treated as an open wound.

Burns, chemical. Such substances as lye, caustic soda, other corrosive fluids, should be kept far beyond the reach of small children. But if an accident happens, strip off all clothing which has come in contact with the chemical. Flood the burned area immediately with a large quantity of water until the chemical is washed away. If possible, rush immediately under bathroom shower. Then contact the doctor immediately for further instructions. Burns from acids should be treated the same way, then rinsed with a baking soda solution. If there is a delay and corrosive liquid has dried, call doctor at once.

Burns, fire, dry heat, and scalds. If the area is relatively small, submerge the burned part immediately in cold running water for several minutes. This relieves the pain and reduces the local reaction to the burn. Cleanse the burn with hexachlorophene soap or any soap available. Apply a mild burn ointment or petroleum jelly. Remember, ointments should be used for small, minor burns only. Next apply a sterile dressing. The exclusion of air will give some pain relief.

If the burn is extensive, home treatment is not indicated. Cover the patient immediately with a clean sheet so burns are not contaminated any more than necessary. Take the patient to the hospital at once! Tetanus booster should be given to all patients burned to any significant degree.

Burns, sunburn. The skin of the baby or small child is tender and burns easily. Sunbaths should be given only in early morning or late afternoon when the sun is not too hot. To start, he should be out no longer than 5 minutes. If the baby tolerates this period of time, the sunbaths can gradually get longer.

If he does happen to get sunburned over a large area, call your physician. A bad sunburn can be very serious, especially with a baby or small child.

If relatively small areas are involved, cold, wet compresses (using cold water) will provide some relief. Cold cream, petroleum jelly, olive oil, or cocoa butter also help. Apply liberally with as little rubbing as possible.

Cuts, See *wounds in which bleeding isn't severe.*

Drowning, See *artificial respiration.*

Drugs, medicines swallowed, See *poisons.*

Earache, See *"ear infection," Illnesses chart.*

Eyes, specks, foreign objects, and caustics. Keep the child from rubbing his eye, since the object may scratch the membrane covering the eyeball. Small specks can be removed by flushing the eye with clear water or an eyewash.

You may also draw the upper eyelid down and away from

the eye, holding it by the lashes. Tears will wash the speck out. If you are unsuccessful in removing the object by these simple means, call your doctor.

If the child gets lime, plaster, or cement in his eyes, wash out immediately with great quantities of water. Then call your doctor at once. Time is important.

Eye wounds. If the eye is lacerated, torn, or damaged to a severe degree by any means cover the eye and take the child to the doctor immediately. A blunt blow to the eye may cause hemorrhage within the chamber of the eye. If you notice bloody discoloration as you look through the pupil, keep the child quiet and contact the doctor at once.

Fainting. The most common form of pallid unconsciousness is fainting. It is usually caused by a temporarily insufficient supply of blood to the brain. The best first aid for fainting is to keep the child lying down, head lowered or legs and hips elevated. Loosen constricting clothing. Sprinkle cold water on face. Open the window and allow fresh air to enter the room.

After the child has regained consciousness, offer him small amounts of a carbonated beverage or juice. Recovery should be rapid, within 5 minutes or less. If unconsciousness is prolonged, convulsions occur, or fainting recurs, see your physician.

If a person feels faint in a crowded place, never try to walk him out. If it is not possible for him to lie down, make him sit down and bend over putting his head between his knees. If a chair is not available, make the child kneel down and bend over as if tying a shoe. Any of these positions will put the head lower than the heart thus forcing the blood supply to return to the head.

Falls. If the baby falls from a high place, put him to bed, keep him as quiet as possible, and have the doctor examine him to be sure he's all right. Watch the child carefully. If he falls asleep, let him do so. But, awaken him at 30 to 60 minute intervals and check to make sure that he is all right.

This is especially important if he vomits, appears pale, or seems dazed and unlike himself. Pay particular attention to his eyes. Unequal pupil size indicates brain damage.

Food poisonings, *See poisons.*

Fractures. A fracture itself is seldom an emergency that requires great speed in treatment. And, great harm can be done if a patient is moved hastily or allowed to stand. Unless essential for safety, do not move or disturb a patient while waiting for the doctor or ambulance.

Examine first for other injuries. Stop serious bleeding by hand pressure on gauze dressing over wound.

If necessary, cut away clothing with great care not to disturb the injured part. Keep patient warm and lying down.

If medical help will be delayed and patient must be transported, do not try to set the bones. Splint the person where he lies using anything that is rigid for an emergency splint—boards, sticks, umbrella, cane, tightly rolled magazine, floor mat or a pillow. The splint should extend above and below the adjacent joints. Tie the splint above and below the fracture. Always apply splints before moving or transporting a person.

Frostbite. Gently cover the frozen part with your hand until it's thawed and circulation is restored, or cover with extra clothing or warmed—not hot—towels or blankets. You may immerse the frozen part in tepid water as long as the water's temperature is below 100 degrees. Do not rub frozen part with snow or anything else. Frozen tissue is fragile, easily damaged. Do not expose frozen part to intense direct heat of hot stove, radiator, or heat lamp.

Gas, inhaled, *See artificial respiration.*

Gun wounds, *See wounds.*

Hiccups often clear up spontaneously with no treatment. Mild cases can often be stopped by getting the child to hold his breath as long as possible, or making him drink slowly a glass of water to which a pinch of baking soda has been added. Pulling his tongue out as far as possible may give immediate relief. Breathing in and out of a paper bag fitted over the face may stop them. Persistent cases should be brought to the attention of a physician.

Hives, *See "hives," Common Diseases and Complaints.*

Infections from cuts, *See wounds, infected.*

Infected wounds, *See wounds.*

Insecticides, swallowed, *See poisoning from drugs.*

Ivy poisoning, *See poisons.*

Nosebleed. Quickest way to stop nosebleeds: Pinch nose between thumb and forefinger for 5 to 10 minutes. Or, a small wedge of cotton moistened with nosedrops may be placed inside the nostril and with the finger against the outside of that nostril apply firm pressure for five minutes. Another way: Put pad of cotton, tissue, or soft cloth under upper lip and press against nose firmly with forefinger laid on lip.

If bleeding persists, plug nostril gently with small strip of loosely rolled gauze. Push backward (not upward) into nostril no farther than little finger can push it. Leave strip of gauze dangling for easy removal. If nosebleeding persists or recurs, call doctor.

Objects swallowed. Tacks, open safety pins, needles and other small sharp objects are frequently swallowed by children. Do not give a laxative. Consult your doctor. Most foreign objects, especially round ones such as a button or small coin, that reach the stomach pass through the bowel harmlessly. Open safety pins, tacks, and sharp objects *usually* pass through without causing any complications. The doctor may follow the progress with an X ray. Never force a child who has swallowed a sharp object to vomit.

If the child chokes, turn him head and face down and with the palm of the hand, forcefully hit the back of the child's chest to dislodge a foreign body in the throat. If he can breathe, it is not necessary to do this before taking the child to the doctor.

Poisoning from drugs, medicines, caustics, insecticides, sedatives, and animal poisons. Call doctor or poison control center at once. Prepare to rush child to hospital but first give immediate first aid. Don't lose time seeking a specific poison antidote. Use simple measures immediately available.

If child is conscious, dilute poison by giving large amounts of water. The fluids may cause vomiting which should be encouraged (*Exceptions: See below*). If syrup of ipecac is available (and it should be in every home where there are children), give 1 tablespoon of the syrup to children over 1 year of age, and 2 teaspoons for those children under 1 year of age. This is a more effective way of ridding the stomach of poisons than the hospital's stomach pump.

If child vomits, hold face downward in your lap, head hanging over. Save the vomit so the physician may examine it. If no vomiting occurs within 20–30 minutes, the same dose of ipecac may be repeated, but once only.

If no syrup of ipecac is available, a less effective method to induce vomiting is to give a glass of warm milk or water and then tickle the back of the throat with the blunt handle of a spoon.

Do not induce vomiting if patient has swallowed lye or corrosive acids or alkalis (may be burns around the face or mouth) such as Lysol, or solution containing phenol, lye, ammonia, drain or toilet-bowl cleaners; or kerosene, gasoline, or turpentine. Never try to make an unconscious, semiconscious, or convulsive patient vomit.

Do not wait for child to vomit but transport him quickly to the doctor or hospital. If no transportation is available, contact the rescue squad. Take the poisonous material which the child has swallowed with you.

Poisoning from food. The most common cause of food poisoning: Eating foods contaminated by improper refrigeration. Cream pies, cream puffs, potato salad, and cold foods containing mayonnaise are the most frequent trouble foods. Depending on the type of food poisoning, pain, cramps, nausea, and vomiting may appear anywhere from 2 hours to a day or two after eating contaminated food. Call the doctor. Put the patient to bed, keep warm. After nausea and vomiting subside, give warm water and other fluids.

Sometimes children eat poisonous mushrooms or berries. Give large dose of Epsom salts after vomiting has been induced. Call your doctor at once or take the patient to a hospital immediately.

Poisoning from plants. Wash the skin with plenty of soap and water, lathering five or six times. Then wash again with rubbing alcohol, rinse in clear water, and dry. If rash develops, a drying lotion such as calamine may help. If rash starts oozing, spreads, and appears infected, call your physician.

Puncture wounds, *See wounds.*

Scalds, *See burns, fire.*

Sedatives, swallowed, *See poisoning from drugs.*

Shock. Expect shock to develop after any serious injury. Always think of shock before taking other time-consuming first-aid steps.

Signs of shock are rapid but weak pulse; pale face; cold, clammy skin; nausea; shallow, irregular breathing; and thirst.

While waiting for the doctor to arrive, have patient lie flat, head level with or lower than rest of body or with legs elevated to height of 12 to 18 inches. Cover patient to prevent loss of body heat. Do not let patient see injury—it will only further upset him. Reassure him. Handle very gently. Pain increases shock.

If the patient is conscious and not vomiting give him a solution consisting of 1 teaspoon of table salt and ½ teaspoon of baking soda dissolved in 1 quart of water. Measure proportions carefully. Allow patient to have all he will drink.

Shock, electrical, *See artificial respiration.*

Splinters, *See wounds.*

Sprains. Many times it is difficult to determine whether a wrist or ankle has been sprained or broken. Have the child lie down in case it's an ankle or leg injury and call the doctor.

Minimize the swelling by putting the injured extremity in cold water or by applying cloths soaked in cold or ice water as soon as possible after the injury. Apply for at least 30 minutes, or longer. If movement causes marked pain, immobilize the injured portion with a pillow splint. Place extremity on pillow, fold up and over leg or arm, and tie with cord: An X ray may be necessary to determine whether the injury is a fracture or sprain.

Stings, *See bites, bees.*

Sunburn, *See burns.*

Toothache. Routine examination by family dentist is best prevention. If a toothache develops, take the child to the dentist as soon as possible. Aspirin or cough syrup containing codeine may be given to relieve discomfort. If there's a cavity in the tooth, put a small bit of cotton around the end of a toothpick and clean it out. Then plug the cavity with another small piece of cotton dipped in oil of cloves using the end of a toothpick to insert the cotton. Drugstores also carry a number of commercial preparations for toothaches. If there is no cavity, experiment with hot and cold packs of sterile gauze on the outside to see which is most effective.

Unconsciousness. Sunstroke, poisoning, gas inhalation, choking, drowning, electric shock, fracture, and concussion are all common causes of unconsciousness.

If breathing is inadequate or stopped, start artificial respiration at once. If breathing is adequate, keep patient lying flat on back, warm, but not hot, loosen constricting clothing, and call a physician.

Never try to give anything by mouth to an unconscious person. Never try to shake an unconscious person to wake him up.

Wounds in which bleeding isn't severe. Before touching the wound, carefully wash your hands with soap and water. If sterile gauze or cotton are not available, use a clean washcloth to gently wash the wound. Soap and water is the best cleanser. Begin at the edge of the wound and wash away from, never toward it. If the wound is contaminated with bits of dirt or stone, pick out with sterile eyebrow tweezers. Flush wound thoroughly with clean tap or, if possible, cooled, boiled, water.

Apply antiseptic to the skin edges—you needn't pour it into the wound. After the antiseptic has dried, apply a clean, sterile dressing. Hold dressing in place with adhesive tape. Change dressing every day. Stitches may be necessary, especially if the wound is gaping. Consult your physician.

Wounds with severe bleeding. Think first of pressure in severe bleeding wound. Don't attempt to clean the wound. Place a sterile gauze pad, clean washcloth, or sanitary napkin over the wound and apply firm, steady pressure with hand, finger, or heel of hand. Pressure (and elevation if arm or leg and fracture is suspected) will control most bleeding. Get child to doctor or hospital at once!

A tourniquet is a dangerous instrument. It is a constricting band around a limb which shuts off blood to points beyond it. Tissues die (gangrene) if deprived of blood too long.

A tourniquet is of value as a first-aid tool *only when there is partial or complete amputation of a body part*—at risk of a limb to save a life. It is usually possible to stop bleeding by applying pressure.

Wounds, infected. Signs of infection in a wound are redness around it which soon develops into a swelling, accompanied by a feeling of heat and throbbing pain. If the wound is in a part of the body which can be dipped into a pan, soak it in warm water in which has been dissolved a heaping tablespoon of table salt or 6 heaping tablespoons of Epsom salts to each quart of water. Keep soaking for at least an hour, adding more warm water as water cools. Soak 3 or 4 times a day. If the injured part can't be immersed, bandage the area with a bulky dressing (small towels or sanitary napkins). Pour the warm solution over the dressing, keeping it wet. Apply the treatment until signs of inflammation have subsided.

Consult a doctor about an infection; a seemingly insignificant one may prove dangerous. This is especially true of infections in or about the nose and forehead.

Wounds of the eye. Have the child close injured eye. Cover with sterile gauze dressing, bandage lightly to avoid pressing on eyeball, and take the child to the doctor at once. Only a doctor should remove foreign objects imbedded in the eye.

Wounds in which foreign bodies remain. Splinters are the wounds most commonly acquired by children. If the foreign body is near the surface, it may be picked out. First clean the skin with soap and water. Then sterilize a needle, knife point, or tweezers by passing through a flame. Don't touch the point after you've sterilized it. Use this to remove the splinter. Apply antiseptic to wound after foreign body has been removed. If the object is buried deeply or is quite large, don't try to remove it. Apply a bandage and take the child to the doctor. If your child has been properly immunized against tetanus, all that is necessary is a tetanus booster. If he hasn't been immunized, skin testing and tetanus antitoxin may be necessary.

Wounds, puncture, and gunshot. These should always have the attention of a doctor, because germs may be carried into the body. Even though you may feel a puncture wound was made with a clean object, the object may pick up organisms from dirty shoes or clothing and carry them into the wound. Home care consists only in washing with soap and water, rinsing under running water and covering with a dressing. *Always see a doctor for treatment of puncture wounds.*

Sources of data used in this chapter are:

Better Homes and Gardens First Aid for Your Family. Des Moines, Iowa, 1960. Meredith Corporation.

Better Homes and Gardens Family Medical Guide. Des Moines, Iowa, 1966. Meredith Corporation.

Accidents in Children. Committee on Accident Prevention, Evanston, Illinois, 1968. American Academy of Pediatrics, Inc.

Accidents Facts, 1968 Edition. Chicago, Illinois. National Safety Council.

Index

Congratulations—But...

what about all those questions and problems that arrive with a new addition to the family? Here are several invaluable books for any new or expectant mother. They are filled with helpful hints for raising healthy children in a happy home. Best of luck and may all your problems be little ones!

☐	12849	**BETTER HOMES AND GARDENS BABY BOOK**	$2.25
☐	11070	**UNDERSTANDING PREGNANCY AND CHILDBIRTH** by Sheldon H. Cherry, M.D.	$1.95
☐	12359	**PREGNANCY NOTEBOOK** by Marcia Morton	$1.95
☐	10996	**NINE MONTHS READING** by Robert E. Hall, M.D.	$1.95
☐	10496	**FEED ME! I'M YOURS** by Vicki Lansky	$1.95
☐	12216	**SIX PRACTICAL LESSONS FOR AN EASIER CHILDBIRTH** by Elisabeth Bing	$2.25
☐	10409	**CHILDBIRTH AT HOME** by Marion Sousa	$1.95
☐	12742	**NAME YOUR BABY** by Lareina Rule	$1.95
☐	12335	**YOUR BABY'S SEX: NOW YOU CAN CHOOSE** by Rorvik & Shettles, M.D.'s	$1.95
☐	12232	**COMPLETE BOOK OF BREASTFEEDING** by M. Eiger, M.D. & S. Olds	$1.95
☐	10105	**IMMACULATE DECEPTION** by Suzanne Arms	$2.50
☐	12844	**PREPARING FOR PARENTHOOD** by Lee Salk	$2.25
☐	12497	**PREGNANCY: THE PSYCHOLOGICAL EXPERIENCE** by Arthur & Libby Colman	$2.25
☐	2360	**MOVING THROUGH PREGNANCY** by Elisabeth Bing	$1.95